Teacher's Guide

Course **4**
Part **A**

Contemporary Mathematics in Context

A Unified Approach

CORE-PLUS MATHEMATICS PROJECT

Course **4**
Part **A**

Contemporary Mathematics in Context

A Unified Approach

Arthur F. Coxford
James T. Fey
Christian R. Hirsch
Harold L. Schoen
Eric W. Hart
Brian A. Keller
Ann E. Watkins
with
Beth E. Ritsema
Rebecca K. Walker

Glencoe
McGraw-Hill

New York, New York   Columbus, Ohio   Chicago, Illinois   Peoria, Illinois   Woodland Hills, California

Glencoe/McGraw-Hill

A Division of The **McGraw·Hill** *Companies*

 This project was supported, in part, by the National Science Foundation.
The opinions expressed are those of the authors and not necessarily those of the Foundation.

Send all inquiries to:
Glencoe/McGraw-Hill
8787 Orion Place
Columbus, OH 43240-4027

ISBN: 0-07-827551-2 (Part A)
ISBN: 0-07-827552-0 (Part B)

Contemporary Mathematics in Context
Course 4 Part A Teacher's Guide

1 2 3 4 5 6 7 8 9 10   004/004   10 09 08 07 06 05 04 03

Dedication

The authors, teachers, and publication staff who have collaborated in developing *Contemporary Mathematics in Context* dedicate this fourth course in the series to the memory of our friend and professional colleague Art Coxford, who passed away on March 5, 2000. Art's breadth of knowledge and experience in mathematics education, his consistent good judgment and hard work, and his good humored leadership were instrumental in all aspects of the Core-Plus Mathematics Project. We will miss his thoughtful contributions to project activities, but he has left an invaluable legacy of creative work and a model of personal and professional commitment and integrity.

Art graduated summa cum laude in Mathematics from Albion College in 1959. He received his master's degree with honors in Mathematics from the University of Michigan in 1960 and taught at Lawrence University in Wisconsin from 1960 to 1962. Returning to Michigan, he began teaching at the University of Michigan High School, and he completed a Ph.D. in Mathematics Education in 1965. Joining the University of Michigan faculty as an assistant professor that year, he was promoted to associate professor in 1969 and to Professor of Education in 1973. Hundreds of Michigan mathematics teachers got their start under his tutelage, and his reputation for fairness and integrity led to important leadership assignments in the School of Education and across the University of Michigan campus.

Throughout his 35-year career at the University of Michigan, Art was a leader in mathematics education at the state and national levels. He served as president of the Michigan Council of Teachers of Mathematics (MCTM) and the School Science and Mathematics Association, as chair of the MCTM and NCTM publications committees, and as editor for four NCTM yearbooks. The consistent theme in his scholarship was improving the learning of secondary school mathematics through development of innovative curriculum materials. With his Michigan colleague Joe Payne, he published Algebra I, Algebra II with Trigonometry, and Advanced Mathematics books. He was on the advisory board of the University of Chicago School Mathematics Project and the lead author of the first edition of the geometry book in the UCSMP secondary series. With Chris Hirsch, he developed books on exploring data and predicting from data, curriculum materials that were key resources in the Making Mathematics Accessible to All project that was a precursor of the Core-Plus Mathematics Project.

On the Core-Plus Mathematics Project, Art was a project director, the lead author of all units in the geometry and trigonometry strand, and a leader in workshops for teachers. He could always be counted on to take on more than his share of the project work, to produce top-notch writing, and to meet consistently the tough deadlines of the curriculum development tasks. When the author team got stuck on tough design or writing problems, Art could be counted on to see a sensible and workable solution and to present his ideas in thoughtful self-effacing style.

Ellen Bacon of Bedford High School, who worked closely with Art since 1992 in classroom testing of curriculum materials, remembers him as "an author who listened to teachers in the field. He always wanted to know what happened when kids completed lessons and what he could do to make them better. But I also remember his warm smile and hearty laugh whenever we met."

About the Core-Plus Mathematics Project

The **Core-Plus Mathematics Project (CPMP)** is a multi-year project funded by the National Science Foundation to develop student and teacher materials for a complete high school mathematics curriculum. Courses 1–3 comprise a core curriculum appropriate for *all* students. The fourth-year course continues the preparation of students for college mathematics.

Development Team

Project Directors

Christian R. Hirsch
Western Michigan University

Arthur F. Coxford
University of Michigan

James T. Fey
University of Maryland

Harold L. Schoen
University of Iowa

Senior Curriculum Developers

Eric W. Hart
Maharishi University of Management

Brian A. Keller
Michigan State University

Ann E. Watkins
California State University, Northridge

Professional Development Coordinator

Beth E. Ritsema
Western Michigan University

Evaluation Coordinator

Steven W. Ziebarth
Western Michigan University

Advisory Board

Diane Briars
Pittsburgh Public Schools

Gail Burrill
University of Wisconsin-Madison

Jeremy Kilpatrick
University of Georgia

Kenneth Ruthven
University of Cambridge

David A. Smith
Duke University

Edna Vasquez
Detroit Renaissance High School

Curriculum Development Consultants

Kenneth A. Ross
University of Oregon

Richard Scheaffer
University of Florida

Paul Zorn
St. Olaf College

Technical Coordinator

James Laser
Western Michigan University

Collaborating Teachers

Emma Ames
Oakland Mills High School, Maryland

Mary Jo Messenger
Howard County Public Schools, Maryland

Valerie Mills
Ann Arbor Public Schools, Michigan

Graduate Assistants

Cos Fi
University of Iowa

Sarah Field
University of Iowa

Kelly Finn
University of Iowa

Gina Garza-Kling
Western Michigan University

Chris Rasmussen
University of Maryland

Heather Thompson
Iowa State University

Roberto Villarubi
University of Maryland

Rebecca Walker
Western Michigan University

Edward Wall
University of Michigan

Marcia Weinhold
Western Michigan University

Production and Support Staff

Kelly MacLean

Anna Seif

Wendy Weaver

Kathryn Wright

Teresa Ziebarth
Western Michigan University

Catherine Kern
University of Iowa

Core-Plus Mathematics Project Field-Test Sites

Special thanks are extended to these teachers and their students who participated in the testing and evaluation of Course 4.

Ann Arbor Huron High School
Ann Arbor, Michigan
  Ginger Gajar
  Brenda Garr

Ann Arbor Pioneer High School
Ann Arbor, Michigan
  Jim Brink

Arthur Hill High School
Saginaw, Michigan
  Virginia Abbott
  Cindy Bosco

Battle Creek Central High School
Battle Creek, Michigan
  Teresa Ballard
  Steven Ohs

Battle Creek Mathematics & Science Center
Battle Creek, Michigan
  Dana Johnson
  Serena Kershner
  Rose Martin
  Lily Nordmoe

Bedford High School
Temperance, Michigan
  Ellen Bacon
  David J. DeGrace

Bloomfield Hills Andover High School
Bloomfield Hills, Michigan
  Jane Briskey
  Cathy King
  Linda Robinson
  Mike Shelly

Brookwood High School
Snellville, Georgia
  Ginny Hanley

Caledonia High School
Caledonia, Michigan
  Jenny Diekevers
  Gerard Wagner

Centaurus High School
Lafayette, Colorado
  Dana Hodel
  Gail Reichert

Clio High School
Clio, Michigan
  Bruce Hanson
  Lee Sheridan
  Paul Webster

Davison High School
Davison, Michigan
  John Bale
  Tammy Heavner

Ellet High School
Akron, Ohio
  Marcia Csipke
  Jim Fillmore

Firestone High School
Akron, Ohio
  Barbara Crucs

Goodrich High School
Goodrich, Michigan
  John Doerr
  Barbara Ravas
  Bonnie Stojek

Grand Blanc High School
Grand Blanc, Michigan
  Charles Carmody
  Linda Nielsen

Grass Lake Junior/Senior High School
Grass Lake, Michigan
  Brad Coffey

Kelloggsville Public Schools
Wyoming, Michigan
  Steve Ramsey

Lakeview High School
Battle Creek, Michigan
  Larry Laughlin
  Bob O'Connor
  Donna Wells

Midland Valley High School
Langley, South Carolina
  Ron Bell
  Janice Lee

North Lamar High School
Paris, Texas
  Tommy Eads
  Barbara Eatherly

Okemos High School
Okemos, Michigan
  Lisa Magee
  Jacqueline Stewart

Portage Northern High School
Portage, Michigan
  Renee Esper
  Pete Jarrad
  Scott Moore

Prairie High School
Cedar Rapids, Iowa
  Judy Slezak

San Pasqual High School
Escondido, California
  Damon Blackman
  Ron Peet

Sitka High School
Sitka, Alaska
  Cheryl Bach Hedden
  Dan Langbauer

Sturgis High School
Sturgis, Michigan
  Craig Evans
  Kathy Parkhurst

Sweetwater High School
National City, California
  Bill Bokesch

Tecumseh High School
Tecumseh, Michigan
  Jennifer Keffer
  Elizabeth Lentz

Traverse City Central High School
Traverse City, Michigan
  Dennis Muth
  Tonya Rice

Traverse City West High School
Traverse City, Michigan
  Tamie Rosenburg
  Diana Lyon-Schumacher
  John Sivek

Ypsilanti High School
Ypsilanti, Michigan
  Steve Gregory
  Mark McClure
  Beth Welch

Overview of Course 4

Part A

Unit 1 ▶ Rates of Change

Rates of Change develops student understanding of the fundamental concepts underlying calculus and their applications.

Topics include average and instantaneous rates of change, derivative at a point and derivative functions, accumulation of continuously varying quantities by estimation, the definite integral, and intuitive development of the fundamental theorem of calculus.

Lesson 1 *Instantaneous Rates of Change*
Lesson 2 *Rates of Change for Familiar Functions*
Lesson 3 *Accumulation at Variable Rates*
Lesson 4 *Looking Back*

Unit 2 ▶ Modeling Motion

Modeling Motion develops student understanding of two-dimensional vectors and their use in modeling linear, circular, and other nonlinear motion.

Topics include concept of vector as a mathematical object used to model situations defined by magnitude and direction; equality of vectors, scalar multiples, opposite vectors, sum and difference vectors, position vectors and coordinates; and parametric equations for motion along a line and for motion of projectiles and objects in circular and elliptical orbits.

Lesson 1 *Modeling Linear Motion*
Lesson 2 *Simulating Linear and Nonlinear Motion*
Lesson 3 *Looking Back*

Unit 3 ▶ Logarithmic Functions and Data Models

Logarithmic Functions and Data Models develops student understanding of logarithmic functions and their use in modeling and analyzing problem situations and data patterns.

Topics include inverses of functions; logarithmic functions and their relation to exponential functions, properties of logarithms, equation solving with logarithms; logarithmic scales and re-expression, linearizing data, and fitting models using log and log-log transformations.

Lesson 1 *Inverses of Functions*
Lesson 2 *Logarithmic Functions*
Lesson 3 *Linearizing Data*
Lesson 4 *Looking Back*

Unit 4 ▶ Counting Models

Counting Models extends student ability to count systematically and solve enumeration problems, and develops understanding of, and ability to do, proof by mathematical induction.

Topics include systematic counting, the Multiplication Principle of Counting, combinations, permutations; the Binomial Theorem, Pascal's triangle, combinatorial reasoning; the General Multiplication Rule for Probability; and the Principle of Mathematical Induction.

Lesson 1 *Methods of Counting*
Lesson 2 *Counting Throughout Mathematics*
Lesson 3 *The Principle of Mathematical Induction*
Lesson 4 *Looking Back*

Overview of Course 4

Part A (continued)

Unit 5 ▶ Binomial Distributions and Statistical Inference

Binomial Distributions and Statistical Inference extends student understanding of the binomial distribution, including its exact construction and how the normal approximation to the binomial distribution is used in statistical inference to test a single proportion and to compare two treatments in an experiment.

Topics include binomial probability formula; shape, mean, and standard deviation of a binomial distribution; normal approximation to a binomial distribution; hypothesis test for a proportion; design of an experiment; randomization test; and hypothesis test for the difference of two proportions.

Part B

Unit 6 ▶ Polynomial and Rational Functions

Polynomial and Rational Functions extends student ability to use polynomial and rational functions to represent and solve problems from real-world situations while focusing on symbolic and graphic patterns.

Topics include factored and expanded symbolic forms, computational complexity, connections between symbolic and graphical representations, multiplicity of zeroes, end behavior; Factor Theorem, Remainder Theorem, complex numbers and their use in the solution of polynomial equations, Fundamental Theorem of Algebra; equivalent forms of rational expressions; horizontal, vertical, and oblique asymptotes; and optimization.

Unit 7 ▶ Functions and Symbolic Reasoning

Functions and Symbolic Reasoning extends student ability to manipulate symbolic representations of exponential, logarithmic, and trigonometric functions; to solve exponential and logarithmic equations; to prove or disprove that two trigonometric expressions are identical and to solve trigonometric equations; to reason with complex numbers and complex number operations using geometric representations and to find roots of complex numbers.

Topics include equivalent forms of exponential expressions, definition of e and natural logarithms, solving equations using logarithms and solving logarithmic equations; the tangent, cotangent, secant, and cosecant functions; fundamental trigonometric identities, sum and difference identities, double-angle identities; solving trigonometric equations and expression of periodic solutions; rectangular and polar representations of complex numbers, absolute value, DeMoivre's Theorem, and the roots of a complex number.

Overview of Course 4

Part B   (continued)

Unit **8** ▶ Space Geometry

Space Geometry extends student ability to visualize and represent non-regular three-dimensional shapes using contours, cross sections and reliefs and to visualize and represent surfaces and conic sections defined by algebraic equations.
Topics include using contours to represent three-dimensional surfaces and developing contour maps from data; sketching surfaces from sets of cross sections; conics as planar sections of right circular cones and as locus of points in a plane; three-dimensional rectangular coordinate system; sketching surfaces using traces, intercepts and cross sections derived from algebraically-defined surfaces; surfaces of revolution and cylindrical surfaces.

Unit **9** ▶ Informatics

Informatics develops student understanding of the mathematics of information processing, focusing on the basic issues of access, security, and accuracy.
Topics include set theory; modular arithmetic; symmetric-key and public-key cryptosystems; error-detecting codes, including bar codes and check digits.

Unit **10** ▶ Problem Solving, Algorithms, and Spreadsheets

Problem Solving, Algorithms, and Spreadsheets develops student understanding and skill in use of standard spreadsheet operations for mathematical problems, while at the same time reviewing and extending many of the basic topics in Courses 1–3.
Topics include mathematics of finance, modeling population growth, apportionment of power in representative governments, sequences and series, and numerical solution of equations.

Contents

Unit  Rates of Change

Unit 2 Modeling Motion

Unit 5 ▶ Binomial Distributions and Statistical Inference

Correlation of Course 4 to NCTM Standards

The *Contemporary Mathematics in Context* curriculum and the instructional and assessment practices it promotes address the focal points of the National Council of Teachers of Mathematics' *Principles and Standards for School Mathematics*. By design, the **process standards** on Problem Solving, Reasoning and Proof, Communication, Connections, and Representation are an integral part of each lesson of every unit in the curriculum.

The chart below correlates Course 4 units with the **content standards** for grades 9–12 in terms of focus (✓) and connections (+).

Course 4 Units	NCTM Grades 9–12 Content Standards	Number and Operations	Algebra	Geometry	Measurement	Data Analysis and Probability
Correlation of Course 4 to NCTM Standards						
Rates of Change		+	✓	+	✓	+
Modeling Motion		✓	✓	✓	✓	
Logarithmic Functions and Data Models		✓	✓	+	✓	✓
Counting Models		✓	✓	+		✓
Binomial Distributions and Statistical Inference		+	+	+		✓
Polynomial and Rational Functions		✓	✓	+	+	+
Functions and Symbolic Reasoning		✓	✓	✓	+	
Space Geometry			✓	✓	+	+
Informatics		✓	+			+
Problem Solving, Algorithms, and Spreadsheets		+	✓	+	✓	+

Curriculum Overview

▶ Introduction

The first three courses in the *Contemporary Mathematics in Context* series provided a common core of broadly useful mathematics for all students. They were developed to prepare students for success in college, in careers, and in daily life in contemporary society. Course 4 continues the preparation of students for college mathematics. Formal and symbolic reasoning strategies, the hallmarks of advanced mathematics, are developed here as complements to more intuitive arguments and numerical and graphical approaches to problems developed in Courses 1–3.

Course 4 of the *Contemporary Mathematics in Context* curriculum shares many of the mathematical and instructional features of Courses 1–3.

■ Unified Content

Course 4 continues to advance students' mathematical thinking along interwoven strands of algebra and functions, statistics and probability, geometry and trigonometry, and discrete mathematics. These strands are unified by fundamental themes, by common topics, and by mathematical habits of mind or ways of thinking.

■ Mathematical Modeling

The curriculum emphasizes mathematical modeling including the processes of data collection, representation, interpretation, prediction, and simulation. Models developed in Course 4 come from many diverse areas including physics, economics, navigation, sports, health care, finance, biology, information processing, political science, sociology, and engineering.

■ Technology

Numerical, graphics, and programming/link capabilities such as those found on many graphing calculators are assumed and appropriately used throughout the curriculum. This use of technology permits the curriculum and instruction to emphasize multiple representations (verbal, numerical, graphical, and symbolic) and their use in modeling mathematical situations. Course 4 also introduces the use of spreadsheets as a problem-solving tool and the Internet as a source of rich applications.

■ Active Learning

Instructional materials promote active learning and teaching centered around collaborative small-group investigations of problem situations followed by teacher-led whole class summarizing activities that lead to analysis, abstraction, and further application of underlying mathematical ideas. Students are actively engaged in exploring, conjecturing, verifying, generalizing, applying, proving, evaluating, and communicating mathematical ideas.

■ Multi-dimensional Assessment

Comprehensive assessment of student understanding and progress through both curriculum-embedded assessment opportunities and supplementary assessment tasks supports instruction and enables monitoring and evaluation of each student's performance in terms of mathematical processes, content, and dispositions.

▶ Unified Mathematics

Contemporary Mathematics in Context, Course 4 formalizes and extends important mathematical ideas drawn from four strands, with a focus on the mathematics needed to be successful in college mathematics and statistics courses.

■ Algebra and Functions

The Algebra and Functions strand develops student ability to recognize, represent, and solve problems involving relations among quantitative variables. Central to the development is the use of functions as mathematical models. In Course 4, students extend their toolkits of function models to include logarithmic functions, polynomial functions, and rational functions. Function families are revisited in terms of the fundamental ideas of rates of change and accumulation. Increased attention is given to analysis of symbolic representations of functions. Students extend their skills in *symbolic manipulation*—rewriting expressions in equivalent forms, often to solve equations—and in *symbolic reasoning*—making inferences about symbolic relations and connections between symbolic representations and graphical, numerical, and contextual representations.

■ Statistics and Probability

The primary role of the Statistics and Probability strand is to develop student ability to analyze data intelligently, to recognize and measure variation, and to understand the patterns that underlie probabilistic situations. Graphical methods of data analysis, simulations, sampling, and experience with the collection and interpretation of real data are featured. In Course 4, ideas of probability distributions and data analysis are merged in the development of methods for testing a hypothesis. Work in the strand concludes with the design of experiments to produce data from which reliable conclusions can be drawn.

■ Geometry and Trigonometry

The primary goal of the Geometry and Trigonometry strand is to develop visual thinking and the ability to construct, reason with, interpret, and apply mathematical models of patterns in visual and physical contexts. In Course 4, concepts and methods of algebra, geometry, and trigonometry become increasingly intertwined in the development of models for describing and analyzing motion in two-dimensional space and surfaces in three-dimensional space.

■ Discrete Mathematics

The Discrete Mathematics strand develops student ability to model and solve problems involving enumeration, sequential change, decision-making in finite settings, and relationships among a finite number of elements. Key themes are existence (Is there a solution?), optimization (What is the best solution?), and algorithmic problem-solving (Can you efficiently construct a solution?). A fourth theme introduced in Course 4 is that of proof, and in particular, proof by mathematical induction. Abstract thinking required to construct proofs in discrete settings is also capitalized on in the development of combinatorial techniques that augment informal methods of systematic counting developed in prior courses. An introduction to the mathematics of information processing concludes work in this strand.

These four strands are connected within units by fundamental ideas such as symmetry, recursion, functions, re-expression, and data analysis and curve-fitting. The strands also are connected across units by mathematical habits of mind, such as visual thinking, recursive thinking, searching for and explaining patterns, making and checking conjectures, reasoning with multiple representations, inventing mathematics, and providing convincing arguments and proofs. The strands are unified further by the fundamental themes of data, representation, shape, and change. Important mathematical ideas are frequently revisited through this attention to connections within and across strands, enabling students to develop a robust and connected understanding of mathematics.

▶ Organization of Course 4

With the increasingly quantitative nature of undergraduate programs, it is important that college-bound students study at least four years of college preparatory mathematics in high school. This view is reflected in the NCTM Standards for high school mathematics. Since not all undergraduate majors require calculus, the developers have designed Course 4 to allow considerable flexibility in tailoring a course to best prepare students for various undergraduate programs.

Students intending to pursue college majors in the *mathematical, physical, and biological sciences, or engineering* are best served by the units in Path A listed on page xx. Students intending to pursue college majors in the *social, management, and some of the health sciences or humanities* are better served by the units in Path B listed on page xx. Omission of indicated lessons will not affect the continuity or cohesion of the course for these students. Depending on time available, additional units of study can be selected based on student performance and interests. Further, all teachers may want to explore with their classes selected topics introduced in Units 6 and 7 that may appear on college mathematics placement exams.

Path A: Leading to Calculus	Path B: Leading to Other Mathematics
Unit 1	Unit 1
Unit 2	Unit 2 (omit Lesson 2)
Unit 3	Unit 3
Unit 4	Unit 9
Unit 6	Unit 4 (omit Lesson 3)
Unit 7	Unit 5
Unit 5, 8, or 10	Unit 10

In planning sequence and timing of appropriate units in either path, you should also consider the opportunity to use lessons from Unit 10, "Problem Solving, Algorithms, and Spreadsheets," in a variety of ways. That unit introduces a versatile and powerful tool that is used in a wide variety of applications of mathematics and is structured so that the individual lessons are somewhat independent of each other. Thus, you might want to cover the first lesson or two early in the school year and other lessons at appropriate points thereafter. In lieu of computers, the specially-designed spreadsheet software for TI-89 and TI-92 calculators, available from the publisher, can be used with Unit 10.

▶Instructional Model

The manner in which mathematical ideas are developed can contribute significantly to the quality of student learning and depth of understanding. Lessons are therefore organized around a four-phase cycle of instructional activities designed to be completed by students working collaboratively in groups of two to four students.

In Class The four-phase cycle of classroom activities—*Launch, Explore, Share and Summarize,* and *Apply*—is designed to actively engage students in investigating and making sense of problem situations, in constructing important mathematical concepts and methods, in generalizing and proving mathematical relationships, and in communicating, both orally and in writing, their thinking and the results of their efforts. The summary below describes these phases of classroom instruction.

In-Class Instruction

LAUNCH   full-class discussion

Think About This Situation

The lesson begins with a teacher-led discussion of a problem situation and of related questions to **think about**. This discussion sets the context for the student work to follow and helps to generate student interest; it also provides an opportunity for the teacher to assess student knowledge and to clarify directions for the group activities. *Teacher is director and moderator.*

INVESTIGATION 1

Classroom activity then shifts to having students **investigate** focused problems and questions related to the launching situation by gathering data, looking for patterns, constructing models and meanings, and making and verifying conjectures. As students collaborate in small groups, the teacher circulates from group to group providing guidance and support, clarifying or asking questions, giving hints, providing encouragement, and drawing group members into the discussion to help groups work more cooperatively. The unit materials and related questions posed by students drive the learning. *Teacher is facilitator.*

SHARE AND SUMMARIZE full-class discussion

Checkpoint

A teacher-led full-class discussion (referred to as a Checkpoint) of concepts and methods developed by different small groups then provides an opportunity to **share** progress and thinking. This discussion leads to a class **summary** of important ideas or to further exploration of a topic if competing perspectives remain. Varying points of view and differing conclusions that can be justified should be encouraged. *Teacher is moderator.*

APPLY individual task

On Your Own

Finally, students are given a task to complete on their own to **assess** their initial understanding of concepts and methods. The teacher circulates in the room assessing levels of understanding. *Teacher is intellectual coach.*

Out of Class In addition to the classroom investigations, *Contemporary Mathematics in Context* provides sets of MORE tasks, which are designed to engage students in *Modeling* with, *Organizing*, *Reflecting* on, and *Extending* their mathematical understanding. MORE tasks are provided for each lesson in the CPMP materials and are central to the learning goals of each lesson. These tasks are intended primarily for individual work outside of class. Selection of MORE tasks should be based on student performance and the availability of time and technology. Also, students should exercise some choice of tasks to pursue, and at times they should be given the opportunity to pose their own problems and questions to investigate. The chart on page xxii describes the types of tasks in a typical MORE set.

MORE: Out-of-Class Activities

Modeling	*Modeling* tasks are related to or provide new contexts to which students can apply the ideas and methods that they have developed in the lesson.
Organizing	*Organizing* tasks offer opportunities for integrating the formal mathematics underlying the mathematical models developed in the lesson and for making connections with other strands.
Reflecting	*Reflecting* tasks encourage thinking about thinking, about mathematical meanings, and about processes, and promote self-monitoring and evaluation of understanding.
Extending	*Extending* tasks permit further, deeper, or more formal study of the topics under investigation.

Following each MORE set, there is a Preparing for Undergraduate Mathematics Placement (PUMP) exercise set providing practice in skills and reasoning techniques commonly assessed on college mathematics placement tests. These exercises are presented in a multiple-choice format, as commonly found on such tests.

Summarizing Activities In the *Contemporary Mathematics in Context* curriculum, students learn mathematics by doing mathematics. However, it is important that students prepare and maintain summaries of important concepts and methods that are developed. To assist in this matter, the "On Your Own" task in the final lesson of each unit asks students to prepare, in outline form, a summary of the important ideas developed in the unit. Templates to guide preparation of these unit summaries can be found in the *Teaching Resources*. In addition, students should create a Math Toolkit that organizes important class-generated ideas and selected Checkpoint responses as they complete investigations. "Constructing a Math Toolkit" prompts are provided in this *Teacher's Guide* to assist in identifying key concepts and methods as they are developed by students. (See *Teaching Resources* Master 36 for a blackline master that can be used for student Math Toolkit entries.)

▶Curriculum-Embedded Assessment

Assessing what students know and are able to do is an integral part of *Contemporary Mathematics in Context* and there are opportunities for assessment in each phase of the instructional cycle. Initially, as students pursue the investigations that make up the curriculum, the teacher is able to informally assess student understanding of mathematical processes, content, and their disposition toward mathematics. Then at the end of each investigation, the Checkpoint and class discussion provide an opportunity for teachers to assess the levels of understanding that various groups of students have reached as they share and summarize their findings. Finally, "On Your Own" problems, tasks in the MORE sets, and exercises in the PUMP sections provide further opportunities to assess the level of understanding of each individual student.

A more detailed description of the CPMP assessment program is given on pages xxvii–xxxii of this text and in *Implementing the Core-Plus Mathematics Curriculum*.

Implementing the Curriculum

▶ Planning for Instruction

The *Contemporary Mathematics in Context* curriculum is not only changing what mathematics all students have the opportunity to learn, but also changing how that learning occurs and is assessed. Active learning is most effective when accompanied with active teaching. Just as the student text is designed to actively engage students in doing mathematics, the teacher's resource materials are designed to support teachers in planning for instruction; in observing, listening, questioning, facilitating student work, and orchestrating classroom discussion; and in managing the classroom.

The *Teacher's Guide* provides suggestions, based on the experiences of field-test teachers, for implementing this exciting new curriculum in your classroom. You probably will find new ideas that can be overwhelming. The developers highly recommend that teachers who are teaching *Contemporary Mathematics in Context* for the first time do so at least in pairs who share a common planning period.

Each of the items listed below is included in the *Teacher's Guide* for each unit.

- Unit Overview
- Unit Planning Guide listing objectives, suggested timeline, and materials needed
- Instructional notes and suggestions
- Suggested assignments for each MORE set
- Solutions for Investigations and MORE tasks and answers for PUMP exercises
- Unit summary and a look ahead ("Looking Back, Looking Ahead")

The *Teaching Resources* include blackline masters for creating transparencies and handouts. *Assessment Resources* include quizzes for individual lessons, end-of-unit exams, take-home assessment tasks, projects, and a bank of additional assessment tasks for midterm and final examinations. Special calculator spreadsheet software for the TI-89 and TI-92 calculators has been developed to support students' investigations and modeling applications. This software is available on disc for downloading from Macintosh and DOS- or Windows-based (PC) computers.

Each unit of *Contemporary Mathematics in Context* includes either content which may be new to many teachers or new approaches to familiar content. Thus, a first step toward planning the teaching of a unit is to review the scope and sequence of the unit. This review provides an overall feel for the goals of the unit and how it holds together. The *Scope and Sequence* guide shows how the specific mathematical topics fit in the complete four-year curriculum. Working through the student investigations, if possible with a colleague, provides help in thinking about and understanding mathematical ideas that may be unfamiliar.

In the *Teacher's Guide* you will find teaching notes for each lesson in Course 4, including instructional suggestions and sample student responses to investigations and MORE sets. Thinking about the range of possible responses and solutions to problems in a lesson proves to be very helpful in facilitating student work.

Although not stated, it is assumed that students have access to graphing calculators at all times for in-class work and ideally for out-of-class work as well. Downloading and becoming familiar with the specially-designed calculator software will require advanced planning. Use of a computer lab for Units 8 and 10 is optional.

The developers recommend that the homework (MORE) assignment *not* be held off until the end of the lesson or the investigation just preceding the MORE set. Some teachers choose to post the MORE assignment at the beginning of a lesson along with the due date—usually a day or two following planned completion of the lesson. Other teachers prefer to assign particular MORE tasks at appropriate points during the course of the multiday lesson and then assign the remaining tasks toward the end of the lesson. Note that all recommended assignments include provision for student choice of some tasks. This is but one of many ways in which this curriculum is designed to accommodate and support differences in students' interests and performance levels.

It is strongly recommended that student solutions to Organizing tasks be discussed in class. These tasks help students organize and formalize the mathematics developed in context and connect it to other mathematics they have studied. Structuring the underlying mathematics and building connections is best accomplished by comparing and discussing student work and synthesizing key ideas within the classroom.

▶Orchestrating Lessons

The *Contemporary Mathematics in Context* materials are designed to engage students actively in a four-phase cycle of classroom activities. The activities often require both students and teachers to assume roles quite different than those in more traditional mathematics classrooms. Although realistic problem solving and investigative work by students are the heart of the curriculum, how teachers orchestrate the launching of an activity and the sharing and summarizing of results is critical to successful implementation.

Students enter the classroom with differing backgrounds, experience, and knowledge. These differences can be viewed as assets. Engaging the class in a free-flowing give-and-take discussion of how students think about the launch situations serves to connect lessons with the informal understandings of data, shape, change, and chance that students bring to the classroom. Try to maximize the participation of students in these discussions by emphasizing that their ideas and possible approaches are valued and important and that definitive answers are not necessarily expected at this time.

Once launched, a lesson may involve students working together collaboratively in small groups for a period of days punctuated occasionally by brief, whole-class discussion of questions students have raised. In this setting, the lesson becomes driven primarily by the instructional materials themselves. Rather than orchestrating class discussion, the teacher shifts to circulating among the groups and observing, listening, and interacting with students by asking guiding or probing questions. These small-group investigations lead to (re)invention of important mathematics that makes sense to students. Sharing and agreeing as a class on the mathematical ideas that groups are developing is the purpose of the Checkpoints in the instructional materials.

Class discussions at Checkpoints are orchestrated somewhat differently than during the launch of a lesson. At this stage, mathematical ideas and methods still may be under development and may vary for individual groups. So class discussion should involve groups comparing their methods and results, analyzing their work, and arriving at conclusions agreed upon by the class.

The investigations deepen students' understanding of mathematical ideas and extend their mathematical language in contexts. Technical terminology and symbolism are introduced as needed. This sometimes occurs in student materials immediately following a Checkpoint and before the corresponding "On Your Own" task. These connections should be introduced by the teacher as a natural way of closing the class discussion summarizing the Checkpoint.

Managing Classroom Activities

▶ Active Learning and Collaborative Work

The *Contemporary Mathematics in Context* curriculum materials are designed to promote active, collaborative learning and group work for two important reasons. First, a collaborative environment fosters students' ability to make sense of mathematics and develop deep mathematical understandings. Collaborative learning is an effective method for engaging all the students in the learning process, particularly students who have been underrepresented in mathematics classes. Second, practice in collaborative learning in the classroom is practice for real life: students develop and exercise the same skills in the classroom that they need in their lives at home, in the community, and in the workplace.

Value of Individuals

Perhaps the most fundamental belief underlying the use of collaborative learning is that every student is viewed as a valuable resource and contributor. In other words, every student participates in group work and is given the opportunity and time to voice ideas and opinions. Implementing this concept is not easy. It does not happen automatically. In order to set a tone that will promote respect for individuals and their contributions, classroom rules should be established and agreed upon by the learning community. Students should be included in the process of formulating the rules. The teacher should initiate a discussion of group rules and then post them in the classroom. The teacher should model all of the rules correctly to show that "we" begins with "me." Those who do not adhere to the rules must accept the consequences in accordance with classroom or school disciplinary procedures.

Importance of Social Connections

Even in classrooms in which the rules for showing respect have been clearly established, experience has shown that students still cannot talk with one another about mathematics (or social studies, or literature, or any other subject) if they do not first have positive social connections.

One way to develop this kind of common base is through team-building activities. These short activities may be used at the beginning of the year to help students get acquainted with the whole class and may be used during the year whenever new groups are formed to help groupmates know one another better. Team-building activities help students learn new and positive things about classmates with whom they may have attended classes for years, but have not known in depth. The time taken for these quick team builders pays off later in helping students feel comfortable enough to work with the members of their group.

Need for Teaching Social Skills

Experience also has shown that social skills are critical to the successful functioning of any small group. Because there is no guarantee that students of any particular age will have the social skills necessary for effective group work, it often is necessary to teach these skills to build a collaborative learning environment.

These social skills are specific skills, not general goals. Examples of specific social skills that the teacher can teach in the classroom include responding to ideas respectfully, keeping track of time, disagreeing in an agreeable way, involving everyone, and following directions. Though goals such as cooperating and listening are important, they are too general to teach and practice.

One method of teaching social skills is to begin by selecting a specific skill and then having the class brainstorm to develop a script for practicing that skill. Next, the students practice that skill during their group work. Finally, in what is called the processing, the students discuss within their groups how well they performed the assigned social skill. Effective teaching of social skills requires practicing and processing; merely describing a specific social skill is not enough. Actual practice and processing are necessary for students really to learn the skill and to increase the use of appropriate behaviors during group work and other times during class.

One of the premises of collaborative learning is that by developing the appropriate skills through practice, anyone in the class can learn to work in a group with anyone else. Learning to work in groups is a continuous process, however, and the process can be helped by decisions that the teacher makes. *Implementing the Core-Plus Mathematics Curriculum* provides information and support to help teachers make decisions about group size, composition, method of selection, student reaction to working in groups, and the duration of groups. It also provides advice on dealing effectively with student absences.

The culture created within the classroom is crucial to the success of this curriculum. It is important to inculcate in students a sense of inquiry and responsibility for their own learning. Without this commitment, active, collaborative learning by students cannot be effective. In order for students to work collaboratively, they must be able to understand the value of working together. Some students seem satisfied with the rationale that it is important in the business world. Others may need to understand that the struggle of verbalizing their thinking, listening to others' thinking, questioning themselves and other group members, and coming to an agreement increases their understanding and retention of the mathematics while contributing to the formation of important thinking skills or habits of mind.

Issues of helping students to work collaboratively will become less pressing as both you and your students experience this type of learning. You may find it helpful to refer to *Implementing the Core-Plus Mathematics Curriculum* and discuss effective collaborative groups with colleagues a few weeks into the semester.

▶Assessment

Throughout the *Contemporary Mathematics in Context* curriculum, the term "assessment" is meant to include all instances of gathering information about students' levels of understanding and their disposition toward mathematics for purposes of making decisions about instruction. You may want to consult the extended section on assessment in *Implementing the Core-Plus Mathematics Curriculum.*

The dimensions of student performance that are assessed in this curriculum (see chart below) are consistent with the assessment recommendations of the National Council of Teachers of Mathematics in the *Assessment Standards for School Mathematics* (NCTM, 1995). They are much broader than those of a typical testing program.

Assessment Dimensions

Process	**Content**	**Attitude**
Problem Solving	Concepts	Beliefs
Reasoning	Applications	Perseverance
Communication	Representational Strategies	Confidence
Connections	Procedures	Enthusiasm

Sources of Assessment Information

Several kinds of assessment are available to teachers using *Contemporary Mathematics in Context*. Some of these sources reside within the curriculum itself, some of them are student-generated, and some are supplementary materials designed specifically for assessment. Understanding the nature of these sources is a prerequisite for selecting assessment tools, establishing guidelines on how to score assessments, making judgments about what students know and are able to do, and assigning grades.

Curriculum Sources

Two features of the curriculum, questioning and observation by the teacher, provide fundamental and particularly useful ways of gathering assessment information. The student text uses questions to facilitate student understanding of new concepts, how these concepts fit with earlier ideas and with one another, and how they can be applied in problem situations. Whether students are working individually or in groups, the teacher is given a window to watch how the students think about and apply mathematics as they attempt to answer the questions posed by the curriculum materials. In fact, by observing how students respond to the curriculum-embedded questions, the teacher can assess student performance across all process, content, and attitude dimensions described in the chart above.

Specific features in the student material that focus on different ways students respond to questions are the Checkpoint, "On Your Own," and MORE (*M*odeling, *O*rganizing, *R*eflecting, and *E*xtending) sets. Checkpoint features are intended to bring students together, usually after they have been working in small groups, so they may share and discuss the progress each group has made during a sequence of related activities. Each Checkpoint is intended to be a whole-class discussion, so it should provide an opportunity for teachers to assess, informally, the levels of understanding that the various groups of students have reached.

Following each Checkpoint, the "On Your Own" tasks are meant to be completed by students working individually. Student responses to these tasks provide an opportunity for teachers to assess the level of understanding of each student.

The tasks in the MORE sets serve many purposes, including post-investigation assessment. Each type of task in a MORE set has a different instructional purpose. Modeling tasks help students demonstrate how well they understand and can apply the concepts and procedures developed in an investigation. Organizing tasks demonstrate how well students understand connections between the content of an investigation and other mathematical and real-world ideas. In-class discussions based on Organizing tasks are a crucial step in assisting students' development of a full understanding of the mathematical content and connections. Reflecting tasks provide insights into students' beliefs, attitudes, and judgments of their own competence. Extending tasks show how well students are able to extend the present content beyond the level addressed in an investigation. The performance of students or groups of students in each of these types of tasks provides the teacher with further information to help assess applicability, connectedness, and depth of the students' evolving understanding of mathematics.

The exercises in the PUMP sections focus on skills and reasoning strategies that need to be automatic if students are to perform well on timed mathematics placement tests in college. Individual students should monitor their performance on these exercise sets to ensure they have developed the expected level of proficiency.

Finally, an opportunity for group self-assessment is provided in the last element of each unit, the "Looking Back" lesson. These tasks help students pull together and demonstrate what they have learned in the unit and at the same time provide helpful review and confidence-building for students.

Student-Generated Sources

Other possible sources of assessment information are writings and materials produced by students in the form of student mathematics toolkits or journals.

Mathematics Toolkits   Students should create a Math Toolkit that organizes important class-generated ideas and selected Checkpoint responses as they complete investigations. Constructing a Math Toolkit prompts are provided in the *Teacher's Guide* to assist in identifying key concepts and methods as they are developed by students. (See *Teaching Resources* Master 36 for a blackline master to assist students in organizing their Math Toolkits.)

Journals   Student journals are notebooks in which students are encouraged to write (briefly, but frequently) their personal reflections concerning the class, the mathematics they are learning, and their progress. These journals are an excellent way for the teacher to gain insights into how individual students are feeling about the class, what they do and do not understand, and what some of their particular learning difficulties are. For many students, the journal is a non-threatening way to communicate with the teacher about matters that may be too difficult or too time-consuming to talk about directly. Journals also encourage students to assess their own understanding of, and feelings about, the mathematics they are studying. The teacher should collect, read, and respond to each journal at least once a month.

The *Contemporary Mathematics in Context* assessment program provides many items that can be placed in students' portfolios, including reports of individual and group projects.

Math Toolkit or journal entries, teacher-completed observation checklists, end-of-unit assessments, especially the take-home tasks and projects. See *Implementing the Core-Plus Mathematics Curriculum* for additional portfolio information.

Assessment Resources

The *Contemporary Mathematics in Context* teacher resource materials include for each unit a third source of assessment information—*Assessment Resources*. Included in the *Assessment Resources* are end-of-lesson quizzes and end-of-unit assessments in the form of an in-class unit exam, take-home assessment tasks, and projects. Calculators are required in most cases and are intended to be available to students. Teacher discretion should be used regarding student access to their textbook and Math Toolkit for assessments. In general, if the goals to be assessed are problem solving and reasoning, while memory of facts and procedural skill are of less interest, resources should be allowed. However, if automaticity of procedures or unaided recall are being assessed, it is appropriate to prohibit resource materials. Since many rich opportunities for assessing students are embedded in the curriculum itself, you may choose not to use all the lesson quizzes for each unit.

End-of-Lesson Quizzes Two forms of a quiz covering the main ideas of each lesson are provided. These quizzes, which are the most traditional of all the assessment methods and instruments included with the *Contemporary Mathematics in Context* materials, are comprised of fairly straightforward problems meant to determine if students have developed understanding of the important concepts and procedures of each lesson.

In-Class Exams Two forms of in-class exams are provided for each unit and are intended to be completed in a 50-minute class period. The two forms of each exam are not necessarily equivalent, although they assess essentially the same mathematical ideas. Teachers should preview the two versions carefully and feel free to revise or delete items and add new ones if necessary, using the *Assessment and Maintenance Worksheet Builder* CD-ROM.

Take-Home Assessments Take-home assessment tasks are included for each unit. The students or the teacher should choose one or, at most, two of these tasks. These assessments, some of which are best done by students working in pairs or small groups, provide students with the opportunity to organize the information from the completed unit, to extend the ideas of the unit into other areas of interest to them, to work with another student or group of students, and to avoid the time pressure often generated by in-class exams.

Projects Assessment traditionally has been based on evaluating work that students have completed in a very short time period and under restricted conditions. Some assessment, however, should involve work done over a longer time period and with the aid of resources. Thus, assessment projects are included in unit assessments. These projects, which are intended to be completed by small groups of students, provide an opportunity for students to conduct an investigation that extends and applies the main ideas from the unit and to write a summary of their findings.

Midterm or Final Assessment   A bank of assessment tasks, from which to construct semester exams that fit the mathematical emphasis of your course, is also provided.

Scoring Assessments

High expectations of the quality of students' written work will encourage students to reach their potential. Assigning scores to open-ended assessments and to observations of students' performance requires more subjective judgment by the teacher than does grading short answer or multiple-choice tests. It is therefore not possible to provide a complete set of explicit guidelines for scoring open-ended assessment items and written or oral reports. However, some general guidelines may be helpful. When scoring student work on open-ended assessment tasks, the goal is to reward in a fair and consistent way the kinds of thinking and understanding that the task is meant to measure. To score open-ended assessment tasks, teachers should have a general rubric, with several response levels in mind; a specific rubric; and anchor items. The general rubric is the foundation for scoring across a wide range of types of open-ended tasks. The following general rubric can be used for most assessment tasks provided with *Contemporary Mathematics in Context*.

General Scoring Rubric

4 points	Contains complete response with clear, coherent, and unambiguous explanation; includes clear and simple diagram, if appropriate; communicates effectively to identified audience; shows understanding of question's mathematical ideas and processes; identifies all important elements of question; includes examples and counterexamples; gives strong supportive arguments
3 points	Contains good solid response with some, but not all, of the characteristics above; explains less completely; may include minor error of execution but not of understanding
2 points	Contains complete response, but explanation is muddled; presents incomplete arguments; includes diagrams that are inappropriate or unclear, or fails to provide a diagram when it would be appropriate; indicates some understanding of mathematical ideas, but in an unclear way; shows clear evidence of understanding some important ideas while also making one or more fundamental, specific errors
1 point	Omits parts of question and response; has major errors; uses inappropriate strategies
0 points	No response; frivolous or irrelevant response

Assigning Grades

Because the *Contemporary Mathematics in Context* approach and materials provide a wide variety of assessment information, the teacher will be in a good position to assign a fair grade for student work. With such a wide choice for assessment, a word of caution is appropriate: *it is easy to overassess students, and care must be taken to avoid doing so.* A quiz need not be given after every lesson nor an in-class exam after every unit. The developers believe it is best to vary assessment methods from lesson to lesson, and from unit to unit. If information on what students understand and are able to do is available from their homework and in-class work, it may not be necessary to take the time for a formal quiz after each lesson. Similarly, information from project work may replace an in-class exam.

Deciding exactly how to weigh the various kinds of assessment information is a decision that the teacher will need to make and communicate clearly to the students.

Maintaining Skills

The developers have identified a set of paper-and-pencil technical competencies that all students should acquire. To provide additional practice with these core competencies, a special maintenance feature is included in blackline master form in the *Teaching Resources* or on the *Assessment and Maintenance Worksheet Builder* CD-ROM.

The Maintenance Masters contain supplementary sets of exercises that provide periodic review and additional practice of basic skills and symbolic reasoning strategies. Use of the maintenance material following the start of Lesson 2 of each unit will allow students time to work simultaneously on skills during the latter part of a unit without interrupting the flow of the unit. You may wish to allow a few minutes at the end of selected class periods to revisit these skills with various groups of students who need assistance while other groups choose an Extending task to complete.

The maintenance material prepared for each unit spans technical competencies across each of the strands. In each case, the first presented task is a contextual problem, but the remaining tasks are not contextualized. Students should *not* use a calculator for these tasks unless so directed.

▶ Additional Resources

Implementing the Core-Plus Mathematics Curriculum contains expanded information on the scope and sequence of Courses 1–4; on managing classroom activities; and on the assessment program. It also provides a sampling of colleges and universities to which CPMP students have been admitted. A section on communication with parents is also included. You will find it useful to have the implementation guide available for reference throughout the school year.

The Core-Plus Mathematics Project (CPMP) maintains a Web site at www.wmich.edu/cpmp as a resource for schools. You may find the "Frequently Asked Questions" helpful as you think about your uniform district replies to community questions.

In addition, CPMP moderates a listserv that allows teachers to have discussions about mathematical content and implementation of *Contemporary Mathematics in Context*. For additional information and to subscribe to the listserv, email cpmp@wmich.edu.

Rates of Change

UNIT OVERVIEW   The ideas in this unit are a continuation of many of the algebraic concepts and techniques previously studied. The rate of change and total change in a quantity, two key topics in calculus, are further explorations of general numerical patterns, quantitative variables and relationships between those variables, and important patterns of change in those relationships.

Lesson 1 explores how the information in a table or graph for several different variables can be used to estimate and explain the rate of change of those variables at specific points. The variables explored in the investigations of this lesson include distance walked, temperature of a hot drink, and distance traveled by a trapeze flyer. Other contexts occur in the "On Your Own" and MORE tasks.

Lesson 2 continues the exploration of rates of change in various quantities, but with the use of function rules. This is accomplished through interesting situations modeled by linear, quadratic, exponential, and periodic functions. The zoom feature on the graphing calculator is used to make the connection between the rate of change for linear functions and the rate of change for nonlinear functions. This lesson builds on the ideas for estimating the derivative of a function at a point to discover ways to use the rule of a given function and find the rule of its derivative function. This lesson also illustrates the power gained by being able to use the graphing calculator to approximate and, in some cases, write symbolic rules for the derivative functions of linear, quadratic, exponential, trigonometric, and power functions. These derivative function rules are used to explore the symbolic, graphical, and numerical connections between these functions and their derivatives. (See the Technology Tips in Teaching Masters 12–15b and 17–18c.) The derivative rules can be used to assist in describing the rate of change verbally.

Lesson 3 investigates the relationship between the rate of change function of a quantity and the net change in that quantity over a given interval. Net change in the quantity is estimated using simple approximations to the rate function, first for positive rate functions and later for all rate functions. In both cases, the estimated net change is related to combinations of areas of rectangles. The investigations include the relationships between speed and distance traveled, flow rate and net change in volume, and velocity and displacement from an initial point. Consistent with the development of net change, the integral is then introduced as the difference of areas bounded by the rate function. Integrals are estimated using systematic approximations.

Lesson 4 assists students in pulling together the main ideas of the unit. Students are asked to estimate and use the derivative and the definite integral to answer questions about rates of change and accumulation of one variable as another changes.

NOTE: See page xx for a suggested path through Course 4 for students concentrating on mathematics or science, and another path for students concentrating on the humanities or social sciences.

Unit 1 Objectives

- To estimate the rate of change for a variety of quantities using tables of numerical data, graphical representations, and symbolic rules and to develop student ability to relate the rate of change in a quantity to the graph of that quantity

- To recognize that the graphs of many nonlinear functions "look" linear when zoomed in around a point; and thus the rate of change at a point for a nonlinear function can be approximated with the rate of change for a linear function

- To estimate the net change in a quantity whose rate function is given in graphical, tabular, and symbolic forms using systematic approximations to its rate-of-change function and geometric considerations

- To estimate net change in a quantity by systematically approximating areas or using integrals in conjunction with a calculator or computer integration tool

Maintenance Resource

The Teaching Resources for each unit contain a series of masters entitled Maintenance Masters. Items on the Maintenance Masters reflect mathematics skills that students may need to practice periodically over the year. Concepts introduced in a unit may be included on any subsequent Maintenance Masters. The first task presented is a contextual problem, but remaining tasks are not contextualized. Students should *not* use a calculator for these tasks unless so directed.

You may wish to ask students to complete the tasks over a three-day period while they are in the process of completing a multi-day investigation. The developers recommend that Maintenance tasks be assigned at any point after students have completed Lesson 1 of a unit. This allows the students time to get accustomed to the new focus of the unit without interruption. You may wish to allow a few minutes at the end of selected class periods to revisit these skills with various groups of students who need assistance while other groups choose an Extending task.

Preparing for Undergraduate Mathematics Placement Tests (PUMP)

Following each MORE set, there is a PUMP exercise set in multiple choice format to provide practice in skills and reasoning techniques commonly assessed on college mathematics placement tests. The PUMPs can be used to help students develop the automaticity needed for these timed tests.

Unit 1 Planning Guide

Lesson Objectives	Assignments	Suggested Pacing[†]	Materials
Lesson 1 *Instantaneous Rates of Change* • To estimate the rate of change in a quantity for a variety of situations using a table or graph • To describe how the rate of change in a quantity is shown by the shape of the graph • To identify the units associated with the rate of change in a quantity for a variety of situations	**MORE** **after page 6** Students can begin Modeling Task 1 or 3 or Organizing Task 1 from p. 12. **after page 8** Students can begin Modeling Task 2 or Reflecting Task 1 or 3 from p. 12. **page 12** **Modeling:** 1, 2, and choice of one* **Organizing:** 1, 2, and 4 **Reflecting:** 4 and choice of one* **Extending:** 1 and 3 **PUMP**　　　　pages 20–21	**Path A:** Leading to Calculus: 6 days **Path B:** Leading to other college mathematics courses: 8 days	• Teaching Resources 1–7, 36 • Assessment Resources 1–6 • CBLs (optional)
Lesson 2 *Rates of Change for Familiar Functions* • To describe how the rate of change of a function at various points is shown by the shape of the function's graph • To estimate the rate of change of a function at any point on its graph by using the function rule • To understand the similarities and differences in estimating the rate of change for linear and nonlinear functions, and how those methods are related to finding the slope of a straight line • To discover ways to use the rule of a given function to find the rule of its derivative function • To discover some general patterns relating various function types to their derivatives • To explain how the shape of the graph of a function can be used to describe and sketch the graph of its derivative	**MORE** **after page 29** Students can begin Modeling Task 1 from p. 41. **after page 32** Students can begin Reflecting Task 5 from p. 41. **after page 35** Students can begin Modeling Task 2 or 3 from p. 41. **after page 37** Students can begin Modeling Task 4, 5, or 6, or any Extending task from p. 41. **page 41** **Modeling:** 1–3, and 4, 5, or 6* **Organizing:** 1, 4, and 3 or 5* **Reflecting:** 1, 4, 5, and 6 **Extending:** 1 and choice of one* **PUMP**　　　　pages 50–51	**Path A:** 10 days **Path B:** 13 days	• Teaching Resources 8–21 • Assessment Resources 7–12
Lesson 3 *Accumulation at Variable Rates* • To estimate the net change in a quantity from its rate of change graph using systematic approximations and geometric ideas • To describe the idea of a definite integral for a function and to estimate it in various ways	**MORE** **after page 56** Students can begin Modeling Task 1 on p. 65. **after page 60** Students can begin Modeling Task 2 or Extending Task 1 from p. 65. **page 65** **Modeling:** 1, 2, and 3 or 4* **Organizing:** 1, 2, and 4 **Reflecting:** 2 and 3 **Extending:** 1 and choice of one* **PUMP**　　　　pages 72–73	**Path A:** 7 days **Path B:** 9 days	• Teaching Resources 22–33 • Assessment Resources 13–18
Lesson 4 *Looking Back* • To review and test the major objectives of the unit		**Path A:** 2 days **Path B:** 3 days	• Teaching Resources 34–35 • Assessment Resources 19–35

† *See page xix in the front of this text for suggested units to be completed. If your class is composed of students from both paths to college mathematics, you will need to make adjustments to the timeline.*

* *When choice is indicated, it is important to leave the choice to the student.*

Note: *It is best if Organizing tasks are discussed as a whole class after they have been assigned as homework.*

Master 1

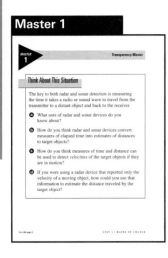

Lesson 1 *Instantaneous Rates of Change*

LESSON OVERVIEW Students need the time and opportunity to develop the concepts that underpin derivatives. The three investigations in this lesson are very straightforward, and your students should be able to move through them quickly. The same set of ideas about estimating average and instantaneous rate of change are introduced and refined in different contexts in the three investigations. Investigation 1 focuses on rate of change at a point. Investigation 2 introduces average rate of change over a time interval. All three investigations emphasize the shape of the graph. Numerical methods of estimating instantaneous rate of change from a graph or table are introduced and refined.

These same ideas are extended in Lesson 2, where function rules are used to generate an estimate of instantaneous rate of change, and where the power of a graphing calculator makes it possible to produce tables of approximate derivatives from which rules for derivative functions can be determined.

Lesson Objectives

- To estimate the rate of change in a quantity for a variety of situations using a table or graph
- To describe how the rate of change in a quantity is shown by the shape of the graph
- To identify the units associated with the rate of change in a quantity for a variety of situations

LAUNCH full-class discussion

Think About This Situation

See Teaching Master 1.

ⓐ Radar devices track airplanes, missiles, cars, baseball pitches, and tennis serves. The United States and Canada operate a radar network known as Space Detection and Tracking System for identifying and monitoring artificial satellites. Police use radar guns to detect speeding cars. There is an optical-radar sensory device developed for use in canes for the blind. Radar is used to aid navigation of aircraft and ships. Sonar was first proposed as a way of detecting icebergs. Sonar devices track and locate submarines and sunken ships. Sonar is also used for detecting depths of fish as well as for medical ultrasounds.

ⓑ Knowing the elapsed time and the speed at which the radio or sound waves travel, the relation between speed, distance, and time (*distance = speed × time*) can be used to get an estimate of the distance to the target.

LAUNCH *continued*

c Knowing the distance of the object from the detector at two times, you can calculate the average velocity of the object by dividing the change in distance by the elapsed time.

d If the reported velocity of the object during a particular time period was constant, you could multiply the velocity by the total elapsed time to obtain the distance traveled. If the reported velocity during a time period varied, you could multiply the elapsed time by the velocity at the beginning of the time interval, by the velocity at the midpoint of the time interval, or by the velocity at the end of the time interval. (The methods for estimating distance with variable velocity will be developed in the lesson, so it is not necessary to introduce them at this time.)

NOTE: Be sure this relationship surfaces in the discussion since students will be using it in the investigation.

EXPLORE   small-group investigation

INVESTIGATION 1▶ Walk That Graph

As a brief introduction to this investigation, you could let students know that they will have a chance to demonstrate the relationship among distance, rate, and time by physically recreating the motion of a moving object. They are going to think about rate of change and try to "clock" the velocity of a moving object at different points, just as if they were operating radar guns.

The main idea in this investigation is to make sense of estimating rate of change at a point by referring to a table or graph. Your students will move through this investigation quickly. If some groups finish early, you might let them begin the "On Your Own," Modeling Task 1, or Investigation 2.

If students use a CBL (calculator-based laboratory), they may find it difficult to match the graphs exactly because of the constraints of the distances at which the CBL functions. They should aim for capturing the *shape* of the graph, not necessarily the scale or exact numbers given. If CBLs are not available, then each group can walk a graph (act out the walk described by the graph), while the other groups critique their demonstrations, in terms of velocity, and starting distance.

Students do not have to reach consensus yet about the best way to estimate rate of change (velocity) at a particular instant. That idea will resurface later.

1. The table values for Part b may be obtained from the graphs in the student text or CBL data.

   a. i. Start 2 m away from the motion detector and walk away from the detector at a constant speed of 0.5 m/s for 6 seconds.

      ii. Start 5 m away from the motion detector, walk toward the detector at a speed of 1 m/s for 3 seconds, and then walk back to the initial position at the same speed.

      iii. Start 6 m away from the detector and begin walking toward the detector at about 2 m/s, gradually slowing down your pace until you essentially stop after 6 seconds, at which time you would be about 1.2 m from the detector.

EXPLORE *continued*

> **iv.** Start 1 m away from the detector and begin walking away from the detector at about 3 m/s, gradually slowing the pace until you stop after 3 seconds. Then, immediately start walking slowly back toward the detector, gradually increasing the pace to about 3 m/s when you are 1 m away from the detector.

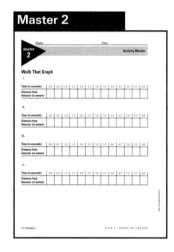

Master 2

b. **See Teaching Master 2.**

The tables that follow give numerical (*time*, *distance*) information about the four different walks graphed in Part a. For students using CBLs, table values will differ, but patterns should be the same since each CBL graph should exhibit the *shape* of the given graph.

i.

Time (in seconds)	0	0.5	1.0	1.5	2.0	2.5	3.0	3.5	4.0	4.5	5.0	5.5	6.0
Distance from Detector (in meters)	2.0	2.25	2.5	2.75	3.0	3.25	3.5	3.75	4.0	4.25	4.5	4.75	5.0

ii.

Time (in seconds)	0	0.5	1.0	1.5	2.0	2.5	3.0	3.5	4.0	4.5	5.0	5.5	6.0
Distance from Detector (in meters)	5.0	4.5	4.0	3.5	3.0	2.5	2.0	2.5	3.0	3.5	4.0	4.5	5.0

iii.

Time (in seconds)	0	0.5	1.0	1.5	2.0	2.5	3.0	3.5	4.0	4.5	5.0	5.5	6.0
Distance from Detector (in meters)	6.0	4.9	4.0	3.3	2.8	2.4	2.1	1.8	1.6	1.5	1.4	1.3	1.2

iv.

Time (in seconds)	0	0.5	1.0	1.5	2.0	2.5	3.0	3.5	4.0	4.5	5.0	5.5	6.0
Distance from Detector (in meters)	1.0	2.4	3.5	4.4	5.0	5.4	5.5	5.4	5.0	4.4	3.5	2.4	1.0

c. The following calculations use the data given in Part b to show various ways of estimating the velocities. Positive velocities indicate movement away from the detector and negative velocities indicate movement toward the detector.

> **i.** For Graph i, the velocity values should be almost constant because the graph is linear. (Here the right endpoints are used for velocity estimates.)
>
> - At 1.5 seconds: $\dfrac{2.75 - 2.50}{1.5 - 1.0} = 0.5$ m/s
> - At 3.0 seconds: $\dfrac{3.50 - 3.25}{3 - 2.5} = 0.5$ m/s
> - At 4.5 seconds: $\dfrac{4.25 - 4.0}{4.5 - 4.0} = 0.5$ m/s

EXPLORE *continued*

Since the graph is linear, all velocities are the same and are equal to the slope of the line.

ii. In Graph ii, the velocity one-quarter of the way into the walk should be negative, because the distance to the motion detector is decreasing. At the halfway point, the velocity should be close to zero because the walker should be changing direction. Three-quarters of the way into the walk, the velocity should be positive because the distance to the motion detector is increasing. (Here the left endpoints are used for velocity estimates.)

- At 1.5 seconds: $\frac{3.0 - 3.5}{2.0 - 1.5} = -1.0$ m/s

- At 3.0 seconds: $\frac{2.5 - 2.0}{3.5 - 3.0} = 1.0$ m/s

  (Using the table values on each side of 3 seconds gives $\frac{0}{1} = 0$ m/s.)

- At 4.5 seconds: $\frac{4.0 - 3.5}{5.0 - 4.5} = 1.0$ m/s

The graph is made up of two linear pieces, one piece showing a walk toward the detector and the other away from the detector. Since these are straight line segments, the velocities are constant and equal to the slope of the line. For the first part of the walk, the velocity is −1 m/s; and for the second part of the walk, the velocity is 1 m/s.

iii. For Graph iii, the absolute value of the velocity, or speed, decreases over the entire length of the walk. Note that the velocity is always negative. (Here the midpoints are used for velocity estimates.)

- At 1.5 seconds: $\frac{2.8 - 4.0}{2.0 - 1.0} = -1.2$ m/s

- At 3.0 seconds: $\frac{1.8 - 2.4}{3.5 - 2.5} = -0.6$ m/s

- At 4.5 seconds: $\frac{1.4 - 1.6}{5.0 - 4.0} = -0.2$ m/s

Since the graph starts off with a rate of change of about −2 and gradually levels off, the velocity starts off at about −2 m/s and gradually approaches zero.

iv. For Graph iv, the velocity at the one-quarter mark will be positive, at the halfway mark the velocity will be zero, and at the three-quarters mark it will be negative. This matches the pattern of the graph which increases and then turns, and decreases. (Here the midpoints are used for velocity estimates.)

- At 1.5 seconds: $\frac{5.0 - 3.5}{2.0 - 1.0} = 1.5$ m/s

- At 3.0 seconds: $\frac{5.4 - 5.4}{3.5 - 2.5} = 0$ m/s (stopped)

- At 4.5 seconds: $\frac{3.5 - 5.0}{5.0 - 4.0} = -1.5$ m/s

Since the graph starts off fairly steep, levels off in the middle, and then becomes steep again, the velocity after 1 second is a fairly large positive value, the velocity in the middle is zero, and the velocity near the end of the walk is a negative value.

d. Students may have used different data, so groups should check to compare patterns and strategies rather than specific answers.

EXPLORE *continued*

2. **a.** Responses may vary. Reasonable responses include calculating the average velocity between the point in question and a previous point, between the point in question and a later point, or between one previous point and one later point. The first three bullets illustrate these three methods, respectively. The fourth method is not as reasonable since the time interval is longer. The last method is not reasonable as it is not a measure of change in distance per change in time.

NOTE: The concept of *deceleration* comes up for the first time in this activity. Rather than defining this term for the students, you can let them use their intuition about what this would mean. Then, you can discuss this concept with the class as part of the Checkpoint discussion.

b. The first group incorrectly calculated the velocity as $\frac{5.0 - 3.5}{5.0 - 4.0} = 1.5$ m/s, while the second group correctly calculated the velocity as $\frac{3.5 - 5.0}{5.0 - 4.0} = -1.5$ m/s. Velocity indicates both speed and direction. Negative velocity indicates that the distance between the walker and the detector is decreasing. In other words, the walker is approaching the detector.

c. A table of values giving time-distance data more frequently, perhaps every tenth of a second, would make it possible to make more accurate velocity estimates.

3. Acceleration occurs when velocity increases. The walker was accelerating when the distance (shown on the graph) was increasing at an increasing rate (between 0 and 3 seconds). Deceleration occurs when the velocity decreases. The walker was decelerating when the distance was increasing at a decreasing rate (between 3 and 6 seconds.)

Master 3

4. **a.** Meters per second (m/s)

b. Meters per second per second or meters per second squared (m/s^2)

SHARE AND SUMMARIZE **full-class discussion**

Checkpoint

See Teaching Master 3.

ⓐ To estimate velocity from a table or a graph, first identify the (*time*, *distance*) coordinates of two points near the time for which you want the velocity estimate. Then subtract the distances and divide this by the difference of the corresponding times.

ⓑ Velocity is expressed as a ratio of change in position over change in time.

ⓒ Acceleration can be estimated by finding the ratio of change in velocity to the length of the corresponding time interval. It also can be estimated by noting the shape of the graph. If the velocity is increasing rapidly, there must be high acceleration. If the velocity is slowing down, then negative acceleration or deceleration is occurring.

ⓓ Acceleration is expressed as a ratio of change in velocity over change in time.

APPLY individual task

▶**On Your Own**

a. The velocity at 3.5 seconds into the walk is approximately $\frac{3.5 - 3.0}{3.75 - 3.25} = 1$ m/s.

b. Since the graph is leveling off, the velocity is decreasing and so the walker is decelerating.

MORE
ASSIGNMENT   *pp. 12–19*

Students can now begin Modeling Task 1 or 3 or Organizing Task 1 from the MORE assignment following Investigation 3.

EXPLORE small-group investigation

INVESTIGATION 2 Chilling Out

   In this investigation, students are encouraged to again think about rate of change (of temperature) at specific points, in terms of the slope of the graph and of numerical calculations over defined intervals. Average rate of change, (*ending temperature – beginning temperature*) ÷ *elapsed time*, is introduced and compared to instantaneous rate of change. All the estimates that students have been finding in these first two investigations are really average rates of change, since they have no way of using a zero-width time interval. As students work on this investigation, you can bring this idea to their attention. How can you find a true instantaneous rate of change? (You have to find rates over smaller and smaller intervals, and hope that as the interval tends towards zero there is some logical limit to the values of the rates of change.)

   This investigation needs no introduction, so some groups can work ahead on this while other groups are still finishing Investigation 1.

1. **Group I**   The change in temperature is fairly rapid at first (about 4°C/min) and then, as time goes on, gradually levels off. After 40 minutes, the temperature appears to remain constant at about 20°C.

   Group II   The temperature decreases at a constant rate of 2°C/min.

   Group III   The temperature decreases very slowly at first and then, as time goes on, begins to decrease more rapidly.

2. **a.**   Degrees Celsius per minute (°C/min)

   b.   Estimates for rate of change may vary since they must be calculated from graphical information. All rates should be negative since the liquid is cooling. Encourage students to interpret the meaning of the negative sign.

   Pattern Reported by Group I

   Rate of cooling after 8 minutes: $\frac{60 - 85}{12 - 4} \approx -3.1$°C/min

   Rate of cooling after 20 minutes: $\frac{32 - 50}{24 - 16} = -2.25$°C/min

   Rate of cooling after 32 minutes: $\frac{22 - 28}{36 - 28} = -0.75$°C/min

EXPLORE *continued*

Pattern Reported by Group II

Rate of cooling after 8 minutes: $\frac{76-92}{12-4} = -2°\text{C/min}$

Rate of cooling after 20 minutes: $\frac{52-68}{24-16} = -2°\text{C/min}$

Rate of cooling after 32 minutes: $\frac{28-44}{36-28} = -2°\text{C/min}$

Pattern Reported by Group III

Rate of cooling after 8 minutes: $\frac{93-98}{12-4} \approx -0.6°\text{C/min}$

Rate of cooling after 20 minutes: $\frac{70-87}{24-16} \approx -2.1°\text{C/min}$

Rate of cooling after 32 minutes: $\frac{34-61}{36-28} \approx -3.4°\text{C/min}$

c. **Pattern Reported by Group I**

The rate of cooling (in absolute value) after 8 minutes is greater than the rate of cooling after 20 minutes, which is greater than the rate of cooling after 32 minutes. This decrease in the rate of cooling is shown by the continual decrease in the steepness of the graph.

Pattern Reported by Group II

Since the graph is linear, the rate of cooling is constant.

Pattern Reported by Group III

The rate of cooling (in absolute value) after 8 minutes is less than the rate of cooling after 20 minutes, which is less than the rate of cooling after 32 minutes. This increase in the rate of cooling is shown by the continual increase in the steepness of the graph.

d. A table of values giving time-temperature data every minute would help make more accurate estimates.

3. a. $\frac{-80°\text{C}}{40 \text{ min}} = -2°\text{C/min}$

b. On the graph from Group I, the average rate of change of $-2°$C/min is close to the estimate of instantaneous rate of change after 20 minutes. At 8 minutes, the rate of change is less than $-2°$C/min, and at 32 minutes it is greater than $-2°$C/min.

For the linear graph from Group II, the instantaneous rate of change is always the same as the average rate of change.

For the graph from Group III, the rate of change at 8 minutes is greater (less negative) than the overall average, at 20 minutes the instantaneous rate of change is close to the overall average, and at 32 minutes the instantaneous rate of change is less (more negative) than the overall average.

4. The first cooling pattern would be closest to experimental data, because the water would cool more quickly at first when the difference in water temperature and room temperature is greatest. Also, that graph is the only situation where the temperature of the water levels off to match the room temperature.

SHARE AND SUMMARIZE full-class discussion

Checkpoint

Master 4

See Teaching Master 4.

a Pick two times close together. Then, calculate the difference in temperature divided by the difference in time.

b Degrees per unit of time is the unit for change in temperature.

c In both cases, you estimate the rate of change by forming the quotient of the change in the quantity being measured divided by the change in time.

> **Master 4**
>
> **Checkpoint**
>
> Suppose you have used a temperature probe to collect data about the temperature of some liquid as time passes.
>
> **a** How can that data be used to estimate the rate of change in temperature?
>
> **b** What units would be used to report rate of change in temperature?
>
> **c** How is estimating rate of change in temperature similar to estimating rate of change in velocity of a moving object?
>
> *Be prepared to share your thinking with the class.*

APPLY individual task

On Your Own

Estimates for rate of change may vary since they must be calculated from graphical information.

a. $\frac{22 - 50}{32 - 16} \approx -1.75°C/min$

b. Approximately $\frac{30 - 35}{26 - 22} \approx -1.25°C/min$

c. It is not a good estimate because it is the average change over a 16-minute interval, not the instantaneous change at a point. To get a better estimate, the interval should be made much smaller.

MORE

ASSIGNMENT   *pp. 12–19*

Students can now begin Modeling Task 2 or Reflecting Task 1 or 3 from the MORE assignment following Investigation 3.

EXPLORE small-group investigation

INVESTIGATION 3 In the Swing of Things

In this investigation, the concepts discussed earlier appear in another context. The idea of average rate of change (velocity in this context) is expanded. You may wish to have a class discussion about the graphs, since students often misinterpret what is happening in these graphs. They may think that only half of a swing is pictured, from one side of the swing to the other, rather than the correct interpretation that this is a swing from one side to the other *and back again*. It may be that their mental picture of the path of a swing is distracting them from the distance/time information on the axes. The distance from takeoff starts and ends at 0. The peak of the graph is at the end of a single arc, not in mid-arc.

Some groups may complete Investigation 3 and the Checkpoint ahead of others. These groups could make a mini-report to you, to satisfy you that they understand the main ideas, and then go on to a MORE assignment. When everyone has finished the investigation, you should have a large group discussion of the Checkpoint.

EXPLORE *continued*

1. **a.** The pattern in Graph ii is more likely because trapeze flyers will slow down as they approach the farthest point from the take-off point in their swing. Graph ii shows this change in speed because it flattens out in the middle of the graph.

   b. The trapeze is traveling fastest at the points where the steepness of the graph is greatest. In Graph i, the trapeze will be at the point farthest from the take-off point. In Graph ii, the trapeze will be at the bottom of the swing both going and coming. These points are located on the following graphs.

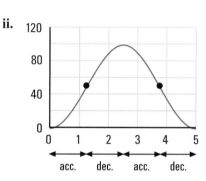

   c. The trapeze is accelerating and decelerating in the places indicated on the graphs above. The trapeze is accelerating in regions where the steepness of the graph increases. Similarly, the trapeze is decelerating in regions where the steepness of the graph decreases.

2. **a.** The first table corresponds to Graph ii and the second table corresponds to Graph i.

   b. As in previous investigations, estimation methods may vary. The following velocity estimates are based on the first table.

   Velocity after 0.5 second: $\frac{35-0}{1.0-0} = 35$ ft/sec

   Velocity after 1.5 seconds: $\frac{90-35}{2.0-1.0} = 55$ ft/sec

   Velocity after 2.5 seconds: $\frac{90-90}{3.0-2.0} = 0$ ft/sec

   Velocity after 3.5 seconds: $\frac{35-90}{4.0-3.0} = -55$ ft/sec

   c. As time increases from 0.5 second to 1.5 seconds, the steepness of the graph increases. The velocity estimate at 0.5 second is therefore less than the velocity estimate at 1.5 seconds. At 2.5 seconds, the graph is flat, which corresponds to a velocity estimate of 0 ft/sec. At 3.5 seconds, the steepness of the graph is the same as at 1.5 seconds. Therefore, the velocity estimates have opposite signs, but equal absolute values. (The graph on the next page illustrates these points.)

EXPLORE *continued*

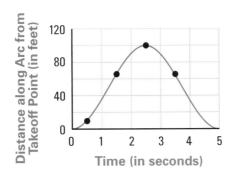

d. A table of values giving time-distance data more frequently, perhaps every tenth of a second, would allow for more accurate velocity estimates.

3. a. Estimates will depend on the interval used. Since *rate* • *time* = *distance*, $r = \frac{\Delta d}{\Delta t} = \frac{65 - 35}{1.5 - 1} = 60$ ft/sec. This maximum speed occurs at approximately 1.25 seconds and 3.75 seconds. At 1.25 seconds the velocity is 60 ft/sec; at 3.75 seconds the velocity is -60 ft/sec.

b. The average speed for a complete trip is $\frac{200}{5} = 40$ ft/sec, which is greater than the speed estimate at 0.5 second and 2.5 seconds and less than the speed estimates at 1.5 seconds and 3.5 seconds.

SHARE AND SUMMARIZE full-class discussion

Checkpoint

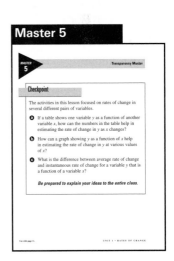

Master 5

See Teaching Master 5.

ⓐ To estimate the rate of change at a particular point, take two nearby points (or one nearby point and the particular point) and divide the difference in their *y*-values by the difference in their *x*-values.

ⓑ If the graph is linear, then the rate of change is the slope of the graph. For nonlinear graphs, the rate of change at a particular point can be estimated by the steepness (slope) of the graph near the point. The velocity is positive if the graph is increasing, and negative if the graph is decreasing.

ⓒ The average rate of change would be calculated over a given time period. The instantaneous rate of change would be estimated by an average rate of change for a time period that is very, very small.

NOTE: This is the first Math Toolkit entry for Course 4. Students should have retained their toolkits from Courses 1, 2, and 3. Those toolkits should contain the important mathematical ideas from the first three courses of this curriculum. See Teaching Master 36.

CONSTRUCTING A MATH TOOLKIT: After discussing the Checkpoint, students should summarize their understanding of average and instantaneous rates of change and how these can be estimated from tables or graphs in their Math Toolkit.

APPLY individual task

▶On Your Own

a. The profit after 8 days is approximately $200,000. Calculate the rate of change:
$\frac{300 - 125}{10 - 6} = 43.75$ or $43,750 per day.

b. The profit after 26 days is approximately $900,000. Calculate the rate of change:
$\frac{880 - 1,000}{27 - 25} = -60$ or $-$60,000 per day.

c. The rate of change is greatest at about the tenth day. Calculate the rate of change:
$\frac{550 - 200}{12 - 8} = 87.5$ or $87,500 per day.

d. The patterns of increase and decrease seem reasonable since more shopping takes place the closer it gets to Christmas and very little if any shopping takes place on Christmas. Immediately after Christmas people return unwanted presents. This accounts for the decrease in profit between December 25 and December 27.

MORE

ASSIGNMENT *pp. 12–19*

Modeling: 1, 2, and choice of one*

Organizing: 1, 2, and 4

Reflecting: 4 and choice of one*

Extending: 1 and 3

*When choice is indicated, it is important to leave the choice to the student.
NOTE: It is best if Organizing tasks are discussed as a whole class after they have been assigned as homework.

MORE independent assignment

Modeling

1. a. i. The oven temperature increases at a fairly constant rate for the first 4 minutes and then begins to increase more slowly, eventually leveling off at about 450°F.

ii. The oven temperature increases slowly, then rapidly, then slowly again as it nears 450°F. This seems to be the most likely pattern of change because an oven at room temperature does not initially heat up quickly. This slow initial increase in oven temperature is shown in Graph ii, whereas Graphs i and iii show a more steady, rapid initial increase in oven temperature.

iii. A constant rate of increase in oven temperature is shown by this graph.

b. Data Pattern A This table matches Graph iii. The linear pattern in the graph corresponds to the constant increase of 25 degrees every minute in the table.

Data Pattern B This table matches Graph ii. The gradual increase at the beginning and end of the graph corresponds to the smaller temperature increases in the table for the first three minutes and the last three minutes. The graph is steepest in the middle, corresponding to much greater temperature increases per minute in the middle of the table.

MORE *continued*

Data Pattern C This table matches Graph i. The table shows the oven temperature initially increasing at a fairly constant rate. As time goes on, this increase becomes less and less, which is reflected in the leveling off of the graph.

c. The estimated rate of heating at 5 minutes is

Data Pattern A $\frac{220-170}{6-4} = 25°\text{F/min}$

Data Pattern B $\frac{210-140}{6-4} = 35°\text{F/min}$

Data Pattern C $\frac{310-250}{6-4} = 30°\text{F/min}$

Since the temperature is measured in degrees Fahrenheit and time in minutes, the rate of heating is reported in degrees Fahrenheit per minute.

2. a. $\frac{700-150}{12 \text{ P.M.} - 10 \text{ A.M.}} = \frac{550}{2} = 275$, a gain of 275 people/hour

   b. $\frac{900-700}{2 \text{ P.M.} - 12 \text{ P.M.}} = \frac{200}{2} = 100$, a gain of 100 people/hour

   c. $\frac{775-900}{4 \text{ P.M.} - 2 \text{ P.M.}} = \frac{-125}{2} = -62.5$, a loss of approximately 62 people/hour

   d. $\frac{150-775}{6 \text{ P.M.} - 4 \text{ P.M.}} = \frac{-625}{2} = -312.50$, a loss of approximately 312 people/hour

   e. $\frac{75-150}{8 \text{ P.M.} - 6 \text{ P.M.}} = \frac{-75}{2} = -37.5$, a loss of approximately 37 people/hour

3. a. Responses may vary. One possible sketch is shown at the right.

   b. Tables of values will vary. Be sure that the data in the table matches the graph drawn in Part a.

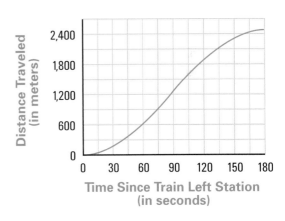

Time (in seconds)	0	15	30	45	60	75	90	105	120	135	150	165	180
Distance (in meters)	0	50	200	400	600	900	1,250	1,600	1,900	2,100	2,300	2,450	2,500

   c. The train starts off slowly then picks up speed reaching its maximum speed halfway through the trip and then begins to slow down as it approaches the station. The train was accelerating during the first half of the trip because its speed was always increasing during this time and it was decelerating during the second half of the trip because its speed was decreasing during this time.

4. Each experiment will have unique data. The patterns should match the patterns from Investigation 3.

NOTE: Students will need a CBL for this task.

Unit 1

MORE *continued*

Organizing

1. **a.** At 0.5 second, the speed is about $\frac{28.5 - 11.5}{0.75 - 0.25} = 34$ ft/sec. Since the ball is traveling up, its velocity is 34 ft/sec. At 2.5 seconds, the speed is about 30 ft/sec, but since the ball is coming down, its velocity is -30 ft/sec.

   b. Speed is always positive, while velocity can be positive or negative. If the ball is going up, then its velocity is positive. If the ball is coming down, then its velocity is negative. In both cases, speed is the absolute value of the velocity. Both the table and the graph show increasing values in the height when the velocity is positive and decreasing values in the height when the velocity is negative.

2. **a.**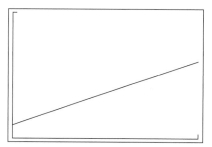

   A linear function with positive slope would match this pattern.

   b.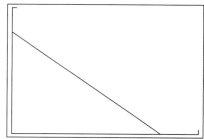

   A linear function with negative slope would match this pattern.

   c.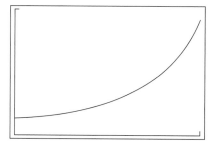

   An exponential growth or power function would match this pattern.

   d.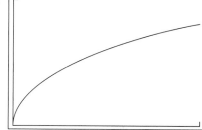

   A square root or cube root function would match this pattern.

   e.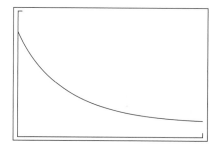

   An exponential decay function would match this pattern. (A power function with negative exponent would give a decrease, but not a *y*-intercept.)

MORE *continued*

3. From 0 to 5 seconds, the distance to the radar detector is decreasing, so the velocity during this time period is negative and the speed of the car is decreasing. At 5 seconds, the car is passing the radar gun location so the velocity is 0 ft/sec for an instant. After 5 seconds, the car is traveling away from the radar detector, the velocity is positive. Both the speed and the velocity are increasing.

4. **a.** $\frac{d(5) - d(1)}{5 - 1}$ ft/sec

   b. $\frac{d(6) - d(0)}{6 - 0}$ ft/sec

   c. $\frac{d(b) - d(a)}{b - a}$ ft/sec

   d. Responses may vary, but should indicate evaluating the distance function close to $t = 3$, for example, $\frac{d(3.1) - d(3)}{0.1}$ ft/sec.

   e. One possible estimate is $\frac{d(a + 0.1) - d(a)}{0.1}$ ft/sec.

Reflecting

1. **a.** Responses may include motion detector, radar detector, and sonar detector.

   b. Response should include mention of appropriate units, such as meters per second, feet per minute, and so on. To estimate the rate of change in that quantity at any point in time, choose an interval containing the point and compute the average rate of change over that interval.

2. The ride will be slowest at the very top of a hill on the roller coaster because you essentially stop for an instant. The ride will be fastest at the bottom of a hill because the speed continues to increase until you reach the bottom, at which point you start to go uphill, losing speed.

3. No, Maurice ran the 10 m between 50 and 60 m faster (11.9 m/s) than any other 10 m of the race. However, his speed for the last 50 m of the race is almost constant.

4. Yes, the instantaneous rate of change is approximated by using the average rate of change for a very small time interval, theoretically approaching zero. (Some students may realize that if they could find this average for an interval of width 0, that would be exactly the instantaneous rate of change.)

Extending

1. **a.** By using the data from the table or by reading approximate coordinates for a number of points on the given graph and using quadratic regression with a graphing calculator, you will come up with a function rule close to $d(t) = -16t^2 + 50t$.

   b. Using the function rule in Part a, the maximum point is (1.5625, 39.0625). The velocity at this point should be 0 ft/sec. To check, calculate something like $\frac{d(1.6625) - d(1.4625)}{0.2}$ which is 0 ft/sec.

MORE *continued*

2. **a.** As time increases, the speed increases slowly, then more rapidly, and finally begins to level off.

    b. The car seems to be accelerating most rapidly at about 5 seconds. The car accelerates most rapidly when the rate of change in the speed is the greatest, that is, where the graph is steepest and the table shows the greatest change in speed per second increase in time.

    c. The acceleration at 4 seconds is approximately $\frac{50-22}{5-3} = 14$ mph/sec. Since the speed is reported in mph and time in seconds, the acceleration is given in miles per hour per second.

    d. ■ $\left(\frac{50\text{ miles}}{1\text{ hour}}\right)\left(\frac{1\text{ hour}}{3,600\text{ seconds}}\right)(10\text{ seconds}) \approx 0.14$ mi

    ■ $\left(\frac{75\text{ miles}}{1\text{ hour}}\right)\left(\frac{1\text{ hour}}{3,600\text{ seconds}}\right)\left(\frac{5,280\text{ feet}}{1\text{ mile}}\right)(8\text{ seconds}) = 880$ ft

    e. The mean speed during the 10-second trip, found using the table values, is 55 mph. Thus, the total distance traveled would be approximately 0.15 mi, or 806.7 ft.

3. **a.** Using the recursive equation $P_t = 1.5P_{t-1}$ and the initial value $P_0 = 10$,

    $$P_0 = 10$$
    $$P_1 = 1.5P_0 = 1.5(10)$$
    $$P_2 = 1.5P_1 = 1.5(1.5)(10) = 1.5^2 \cdot 10$$
    $$P_3 = 1.5P_2 = 1.5(1.5^2)(10) = 1.5^3 \cdot 10$$

    By this pattern $P_t = 10(1.5^t)$.

    b. The constant 1.5 is the exponential growth rate factor. It says that the population at any time is 1.5 times the population one time unit earlier.

    c. $P_t - P_{t-1} = 0.5P_{t-1}$
    $$P_t = P_{t-1} + 0.5P_{t-1}$$
    $$P_t = 1.5P_{t-1}$$

    d. This calculation shows that the population increase over any time period is equal to one-half the population at the beginning of that period.

    e. $y = 10(1.5^x)$

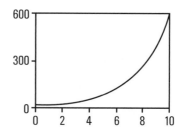

MORE *continued*

The instantaneous rate of change in population can be estimated at any time t by calculating $\dfrac{P(t + 0.01) - P(t - 0.01)}{0.02}$. In general, you will find that these estimates (people or fruit flies or bacteria per unit of time) will increase over time. This is shown in the fact that the graph of $P(t) = 10(1.5^t)$ is a curve that bends upward as time increases. The cruder approximation calculated by the formula in Part d also shows a rate of change (population per unit of time) that is increasing as the population increases over time.

4. a. The ball travels the shortest distance in the straight line ramp in the middle. For the other two curve ramps, the distances appear to be about the same.

   b. Imagine a strobe light flashing at regular intervals. (See the diagrams below.) The ball has the greatest speed for the steepest descent ramp, which is the first ramp. The ball has the slowest speed for the third ramp. The speed is determined by the component of gravity acting on the ball in the direction of the motion. For the first ramp, the component is very large (the ball is almost dropping vertically). For the second ramp, a medium fraction of the force due to gravity is acting on the ball. For the last ramp, only a small fraction of the force due to gravity is pointed towards the direction of motion.

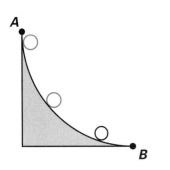 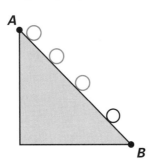 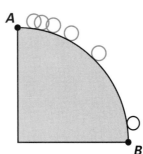

   c. To answer this question, consider the energy of the ball at *A* and *B*. The energy of position of the ball depends only on the positions of *A* and *B*, which are the same for each ramp. The difference in energy, if none is lost to friction, is converted entirely to energy of motion, which is equal to $\frac{1}{2}mv^2$. Since the mass of the ball is the same for each ramp, the magnitude of the velocity is also the same (though the direction is different).

   d. Based on the strobe light diagram and the thinking above, the ball will reach the bottom in the order of the diagrams.

   e. Possible graphs of the speed as a function of distance for each corresponding ramp are

i. 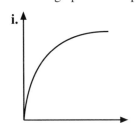 ii. 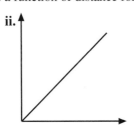 iii.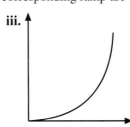

See Masters 6a–6e for Maintenance tasks that students can work on following Lesson 1.

See Assessment Resources pages 1–6.

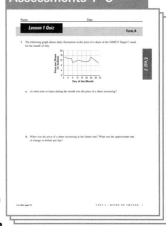

Assessments 1–3

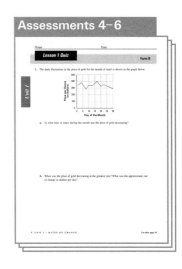

Assessments 4–6

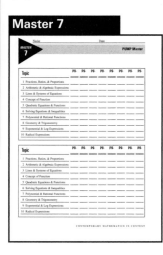

Master 7

REVIEW AND PRACTICE individual task

▶ **PUMP**

The ten exercises in the PUMP sections are drawn from ten general areas that are typically tested on college placement tests. The exercises are in the same order in each set. The Teaching Resources includes Master 7—a record sheet that students can use to keep track of their progress and performance on the PUMP sets. If students are consistently missing the same number exercise(s), you may want to suggest extra work on similar exercises. You may wish to assign the PUMP before the end of the lesson, particularly if a MORE assignment is not appropriate for a particular day's homework.

Answers

1. (c)   6. (a)

2. (d)   7. (c)

3. (e)   8. (a)

4. (a)   9. (e)

5. (e)   10. (d)

Lesson 2 *Rates of Change for Familiar Functions*

LESSON OVERVIEW The first investigation in this lesson relates familiar function models and their graphs to average and instantaneous rates of change. Essentially, students are repeating their efforts from Lesson 1, but not by using numerical data provided in a table or read from a graph. By the end of the second investigation, students should be able to estimate average and instantaneous rates of change for any function, given the equation. This process lends itself to using graphing calculators; for example, $y_2 = \frac{y_1(x + 0.1) - y_1(x - 0.1)}{0.2}$ provides a handy table for estimates of rates of change for $y_1 = f(x)$. (See Technology Tips in Teaching Masters 12 and 13 for use with Investigation 3.) The goal in Investigations 1 and 2 is *not* to find derivative functions.

In Investigations 3 through 5, students make the leap from a numerical method of approximating rates of change at specific points to conjecturing about the form of derivative functions for familiar types of functions. Investigation 3 gives them the opportunity to conjecture about the derivative functions for quadratic functions and for linear functions. They do not have to have a formula in response to "What is the derivative function for a quadratic?" It is more important that it make sense to them that the derivative function for a quadratic should be a linear function. In Investigation 4, students generate tables and graphs for estimated derivative functions for other types of functions given the function rules. They consider the shape of the estimate of the derivative function and how this seems to relate to the original function or changes in the parameters in the original function. In Investigation 5, students sketch a graph of the derivative function without doing any calculation, just by interpreting the slopes at different points on the function graph.

Lesson Objectives

- To describe how the rate of change of a function at various points is shown by the shape of the function's graph
- To estimate the rate of change of a function at any point on its graph by using the function rule
- To understand the similarities and differences in estimating the rate of change for linear and nonlinear functions, and how those methods are related to finding the slope of a straight line
- To discover ways to use the rule of a given function to find the rule of its derivative function
- To discover some general patterns relating various function types to their derivatives
- To explain how the shape of the graph of a function can be used to describe and sketch the graph of its derivative

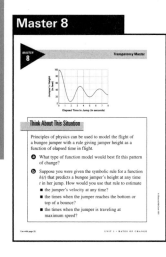

Master 8

LAUNCH full-class discussion

Think About This Situation

See Teaching Master 8.

ⓐ The bouncing pattern looks somewhat like a cosine or sine function, but the oscillations decrease in amplitude over time. (There are several ways to accomplish this "damped vibration." Students are not expected to be able to figure out a specific function that will do the job.)

ⓑ ■ To estimate the velocity at any particular time, compute the average rate of change of the function $h(t)$ over a small interval containing that time. The resulting velocity should be positive if $h(t)$ is increasing and negative if $h(t)$ is decreasing over the time interval.

■ Use the rule to create the graph or table from which estimates of the times when the graph is at a peak (corresponding to the top of the bounce) or valley (corresponding to the bottom of the bounce) can be made. Alternatively, you could estimate the times when the jumper reaches the bottom or top of a bounce by looking for times when the velocity estimate is 0.

■ The times when the jumper is traveling at maximum speed could be estimated from the graph by looking for the places where the graph is steepest, that is, where the magnitude (or absolute value) of the ratio of the change in height over a small elapsed time period is greatest.

EXPLORE small-group investigation

INVESTIGATION 1 ▷ Reasoning with Rules About Rates

There is no Checkpoint until after Activity 13. As in Lesson 1, you can let students work at their own pace through the activities without any need for introductions or large-group summaries. If you are concerned about letting your students work for a long period without drawing everyone together to compare answers and discuss differences, you may wish to summarize each set of activities as a class following each function type. Another alternative is to prepare answers for selected questions on transparencies or allow students to consult the *Teacher's Guide*. Students can then pause briefly and check answers as needed.

At some point in this investigation, you may find students are using their calculators to set up tables so that they can produce estimates of instantaneous rates of change at any desired point, instead of doing these calculations one point at a time. This is a transitional step to creating a derivative function. The answers they get are still estimates, but the fact that they are using a formula on the function screen of a calculator can help you to introduce the idea that the rate of change at a point is related in a patterned, functional way to the independent variable.

EXPLORE *continued*

One method students may suggest to estimate the rate of change at a point is indicated below. Define a function in the $\boxed{Y=}$ menu. Then, on the home screen, evaluate the difference equation. Better estimates can be obtained using $\boxed{2nd}$ ANS and editing the numerical values.

```
Plot1 Plot2 Plot3
\Y1 ▤3X²–3X
\Y2 =
\Y3 =
\Y4 =
\Y5 =
\Y6 =
\Y7 =
```

```
(Y1(2.47)–Y1 (2.4))/(2.47
–2.4)
                    11.61
(Y1(2.47)–Y1(2.46))/(2.47
–2.46)
                    11.79
```

Linear Functions

In Activities 1–3, students review the rate of change of a linear function. Most students will go directly to the parameter for slope. If some seem to want to redo calculations similar to Lesson 1, you can let that happen; they will soon realize that is unnecessary.

1. **a.** 525 mph

    b. The plane always travels at 525 mph.

    c. For every 1-hour increase, the (*time*, *distance*) table will show an increase in distance of 525 mi. The graph will be linear with a slope of 525.

2. **a.** For each dollar increase in selling price, the number of CDs sold will decrease by 5 (5,000).

    b. For every dollar increase in price, the (*price*, *sales*) table will show a decrease of 5 (5,000) in the number of CDs sold. The graph will be linear, with a slope of –5.

3. **a.** b

    b. For every unit increase in x, y changes by b units. The graph will be linear with slope b. For a function with a linear rule, the rate of change is the coefficient of the independent variable.

    c. $b = \frac{y-a}{x}$

Quadratic Functions

In Activities 4–8, students estimate rates of change at specific points on the graph of a quadratic function. While they are learning to make sense of using the equation to do this, you might want to ask if there is a pattern to the rates of change. It is very easy and useful to be able to immediately deduce the rate of change at any point on a linear function, just by observing the equation. It would be useful to be able to do this for quadratic functions also. Ask your students to compare the two situations.

EXPLORE *continued*

Why can't they give one rate of change for *any* point on a quadratic, as they could for a linear function? (Because the rate of change changes.) Does the rate of change for a quadratic function change randomly? (That there is a pattern to the rates of change foreshadows finding a symbolic model for rate of change—the derivative function.)

4. **a.** The diver hits the surface when the height equals 0. Solving $30 - 4.9t^2 = 0$ gives $t = \sqrt{\dfrac{30}{4.9}} \approx 2.47$ seconds.

NOTE: Before continuing, make sure that students discuss this problem. Activities that follow will lead students through various ways to estimate the diver's speed.

   b. The average velocity of the diver from takeoff to hitting the water is $\dfrac{h(0) - h(2.47)}{0 - 2.47}$ $= \dfrac{30 - 0}{0 - 2.47} \approx -12$ m/s.

   c. His average speed is approximately 12 m/s. As time increases, his speed will gradually increase until he hits the water. This increase in speed is shown by the continual increase in the steepness of the graph of $h(t)$.

5. Group strategies will vary.

NOTE: When finding average speeds, students might be tempted to arrange the terms in the numerator and denominator so that both are positive, but at this point it is important for them to be consistent in how they calculate the differences. Students can then think about when the rate of change is positive and when it is negative and what that means.

6. **a.** $\dfrac{h(1) - h(2.47)}{1 - 2.47} \approx \dfrac{25.1 - 0.10559}{1 - 2.47} \approx -17$ m/s

The average speed is 17 m/s. (–17 m/s is the velocity, which takes direction into account).

   b. $\dfrac{h(2) - h(2.47)}{2 - 2.47} \approx -21.9$ m/s. The average speed is approximately 21.9 m/s.

   c. $\dfrac{h(2.4) - h(2.47)}{2.4 - 2.47} \approx -23.9$ m/s. The average speed is approximately 23.9 m/s.

   d. $\dfrac{h(2.46) - h(2.47)}{2.46 - 2.47} \approx -24.2$ m/s. The average speed is approximately 24.2 m/s.

   e. Parts a–d suggest that the diver hits the water with an approximate speed of 24.2 m/s.

7. **a.** Here are three methods students might use

$\dfrac{h(1) - h(0.99)}{1 - 0.99} \approx -9.75$ m/s

$\dfrac{h(1.01) - h(1)}{1.01 - 1} \approx -9.85$ m/s

$\dfrac{h(1.01) - h(0.99)}{1.01 - 0.99} \approx -9.8$ m/s

A good estimate of the diver's speed is 9.8 m/s.

EXPLORE *continued*

b. As in Part a, students may try any number of methods, including:

$$\frac{h(2) - h(1.99)}{2 - 1.99} \approx -19.55 \text{ m/s}$$

$$\frac{h(2.01) - h(2)}{2.01 - 2} \approx -19.65 \text{ m/s}$$

$$\frac{h(2.01) - h(1.99)}{2.01 - 1.99} \approx -19.6 \text{ m/s}$$

A good estimate of the diver's speed is 19.6 m/s.

c. Here are two methods that students might try:

$$\frac{h(0.01) - h(0)}{0.01 - 0} \approx -0.049 \text{ m/s}$$

$$\frac{h(0.001) - h(0)}{0.001 - 0} \approx -0.0049 \text{ m/s}$$

It appears that the instant he takes off from his dive, his speed is 0 m/s.

8. Since the diver is always going in the same direction and that direction is clear to everybody, speed can be used instead of velocity.

Exponential Functions

Activities 9 and 10 repeat the effort of finding instantaneous and average rates of change for an exponential function. This time the important difference is that the rate of change always increases. In fact, the rate of change changes in the same way that the original function does. As students work on these activities, remind them of the big picture. You want to know if there is a pattern in how the rate of change is changing. How is this pattern similar to or different from the patterns they observed for linear and quadratic functions?

9. Note that choices of points and rounding errors will account for some differences in answers. Have students with different answers explain their methods so students can see how rounding errors can affect the final answers.

a. ■ $\frac{100(2^{0.2(20)}) - 100(2^0)}{20 - 0} = 75$ flies/day

■ Responses may vary, depending on the estimation strategy. However, estimates for the growth rate should be close to the following:

Day 0: $\frac{100(2^{0.2(0.01)}) - 100(2^0)}{0.01 - 0} \approx 14$ flies/day

Day 10: $\frac{100(2^{0.2(10.1)}) - 100(2^{0.2(9.9)})}{10.1 - 9.9} \approx 55$ flies/day

Day 20: $\frac{100(2^{0.2(20.1)}) - 100(2^{0.2(19.9)})}{20.1 - 19.9} \approx 222$ flies/day

b. ■ $\frac{100(2^{0.2(40)}) - 100(2^{0.2(20)})}{40 - 20} = 1,200$ flies/day

■ Responses may vary, depending on the estimation strategy. However, estimates for the growth rates should be close to the following:

Day 20: Approximately 222 flies/day

Day 30: $\frac{100(2^{0.2(30.1)}) - 100(2^{0.2(29.9)})}{30.1 - 29.9} \approx 887$ flies/day

Day 40: $\frac{100(2^{0.2(40.1)}) - 100(2^{0.2(39.9)})}{40.1 - 39.9} \approx 3,549$ flies/day

EXPLORE *continued*

10. Student sketches should have the axes labeled. Since students know the general shape of exponential functions, they might produce the graph with their calculator or plot a few points.

   From Activity 9, students will see that as time increases, the rate of growth increases very rapidly. This continual rapid increase in the rate of growth is reflected in the graph by the way it becomes steeper and steeper as time increases. The average rate of change from one day to a later day is between the instantaneous rates of change at the two days but closer to the lower rate of change due to the rapid growth rate.

Trigonometric Functions

   In the final activities of this lesson, students find that they must apply the computational method they have been using with care. When the original function is periodic, the rate of change changes in a periodic way, so that you can predict when the greatest rates of change will occur, and you can also predict when the rate of change will change its sign. They find out that care must be taken not to average a rate of change over an inappropriate interval.

   If your students have been working at their own pace, you may find that groups have reached this point at very different times, so you will have to be ready with a MORE assignment for early finishers. When everyone has caught up, draw the class together for a large group discussion of the Checkpoint.

11. **a.** The water depth increases to a maximum value of 24 ft, then decreases to a minimum value of 6 ft, and then increases again to 24 ft. This pattern repeats about every 12 hours.

   b. At $t = 0$, the water depth is 15 ft.

   At $t = 3$, the water depth is approximately 24 ft.

   At $t = 6$, the water depth is approximately 16.3 ft.

   At $t = 9$, the water depth is approximately 6.2 ft.

   At $t = 12$, the water depth is approximately 12.5 ft.

   c. The average rate of change in water depth for:

   i. $0 \le t \le 3$ is approximately $\frac{24 - 15}{3} = 3$ ft/hr;

   ii. $3 \le t \le 6$ is approximately -2.6 ft/hr;

   iii. $6 \le t \le 9$ is approximately -3.4 ft/hr;

   iv. $9 \le t \le 12$ is approximately 2.1 ft/hr.

EXPLORE *continued*

d. $\frac{D(6) - D(0)}{6 - 0} \approx 0.21$ ft/hr

$\frac{D(12) - D(6)}{12 - 6} \approx -0.63$ ft/hr

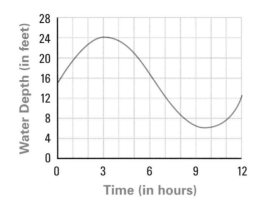

From the above calculations, you might conclude that the water depth stays almost constant between $t = 0$ and $t = 6$ hours, but the graph at the right shows that this is not the case. The water depth is almost the same at these two times, but in between the water depth increases, reaches its maximum depth, and then decreases.

You might also conclude that the water depth only decreases between $t = 6$ and $t = 12$ hours (-0.63 ft/hr). However, the graph above tells a different story. Although the water depth is decreasing at first, it reaches a minimum depth and then increases.

12. a. The average rate of change in water depth for:

$9 \le t \le 10$ is approximately 0.2 ft/hr;

$10 \le t \le 11$ is approximately 2.3 ft/hr.

b. The average rate of change in water depth for:

$9.5 \le t \le 10$ is approximately 0.7 ft/hr;

$10 \le t \le 10.5$ is approximately 1.8 ft/hr.

c. The average rate of change in water depth for:

$9.9 \le t \le 10$ is approximately 1.2 ft/hr;

$10 \le t \le 10.1$ is approximately 1.4 ft/hr.

d. The pattern suggests the rate of change in water depth at $t = 10$ is approximately 1.3 ft/hr.

e. The graph reaches its minimum at about $t = 9.5$ and then increases as time goes on. Also, the graph increases in steepness between $t = 9.5$ and $t = 11$. Therefore, the rate of change estimates which use points to the left of $(10, D(10))$ will underestimate the rate of change at $t = 10$ and the estimates which use points to the right of $(10, D(10))$ will overestimate the rate of change.

Master 9

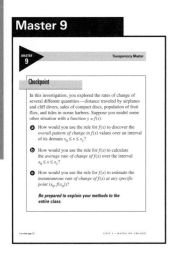

EXPLORE *continued*

13. In the graph at the right, points labeled *A* are where the tide is moving in most rapidly, points labeled *B* are where the tide is moving out most rapidly, and points labeled *C* are where the tide is moving in or out most slowly. The period of this graph is 4π or approximately 12.6. (You may wish to encourage students to examine the table of values as well as the graph to see these patterns.)

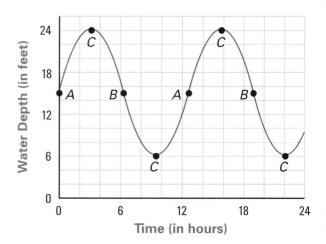

a. The times when the water is moving in most rapidly are $t = 0 + 12.6n$, $n = 0, 1, 2, \ldots$. At points *A*, the rate of change in water depth is approximately $\frac{D(12.6) - D(12.5)}{12.6 - 12.5} \approx 4.5$ ft/hr.

b. The times when it is moving out most rapidly are $t = 6.3 + 12.6n$, $n = 0, 1, 2, \ldots$. At points *B*, the rate of change in water depth is approximately $\frac{D(6.3) - D(6.2)}{6.3 - 6.2} \approx -4.5$ ft/hr.

c. The times when it is moving in or out most slowly are $t = 3.15 + 6.3n$, $n = 0, 1, 2, \ldots$. At points *C*, the rate of change in water depth is approximately $\frac{D(3.2) - D(3.1)}{3.2 - 3.1} \approx 0$ ft/hr.

SHARE AND SUMMARIZE   full-class discussion

Checkpoint

See Teaching Master 9.

Before the Checkpoint, you may wish to provide an opportunity for students to pull together the ways in which the patterns for the rates of change were different for all the types of functions that they investigated. You might start them off by writing on the overhead:

> "Linear function: the most noticeable thing was that the rate of change was constant, and in fact is the slope of the original function."

> "Quadratic function: the most noticeable thing was that . . ." (Students might say that the rate of change changed in a symmetric way, negative for some *x*-values and positive for others.)

> "Exponential function . . ." (Students might observe that the rate of change gets ever faster, that is, the rate is constantly accelerating.)

> "Periodic function . . ." (Students might describe the rate of change as periodic also, that is, it predictably accelerates and decelerates at set intervals, and switches from positive to negative rates at the same intervals.)

SHARE AND SUMMARIZE *continued*

a Responses may vary. Students should make reference to using the function rule to produce a graph or table, at least for functions that are nonlinear. If the graph is increasing, then the rate of change is positive and if the graph is decreasing, the rate of change is negative. Also, the steeper the graph is, the greater (in absolute value) the rate of change.

b Compute the following ratio: $\frac{f(x_1) - f(x_0)}{x_1 - x_0}$.

c You could calculate the average rate of change over the interval defined by two points very close to $(x_0, f(x_0))$, one with x-value slightly less than x_0 and one with x-value slightly greater than x_0. Alternately, you could calculate the average rate of change over the interval defined by $(x_0, f(x_0))$ and a point very close to it, such as $(x_0 + 0.1, f(x_0 + 0.1))$.

CONSTRUCTING A MATH TOOLKIT: Students should summarize the methods of using function rules to discover overall patterns of change, to calculate the average rate of change over an interval, and to estimate the instantaneous rate of change at a point.

APPLY individual task

▶**On Your Own**

a. Responses should be fairly close to the following. The following coordinates are used in calculating the average velocities:

Starting point: (0, 93)

Bottom of the first fall: (1.8, 4)

Top of the first bounce: (3.4, 50)

Bottom of the second fall: (5, 19)

Top of the second bounce: (6.6, 42)

Based on the values above, the jumper's average velocity:

■ from the start to bottom of first fall is −49.4 ft/sec;

■ from the bottom of first fall to top of first bounce is 28.8 ft/sec;

■ from the top of first bounce to bottom of second fall is −19.4 ft/sec;

■ from the bottom of second fall to top of second bounce is 14.4 ft/sec.

b. The average velocity of the jumper in the time interval:

■ from $t = 0$ to $t = 0.5$ is $\frac{h(0.5) - h(0)}{0.5 - 0} \approx -20.5$ ft/sec;

■ from $t = 0.5$ to $t = 1.0$ is $\frac{h(1.0) - h(0.5)}{1.0 - 0.5} \approx -80.5$ ft/sec;

■ from $t = 1.0$ to $t = 1.5$ is $\frac{h(1.5) - h(1.0)}{1.5 - 1.0} \approx -64$ ft/sec;

■ from $t = 1.5$ to $t = 2$ is $\frac{h(2) - h(1.5)}{2 - 1.5} \approx -10$ ft/sec.

c. Responses may vary slightly, depending on the method used, but should produce similar results. The jumper's estimated instantaneous velocity at:

■ (0.5, 82.951) is $\frac{h(0.5) - h(0.49)}{0.5 - 0.49} \approx -65$ ft/sec;

APPLY *continued*

- (1.0, 42.7) is $\dfrac{h(1.0) - h(0.99)}{1.0 - 0.99} \approx -83$ ft/sec;

- (1.5, 10.679) is $\dfrac{h(1.5) - h(1.49)}{1.5 - 1.49} \approx -40$ ft/sec;

- (2.0, 5.6679) is $\dfrac{h(2) - h(1.99)}{2 - 1.99} \approx 17$ ft/sec.

d. In Part b, students should note that although the time intervals are the same length, the average velocity is different for each interval. This is due to the fact that the change in the jumper's height is not the same over each interval. From 0–0.5 second, the graph is not as steep as it is from 0.5–1.0 second. Thus, the average velocity for the first time interval is less (in absolute value) than the average velocity for the second time interval.

In Part c, students should note that at 0.5 second, 1.0 second, and 1.5 seconds the velocity is negative because the graph is decreasing, but that at 2 seconds, the velocity is positive because the graph is increasing.

Also, the steeper the graph, the larger the velocity (in absolute value), so, for example, since the graph is steeper at 1 second than at 0.5 second, 1.5 seconds, or 2 seconds, the velocity is greater (in absolute value).

e. The time at which the bungee jumper is falling at the greatest velocity is approximately 0.8 seconds. This time corresponds to the point on the graph where the graph is the steepest. From a table, you could locate this point by looking for the time interval where there is the greatest change in height for equal changes in time.

MORE

ASSIGNMENT *pp. 41–49*

Students can now begin Modeling Task 1 from the MORE assignment following Investigation 5.

EXPLORE small-group investigation

INVESTIGATION 2 The Linear Connection

The main idea in this investigation is that finding a rate of change depends on treating a curve as if it were a series of very short line segments which approximate the curve. Making the segments as short as possible makes the estimation process more accurate. This is, of course, the process which is taken to its logical limit in finding derivative functions. Be sure to ask students why you want the "segment" to be as short as possible. At this point your students have noticed a pattern in rates of change for different functions, but probably do not suspect that the rate of change is a familiar function of *x* also. (However, if they have been using the function screen of their calculators to enter the estimator rule, you can take advantage of this in the discussion in Investigation 3.) Before doing Activity 2, be sure the students know how to use the zoom box feature of their calculator. There may be students in your class who can demonstrate this feature.

EXPLORE *continued*

1. **a.** You could find the rate of change (slope of the line) by computing any of the following ratios: $\frac{y_3 - y_1}{x_3 - x_1}$ or $\frac{y_2 - y_1}{x_2 - x_1}$ or $\frac{y_3 - y_2}{x_3 - x_2}$.

   b. You could estimate the rate of change by computing any of the following ratios: $\frac{y_3 - y_1}{x_3 - x_1}$ or $\frac{y_2 - y_1}{x_2 - x_1}$ or $\frac{y_3 - y_2}{x_3 - x_2}$. (Students may have other suggestions.)

   c. The methods are similar because you compute exactly the same quotient for each. The methods are different in that the quotient gives the exact rate of change for a linear function, but only gives an estimate for a nonlinear function.

2. **a–c.** The closer you zoom in to (3, 9), the more nearly linear the graph looks. This happens at any point you zoom in on for all of the functions in this activity.

3. The particular points students use to make the estimates may vary, but the difference between the *x*-values should be very small in order to give a fairly good estimate. Here are some reasonable estimates:

   a. The rate of change in $f(x)$ at (3, 9) is approximately 6.

   b. The rate of change in $g(x)$ at (3, 2.5) is approximately –1.7.

   c. The rate of change in $h(x)$ at $\left(\frac{\pi}{2}, 0\right)$ is –1.

   When finding the slope of a linear function, you choose two points on the line and compute the difference in the *y*-values divided by the difference in the *x*-values. Moreover, the rate of change in the function is the same as the slope for linear functions. From Activity 2, the graph looks linear when you zoom in on a nonlinear function at any point. Therefore, if you want to estimate the rate of change of a nonlinear function at a particular point, you can zoom in at that point and approximate the nonlinear function with a linear one.

TECHNOLOGY NOTE: ZBox is located under the ZOOM menu. Move the cursor to one corner of the box you wish. Press ENTER to select the corner, then move the cursor to the opposite corner and press ENTER again. The graph will be automatically replotted.

4. **See Teaching Master 10.**
   This activity uses the reverse process of that used in approximating the rate of change of a curve. Velocity is the rate of change of the altitude, so at each time value, draw a small segment with slope that is equal to the velocity. To draw the altitude graph, "connect" the slope segments to give a smooth curve.

   This problem may be approached in a variety of ways. If you wish students to simply think about the slope segment idea without concentrating on the actual height of the rocket, their graphs should have a shape similar to the one

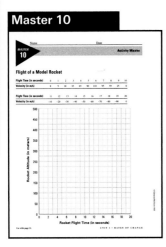

Master 10

EXPLORE *continued*

on the next page. Another approach is to estimate heights by finding the average velocity over each 1-second interval and plot the cumulative heights. A table of average velocities and cumulative heights is given below.

Time	Velocity (in meters per second)	Average Velocity (in meters per second)	Cumulative Height (in meters)
0	0		0
1	5	2.5	2.5
2	10	7.5	10
3	35	22.5	32.5
4	65	50	82.5
5	90	77.5	160
6	110	100	260
7	95	102.5	362.5
8	55	75	437.5
9	25	40	477.5
10	0	12.5	490
11	−10	−5	485
12	−20	−15	470
13	−30	−25	445
14	−40	−35	410
15	−50	−45	365
16	−60	−55	310
17	−70	−65	245
18	−80	−75	170
19	−90	−85	85
20	0	−45	40

EXPLORE *continued*

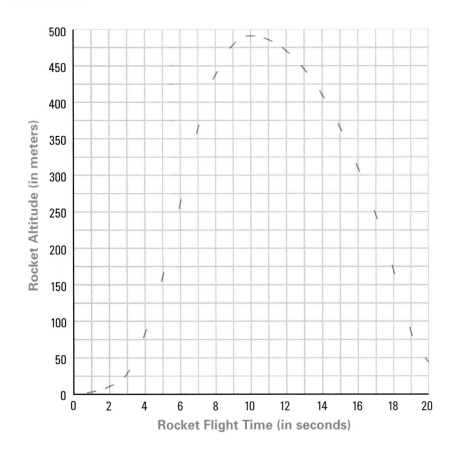

Master 11

Checkpoint

Investigation 2 focused on finding rates of change for functions defined by symbolic rules of various kinds and relating those rates of change to the slopes of graphs.

ⓐ How is finding the rate of change for a nonlinear function $f(x)$ similar to finding the slope of the graph of that function?

ⓑ How is finding the rate of change for a nonlinear function different than for a linear function?

Be prepared to explain your group's ideas to the entire class.

SHARE AND SUMMARIZE   **full-class discussion**

Checkpoint

See Teaching Master 11.

ⓐ To find the rate of change for nonlinear functions, approximate the nonlinear function with a linear one and determine the slope of that line. The smaller the interval, the closer the slope of the line is to the rate of change of the function at a particular point.

ⓑ The rate of change of a function is the slope of the graph for both linear and nonlinear functions. The difference is that for linear functions, the exact value of the slope is known and for nonlinear functions the slope has to be approximated.

CONSTRUCTING A MATH TOOLKIT: Following the Checkpoint discussion, students should write a comparison of finding the rate of change for linear and nonlinear functions.

APPLY individual task

▶ On Your Own

a–d. See the graph at the right.

> You should encourage students to use a large piece of graph paper so that the graph is as large as possible.

e. With each progression the connected points become closer to the actual curve. These segments approximate the curve and can be used to approximate the slope of the curve or the rate of change of the function.

f. The eleven points are $(-5, 25)$, $(-4, 16)$, $(-3, 9)$, $(-2, 4)$, $(-1, 1)$, $(0, 0)$, $(5, 25)$, $(4, 16)$, $(3, 9)$, $(2, 4)$, and $(1, 1)$. Students should see that this scatterplot is closely matched by the graph of $y = x^2$.

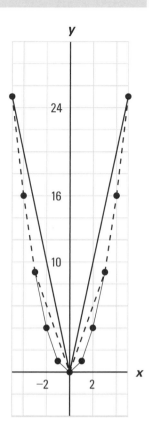

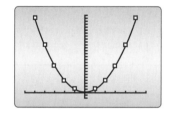

MORE

ASSIGNMENT   *pp. 41–49*

Students can now begin Reflecting Task 5 from the MORE assignment following Investigation 5.

EXPLORE small-group investigation

INVESTIGATION ▶3 Finding Derivative Functions

As an introduction to this investigation, you might review with students their methods of finding the rate of change at a point and try to focus them on the challenge of the next lesson. Put an example on the board or overhead and ask how to find the rate of change at some specified *x*-value. Some students may still prefer to find the rate by using a segment just to the left of a point, or just to the right, but most will have settled on using a segment that straddles the given point. Here are some questions you might ask: What are the advantages and disadvantages of this method? (The calculator makes the calculations easy, but the answers are estimates which many students will find unsatisfyingly inaccurate, particularly if different methods or different lengths of segments have led to different estimates.) Would it not be helpful if you could predict the rate at any point without having to find the rate one point at a time? What would make such an advance possible? (It would be possible if you had a formula/function for rate that depended on *x*.) Do you think that it is possible that there will be one formula/function that will give you

EXPLORE *continued*

instantaneous rate for every function? (No. The patterns you have observed in how the rate changes differ from one type of function to another.) So it must be that the formula/function that you are looking for will depend on the type of the original function. (At this point, students already know that the rate of change is a constant equal to the slope for a linear function, so they have already solved the puzzle for that type.)

As you facilitate groups working through Activities 1–4, you may wish to ask them about the different methods that appear in Activity 1. Will one method consistently overestimate the slope? Underestimate? (It depends on the function. Sometimes taking the segment right before a point will lead to an underestimate, sometimes not. It depends on the shape of the curve close to that point.) Why are the estimates for rate for $y = x^2$ higher for Group 2 than for Group 4? (This is tricky to answer because the sign of the rate/slope changes. The curve is steeper as x increases on the right of the y-axis (when $x > 0$), so estimates using segments to the right of the point tend to be too high. On the other hand, estimates will still be too high using the same method for points on the left of the y-axis, even though the curve is less steep, because now you are comparing negative slopes.) This discussion foreshadows work students may do in calculus.

1. **a.** Group 1 decided to use the given point and one slightly to the right and picked the points $(4, 4^2)$ and $(4.1, 4.1^2)$.

   b. Group 2 had the same idea and picked the points $(4, 4^2)$ and $(4.1, 4.1^2)$ also, but they simplified the denominator.

   c. Group 3 decided to use the given point and one slightly to the left and picked the points $(4, 4^2)$ and $(3.9, 3.9^2)$.

   d. Group 4 decided to pick close points on either side of the given point and picked the points $(4.1, 4.1^2)$ and $(3.9, 3.9^2)$.

2. **a.** $f'(4) \approx \dfrac{4.1^2 - 4^2}{4.1 - 4} = 8.1$

   b. $f'(4) \approx \dfrac{4.1^2 - 4^2}{0.1} = 8.1$

   c. $f'(4) \approx \dfrac{4^2 - 3.9^2}{0.1} = 7.9$

   d. $f'(4) \approx \dfrac{4.1^2 - 3.9^2}{0.2} = 8$

   Each of the above estimates could be made more precise by choosing a smaller interval containing the point $(4, 16)$. For example, Group 1 could use the points $(4, 4^2)$ and $(4.01, 4.01^2)$, yielding 8.01. Refinements in Group 4's approach still yield 8.

EXPLORE *continued*

3. **a.** Many students will use one of the methods from Activity 1 simply to generate the values for $f'(x)$, and then from those values they will be able to identify an algebraic rule. Some students, however, may generalize one of the methods from Activity 1. The following table of sample values for $f(x)$ and $f'(x)$ was generated by generalizing Group 4's method.

x	$f(x) = x^2$	$f'(x) = y_2(x)$
−5	25	−10
−4	16	−8
−3	9	−6
−2	4	−4
−1	1	−2
0	0	0
1	1	2
2	4	4
3	9	6
4	16	8
5	25	10

The above table suggests that $f'(x) = 2x$.

b. Adapting Group 2's method yields the following table. (Students might suggest $f'(x) = 2x + 0.1$. If so, you may wish to have them work Extending Task 1.)

x	$f(x) = x^2$	$f'(x) = y_2(x)$
−5	25	−9.9
−4	16	−7.9
−3	9	−5.9
−2	4	−3.9
−1	1	−1.9
0	0	0.1
1	1	2.1
2	4	4.1
3	9	6.1
4	16	8.1
5	25	10.1

EXPLORE *continued*

4. Students should use reasoning similar to that in Activity 3.

   a. $g'(x) = 4$

   This makes sense because $g(x)$ is a linear function and thus, the rate of change is constant and equal to the slope of 4.

   b. $h'(x) = -3.5$

   This makes sense because $h(x)$ is a linear function and thus, the rate of change is constant and equal to the slope of -3.5.

   c. $j'(x) = 2x$

   This makes sense because the graph of $j(x)$ is the graph of $f(x) = x^2$ shifted down 4 units, so the rate of change or derivative should be the same.

   d. $k'(x) = 2x - 4$

   Since the graph of $k(x)$ is a translation of the graph of $f(x) = x^2$, it makes sense that the graph of $k'(x)$ would be a translation of the graph of $f'(x)$.

   e. $m'(x) = 6x$

   Because the graph of $m(x)$ is a stretch of the graph of $f(x) = x^2$, it makes sense that the derivative of $m(x)$ would be a stretch of the derivative of $f(x)$.

5. **This is an extremely important activity. It will be productive to have groups report on their work and discuss this with the entire class. Some students may have generalized this rule in Activity 4, but most students need this direct approach.**

   a. $D(x)$ will produce the desired derivative estimates because near any point $(x, f(x))$, the graph of $f(x)$ is very close to a straight line segment. Since the rate of change of a straight line is the slope of the line, you can approximate $f'(x)$ by computing the slope of the line segment formed by the points $(x + 0.1, f(x + 0.1))$ and $(x - 0.1, f(x - 0.1))$. This slope is equal to $\dfrac{f(x + 0.1) - f(x - 0.1)}{(x + 0.1) - (x - 0.1)} = \dfrac{f(x + 0.1) - f(x - 0.1)}{0.2}$.

   b. By zooming in even closer, you could use the points $(x + 0.01, f(x + 0.01))$ and $(x - 0.01, f(x - 0.01))$, for example, to compute the slope of the line segment. **(See Technology Tips (Masters 12–15b) for Investigation 3 of Lesson 2.)**

   c. Let $y_1 = 3x^2$ and $y_2 = \dfrac{y_1(x + 0.1) - y_1(x - 0.1)}{0.2}$.

x	$m(x) = 3x^2$	$D(x) = \dfrac{m(x+0.1)-m(x-0.1)}{0.2}$
-3	27	-18
-2	12	-12
-1	3	-6
0	0	0
1	3	6
2	12	12

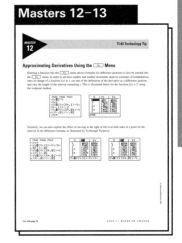

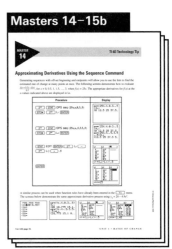

EXPLORE *continued*

6. **a.** For a linear function with rule $f(x) = a + bx$, the derivative function always seems to be a constant.

   b. For a quadratic function with rule $f(x) = a + bx + cx^2$, the derivative function always seems to be linear.

   If students give (a) $f' = b$ and (b) $g' = 2cx + b$ as answers, that is fine, but it is not expected at this point. The general type of function is what is important here.

Master 16

CONSTRUCTING A MATH TOOLKIT: Students should write a definition of the derivative function and explain how to estimate the derivative at a point and how to find a rule that approximates the derivative function.

MORE

ASSIGNMENT *pp. 41–49*

Students can now begin Modeling Task 2 or 3 from the MORE assignment following Investigation 5.

SHARE AND SUMMARIZE full-class discussion

Checkpoint

See Teaching Master 16.

ⓐ To find the derivative of a function at a specific point $(a, f(a))$, find the value of the function at $a + 0.1$ and $a - 0.1$ and then find the difference between those two values and divide by 0.2.

ⓑ To find the derivative of a function, use the method for approximating the rate of change at a point, $f'(x) = \dfrac{f(x + 0.1) - f(x - 0.1)}{0.2}$, for a variety of points and look for a rule to describe the pattern.

ⓒ ■ The derivative of a linear function is constant.
   ■ The derivative of a quadratic function is linear.

APPLY individual task

On Your Own

Students may either estimate using the difference quotient or use the derivative rule (if your class has generalized it) for $f(x) = ax^2$ to answer these questions.

a. $d(t) = 0.5t^2$, so $d'(t) = 0.5(2t) = t$ and $d'(10) = 10$ m/s.

b. The amount of time it takes to go 20 m is needed in order to find the speed after 20 m.

$$d(t) = 0.5t^2$$
$$20 = 0.5t^2$$
$$40 = t^2$$
$$t = \sqrt{40}$$

Thus, $d'(t) \approx 6.3$ m/s.

EXPLORE small-group investigation

INVESTIGATION ▶ 4 Derivatives of Other Function Types

Master 17

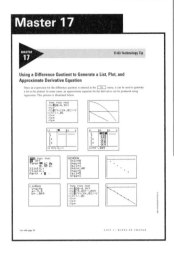

The point of this investigation is to give students an opportunity to conjecture about the derivatives of familiar functions. They may recognize the derivative function from the graph they get for their estimator function, they may ask for a regression to confirm what they see, or they may try their conjectures out to see how well their conjectured derivatives match the estimator function. As before, the shorter the interval, the more accurate the estimates. After Activity 3 you may wish to take time for a large group discussion, and make notes on the board of conjectures. Groups can check each other's conjectures, and extend them. Students do not need a "recipe" list of derivative functions to memorize at this time. They need to spend their time making sense of what a derivative function is, how the derivative function relates to the original function, and noting any patterns they see.

For each part in Activities 1, 2, and 3, students should generate function and derivative graphs using the method from the previous investigation. The following derivative graphs were generated using the rule $\dfrac{f(x + 0.1) - f(x - 0.1)}{0.2}$. The Technology Tips (Masters 14–15b) will help students recall the keystrokes on a TI-83 (TI-89) calculator for using lists to find many values of the approximate derivative, making a scatterplot of the lists, and finding an approximate derivative equation. The Technology Tips from Masters 17–18c show how to use sequences to help find approximate derivatives.

Masters 18a–18c

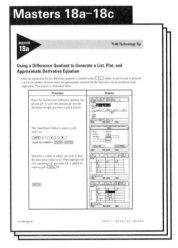

The derivative rules are supplied below for Activities 1–3 for your information, even though students are only asked for the type of function, not an exact derivative rule. Some students may want to find the rules.

1. If students display the graphs of exponential functions and their derivatives on separate screens, they might not notice that the two are different. Inspection of tables side by side or graphs on the same screen will make the similarities of shape but real differences of values apparent. Here, and on following graphs, students who want to find equations for the derivatives can use the estimator function to generate a list of data, and then select an appropriate regression function. Some data will have to be reflected in order to use regression tools.

EXPLORE *continued*

There are calculators and computer software packages that have built into them the ability to give the derivative function for any differentiable function. Students who have access to such technology may wish to use it to verify the patterns they have discovered in this lesson. Tell them that if they take a calculus course, they will develop and understand these relationships more fully.

■ $g(x) = 2^x$ $\qquad\qquad\qquad\qquad\qquad\qquad\qquad$ $g'(x) \approx 0.69(2^x)$

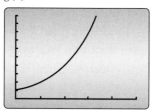
```
WINDOW
 Xmin =0
 Xmax=5
 Xscl =1
 Ymin =0
 Ymax=10
 Yscl =1
 Xres =1
```
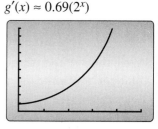

■ $h(x) = 3^x$ $\qquad\qquad\qquad\qquad\qquad\qquad\qquad$ $h'(x) \approx 1.1(3^x)$

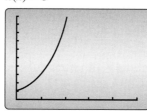
```
WINDOW
 Xmin =0
 Xmax=5
 Xscl =1
 Ymin =0
 Ymax=10
 Yscl =1
 Xres =1
```
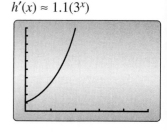

■ $i(x) = 1.5^x$ $\qquad\qquad\qquad\qquad\qquad\qquad\qquad$ $i'(x) \approx 0.405(1.5^x)$

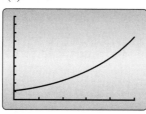
```
WINDOW
 Xmin =0
 Xmax=5
 Xscl =1
 Ymin =0
 Ymax=10
 Yscl =1
 Xres =1
```
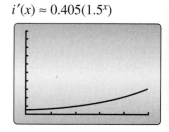

■ $j(x) = 0.8^x$ $\qquad\qquad\qquad\qquad\qquad\qquad\qquad$ $j'(x) \approx -0.22(0.8^x)$

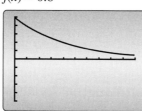
```
WINDOW
 Xmin =0
 Xmax=10
 Xscl =1
 Ymin =-1
 Ymax=1
 Yscl =.2
 Xres =1
```
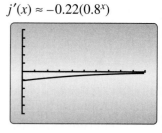

Students will need to reflect $j'(x)$ by multiplying the derivative values by –1 in order to do an exponential regression. Then $j'(x)$ will be the opposite of the exponential regression equation.

■ $k(x) = 2^x + 10$ $\qquad\qquad\qquad\qquad\qquad\qquad$ $k'(x) \approx 0.69(2^x)$

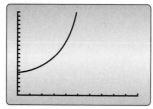
```
WINDOW
 Xmin =0
 Xmax=10
 Xscl =1
 Ymin =0
 Ymax=40
 Yscl =2
 Xres =1
```
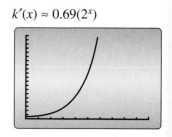

EXPLORE *continued*

■ $m(x) = 5(2^x)$ $\qquad\qquad\qquad\qquad\qquad\qquad$ $m'(x) \approx 5(0.69)(2^x) = 3.45(2^x)$

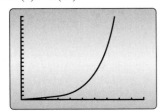

```
WINDOW
 Xmin =0
 Xmax=10
 Xscl =1
 Ymin =0
 Ymax=1000
 Yscl =100
 Xres =1
```

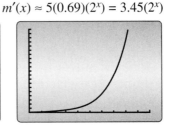

It appears that the derivative of an exponential function is also an exponential function. Reasons for this conclusion will vary, but could include some reference to the way in which the exponential functions increase (or decrease) and how this relates to the derivative function. Here is one possible response: An exponential function is either always increasing (as is the case with exponential growth) or always decreasing (as is the case with exponential decay) and therefore the derivative function, which measures the slope of the graph at each point, should always either be positive or negative. Moreover, since the rate of change of an exponential function continues to increase as *x* increases, the derivative function will also be increasing and hence it is reasonable to expect the derivative function to be an exponential function as well.

2. ■ $f(x) = \sin x$ $\qquad\qquad\qquad\qquad\qquad\qquad$ $f'(x) = \cos x$

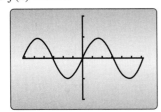

```
WINDOW
 Xmin =-6.28
 Xmax=6.28
 Xscl =1
 Ymin =-2
 Ymax=2
 Yscl =1
 Xres =1
```

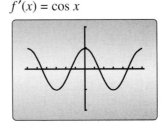

Some students will recognize this as the function $y = \cos x$. If they use sine regression, they will find $f'(x) = \sin\left(x + \frac{\pi}{2}\right)$.

■ $g(x) = \cos x$ $\qquad\qquad\qquad\qquad\qquad\qquad$ $g'(x) = -\sin x$

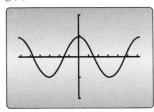

```
WINDOW
 Xmin =-6.28
 Xmax=6.28
 Xscl =1
 Ymin =-2
 Ymax=2
 Yscl =1
 Xres =1
```

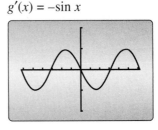

Some students will recognize this as the function $y = -\sin x$. If they use sine regression, they will find $g'(x) = \sin(x + \pi) = -\sin x$.

■ $h(x) = 5 + \sin x$ $\qquad\qquad\qquad\qquad\qquad\qquad$ $h'(x) = \cos x$

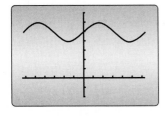

```
WINDOW
 Xmin =-6.28
 Xmax=6.28
 Xscl =1
 Ymin =-2
 Ymax=7
 Yscl =1
 Xres =1
```

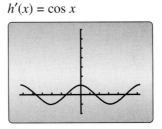

Unit 1

EXPLORE *continued*

■ $i(x) = 3 \sin x$

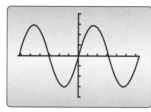

```
WINDOW
Xmin =-6.28
Xmax=6.28
Xscl =1
Ymin =-4
Ymax=4
Yscl =1
Xres =1
```

$i'(x) = 3 \cos x$

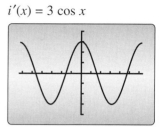

It appears that the derivative of a trigonometric function is also a trigonometric function. A trigonometric function increases and decreases an infinite number of times and hence has an infinite number of maximum or minimum points. Therefore, the derivative function, which is a measure of the function's rate of change, will always oscillate between positive and negative values with an infinite number of maximum or minimum points. Thus, it is reasonable to expect the derivative function to be a trigonometric function as well.

3. ■ $j(x) = x^3$

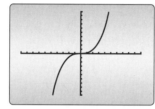

```
WINDOW
Xmin =-10
Xmax=10
Xscl =1
Ymin =-100
Ymax=100
Yscl =10
Xres =1
```

$j'(x) = 3x^2$

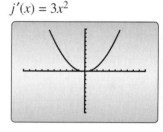

■ $k(x) = x^4$

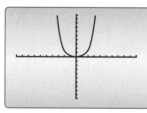

```
WINDOW
Xmin =-10
Xmax=10
Xscl =1
Ymin =-100
Ymax=100
Yscl =10
Xres =1
```

$k'(x) = 4x^3$

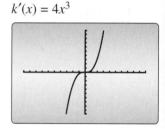

■ $g(x) = x^{1.5}$

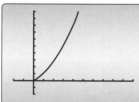

```
WINDOW
Xmin =-2
Xmax=10
Xscl =1
Ymin =-2
Ymax=10
Yscl =1
Xres =1
```

$g'(x) = 1.5x^{0.5}$

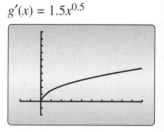

■ $h(x) = x^{-1}$

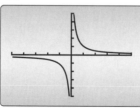

```
WINDOW
Xmin =-5
Xmax=5
Xscl =1
Ymin =-5
Ymax=5
Yscl =1
Xres =1
```

$h'(x) = -x^{-2}$

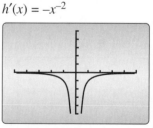

It appears that the derivative of a power function is also a power function. A power function changes from increasing to decreasing only a finite number of times (possibly zero times) and hence has a finite number of maximum or minimum points. Therefore the

EXPLORE *continued*

derivative function, which is a measure of the function's rate of change, will change from positive to negative only a finite number of times and have a finite number of maximum or minimum points. In other words, the derivative function will be a power function as well. Some students may notice that the degree of $f'(x)$ seems to be one less than that of $f(x)$.

Master 19

SHARE AND SUMMARIZE full-class discussion

Checkpoint

See Teaching Master 19.

a The derivative of an exponential function will be an exponential function.

b The derivative of a trigonometric function, if it exists, will also be a trigonometric function.

c The derivative of a power function will be a power function.

APPLY individual task

▶On Your Own

a. A constant function

b. A linear function

c. An exponential function

d. A trigonometric function

e. A power function

EXPLORE small-group investigation

INVESTIGATION ▶5 From Function Graphs to Derivative Graphs

In this investigation, students will explore the relationship between the graph of a function and the derivative of the function. They will study the shape of the function graph to determine the rate at which one variable is changing in relation to the other, and they will use the analysis of the graph of *f*(*x*) to sketch the graph of the derivative *f*′(*x*).

CONSTRUCTING A MATH TOOLKIT: Students should summarize the patterns in the rates of change of linear, quadratic, exponential, and trigonometric functions with appropriate examples.

MORE
ASSIGNMENT *pp. 41–49*

Students can now begin Modeling Task 4, 5, or 6, or any Extending task from the MORE assignment following Investigation 5.

EXPLORE *continued*

1. **a.** The number of absences due to the flu increased at a rate that gradually increased over the first two days of the epidemic and then increased at a rate that gradually decreased until the fifth or sixth day of the epidemic. After the sixth day into the epidemic, the number of absences decreased, reaching the maximum rate of decrease around day 9. After day 9, the number of absences continued to decrease, but the rate of decrease gradually leveled off.

   b. $f'(t)$ is positive for $0 \leq t \leq 5.5$, which says the number of students absent due to the flu is increasing during this time period. $f'(t)$ is 0 somewhere between the fifth and sixth days, which says the number of students absent due to the flu is neither increasing nor decreasing. $f'(t)$ is negative for $5.5 \leq t \leq 13.5$, which says the number of students absent due to the flu is decreasing during this time period. $f'(t)$ is 0 again during the 13th day ($t \approx 13.5$) and then becomes positive again indicating absences are increasing.

   c. Here is one reasonable sketch for $f'(t)$.
   The interval from $0 \leq t \leq 5.5$, where $f'(t)$ is positive, shows when the number of students absent was increasing. The interval $5.5 \leq t \leq 13.5$ where $f'(t)$ is negative shows when the number of students absent was decreasing. The rate of increase in the number of students ill was at a maximum on day 1. This is where the greatest positive slope occurs on the graph of $f(t)$.

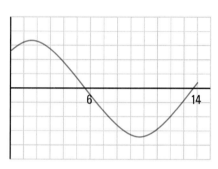

Master 20

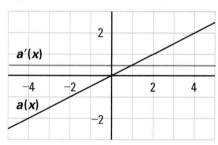

2. **See Teaching Master 20.**
   It is very important that students first do this activity without using their calculators. Calculators may be used to check the sketches afterwards. This is a nice activity for the class to share by having different groups present different problems. You might consider having the groups sketch both the function and the derivative on large sheets of paper and report their work to the class.

   a. Since the rate of change of $a(x)$ is positive and always equal to $\frac{1}{2}$, the derivative $a'(x)$ is always positive and equal to $\frac{1}{2}$.

EXPLORE *continued*

b. As *x* increases from −4 to 4, the rate of change of *f*(*x*) starts out negative, increases to 0 when *x* is 0, and then becomes positive and continues to increase. Therefore, the derivative is negative from −4 to 0, increases to 0 when *x* is 0, and then, becomes increasingly positive for values of *x* greater than 0.

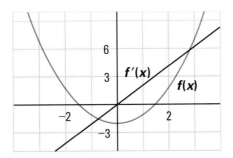

c. As *x* increases from −3 to 7, the rate of change starts off with a near-zero, positive value and then gets larger and larger. Therefore, the derivative *g*′(*x*) is never zero, always positive, and always increasing. At *g*(5) the slope appears to be about 3, so *g*′(5) ≈ 3.

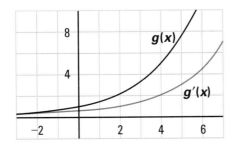

d. The derivative *h*′(*x*) is 0 when *x* is −π, increases to its maximum positive value (1) when *x* is $-\frac{\pi}{2}$, and then decreases to 0 when *x* is 0. From 0 to π, the derivative is negative and decreases to its minimum value (−1) when *x* is $\frac{\pi}{2}$ and then from $\frac{\pi}{2}$ to π, the derivative is still negative but increases from its minimum value back up to 0.

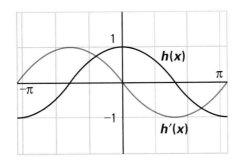

EXPLORE *continued*

e. The derivative is positive for *x* less than about –2.3, at which point it is 0, then it is negative for *x* between –2.3 and 2.3, where it is zero once again, and finally it is positive for *x* greater than approximately 2.3. Moreover, the derivative is decreasing for *x* less than 0 and increasing for *x* greater than 0.

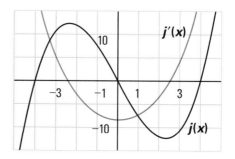

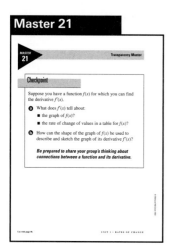

Master 21

SHARE AND SUMMARIZE full-class discussion

Checkpoint

See Teaching Master 21.

ⓐ ■ $f'(x)$ provides information on the slope of the graph of $f(x)$. In particular, it tells you where the graph of $f(x)$ is increasing, where it is decreasing, and where it might have a maximum or a minimum.

■ $f'(x)$ provides information on how fast or how slowly the function values in a table for $f(x)$ are changing at each *x*-value.

ⓑ The derivative $f'(x)$ will be positive when $f(x)$ is increasing, negative when $f(x)$ is decreasing, and 0 when the graph of $f(x)$ is at a peak or valley (that is, a local maximum or minimum). Moreover, the derivative is increasing wherever the slope of the graph of $f(x)$ is increasing and decreasing wherever the slope of the graph of $f(x)$ is decreasing. The derivative will change from positive to negative whenever the function has a peak. When it has a valley, the derivative will change from negative to positive.

Students do not need to be using the local maximum or minimum language until Unit 6, but you may wish to introduce it to students at this time.

CONSTRUCTING A MATH TOOLKIT: Students should explain how the graph of a function and the graph of its derivative are related.

APPLY individual task

▶**On Your Own**

a. ■ $P(t)$ for $0 \leq t \leq 10$

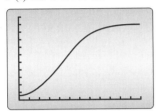

```
WINDOW
 Xmin =0
 Xmax=12
 Xscl =1
 Ymin =0
 Ymax=110
 Yscl =10
 Xres =1
```

■ In the table below, $Y_2 = P'(t)$.

X	Y2
0	3.1435
.5	4.2753
1	5.7285
1.5	7.524
2	9.627
2.5	11.913
3	14.146

X=0

X	Y2
3.5	15.995
4	17.115
4.5	17.263
5	16.406
5.5	14.733
6	12.574
6.5	10.274

X=3.5

X	Y2
7	8.101
7.5	6.2102
8	4.6588
8.5	3.4387
9	2.5078
9.5	1.813
10	1.3024

X=7

■ $P'(t)$ for $0 \leq t \leq 10$

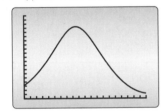

```
WINDOW
 Xmin =0
 Xmax=10
 Xscl =.5
 Ymin =0
 Ymax=20
 Yscl =1
 Xres =1
```

b. Positive values for $P'(t)$ for $0 \leq t \leq 10$ indicate that the percent of the maximum capacity of fish for the lake is increasing, even after 10 years. However, the greatest rate of increase in the fish population occurred after approximately 4.3 years.

MORE
ASSIGNMENT *pp. 41–49*

Modeling: 1–3, and 4, 5, or 6*
Organizing: 1, 4, and 3 or 5*
Reflecting: 1, 4, 5, and 6
Extending: 1 and choice of one*

*When choice is indicated, it is impor-tant to leave the choice to the student.
NOTE: *It is best if Organizing tasks are discussed as a whole class after they have been assigned as homework.*

MORE independent assignment

Modeling

1. a. At 7:00 A.M., the depth would be approximately $20 + 1.5(1) = 21.5$ ft.
At 6:30 A.M., the depth would be approximately $20 + 1.5(0.5) = 20.75$ ft.
At 6:15 A.M., the depth would be approximately $20 + 1.5(0.25) = 20.375$ ft.

MORE *continued*

b. At 1:00 P.M., the depth would be approximately $17 - 0.75(1) = 16.25$ ft.
At 12:30 P.M., the depth would be approximately $17 - 0.75(0.5) = 16.625$ ft.
At 12:15 P.M., the depth would be approximately $17 - 0.75(0.25) = 16.8125$ ft.

2. a. The rate of change is constant at 8.5 dollars or $8.50 per ticket sold.

b. The graph will be a line with a constant rate of change or slope of 8.5.

c. In the following table, $y_1(x) = 8.5x - 3,500$ and $y_2(x) = \frac{y_1(x + 0.01) - y_1(x - 0.01)}{0.02}$. Other methods for approximating the derivative function are acceptable.

X	Y₁	Y₂
0	-3500	8.5
100	-2650	8.5
200	-1800	8.5
300	-950	8.5
400	-100	8.5
500	750	8.5
600	1600	8.5
X=0		

X	Y₁	Y₂
700	2450	8.5
800	3300	8.5
900	4150	8.5
1000	5000	8.5
1100	5850	8.5
1200	6700	8.5
1300	7550	8.5
X=700		

Graph of $P'(x)$

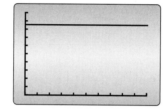

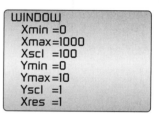

WINDOW
Xmin =0
Xmax=1000
Xscl =100
Ymin =0
Ymax=10
Yscl =1
Xres =1

$P'(x) = \$8.50$ per ticket sold

d. The shape of the graph of $P'(x)$ says that the rate of change in theater profit is always $8.50 per ticket sold.

3. a. The velocities are 34 ft/sec, 2 ft/sec, -14 ft/sec, respectively. The ball is moving fast at first, but then it slows down as gravity pulls it down. The graph shows the curve increasing until it reaches a maximum point. It is at this point that the ball starts returning to the ground. As the ball is going up, the velocity is positive, but as the ball starts coming down, the velocity is negative. (See the graph in Part c.)

b. Answers will vary depending upon the height of the student. For students between 5 and 6 ft tall, answers should be that the ball is falling at approximately 46 ft/sec, or that the velocity is approximately -46 ft/sec.

c. $h(t) = y_1(t) = -16t^2 + 50t$ and $h'(t) = y_2(t) = \frac{y_1(t + 0.01) - y_1(t - 0.01)}{0.02}$. The graph of $h(t)$ is the parabola and the graph of $h'(t)$ is the line in the graph below. Student sketches should resemble these graphs.

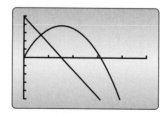

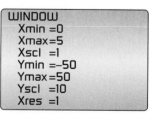

WINDOW
Xmin =0
Xmax=5
Xscl =1
Ymin =-50
Ymax=50
Yscl =10
Xres =1

MORE *continued*

Students might use reasoning such as the following in producing their sketches. Since $h(t)$ is quadratic, $h'(t)$ will be linear. $h'(t)$ will be positive wherever the slope of the graph of $h(t)$ is positive. $h'(t)$ will be negative wherever the slope of $h(t)$ is negative. $h'(t)$ will be 0 wherever the slope of the graph of $h(t)$ is 0. When the slope of the graph of $h(t)$ is positive, the height of the ball is increasing and when the slope of the graph of $h(t)$ is decreasing, the height of the ball is decreasing. Finally, when the slope of the graph of $h(t)$ is 0, the ball is not moving up or down at all.

d. The graph shows that the velocity of the ball starts out positive and decreases linearly until the ball reaches its maximum height, at which point the velocity is zero. After the ball reaches its maximum height, the velocity is negative and continues to decrease linearly until the ball hits the ground.

4. a. In a non-leap year, March 21 corresponds to $d = 80$, June 21 corresponds to $d = 172$, September 21 corresponds to $d = 264$, and December 21 corresponds to $d = 355$.

NOTE: You may need to remind the students to set their calculator mode to radians.

b.

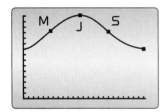

```
WINDOW
  Xmin =0
  Xmax=365
  Xscl =15
  Ymin =0
  Ymax=900
  Yscl =60
  Xres =1
```

The graph indicates that the number of minutes between sunrise and sunset (that is, the number of minutes of daylight) increases until midyear and then decreases until the end of the year. By examining the table of values, the shortest day of the year occurs when $d = 354$ (December 20) and the longest day of the year occurs when $d = 171$ (June 20).

c. On March 21, the rate of change is approximately $\frac{S(80) - S(79.9)}{80 - 79.9} \approx 3.1$ min/day. On the graph, this is shown by a slope of about 3 min/day.

On June 21, the rate of change is approximately $\frac{S(172) - S(171.9)}{172 - 171.9} \approx -0.03$ min/day. On the graph, this is shown by a near-zero slope.

On September 21, the rate of change is approximately $\frac{S(264) - S(263.9)}{264 - 263.9} \approx -3.1$ min/day. On the graph, this is shown by a slope of about –3 min/day.

On December 21, the rate of change is approximately $\frac{S(355) - S(354.9)}{355 - 354.9} \approx 0.05$ min/day. On the graph, this is shown by a near-zero slope.

d. The days are growing longer most rapidly around March 21 and growing shorter most rapidly around September 21. The days are growing longer most slowly just before June 21 and growing shorter most slowly before December 21.

MORE *continued*

e. In the following table, $y_1(x) = 180 \sin(0.0172x - 1.376) + 720$ and $y_2(x) = \frac{y_1(x + 0.01) - y_1(x - 0.01)}{0.02}$. Other methods for approximating the derivative function are acceptable.

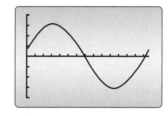

X	Y₁	Y₂
0	543.4	.59928
30	583.59	2.0199
60	659.29	2.9146
90	750.81	3.0503
120	834.3	2.3917
150	888.03	1.1103
180	898	-.4602

X=0

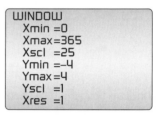

X	Y₁	Y₂
210	861.62	-1.911
240	788.37	-2.864
270	697.31	-3.071
300	612.16	-2.479
330	555.09	-1.241
360	540.97	.32021
390	573.46	1.7979

X=210

$S'(d) = $ Y₂:

WINDOW
Xmin =0
Xmax=365
Xscl =25
Ymin =-4
Ymax=4
Yscl =1
Xres =1

f. The days are increasing in length when $S'(d)$ is positive and decreasing in length when $S'(d)$ is negative. The greater the value of $S'(d)$, the faster day length is increasing; the smaller the value of $S'(d)$, the faster day length is decreasing.

5. a. $T'(40) \approx -0.28$, $T'(60) \approx -0.13$. If the bus is traveling at 40 mph and increases its speed by approximately 1 mph, the trip will take approximately 0.28 hour less. Similarly, if the bus is traveling at 60 mph, a change of 1 mph in speed will correspond to about a 0.13 hour change in time. (You may wish to ask students to connect their understanding to the table and the graph in Part b.)

b. In the following table, $y_1(x) = \frac{450}{x}$ and $y_2(x) = \frac{y_1(x + 0.01) - y_1(x - 0.01)}{0.02}$. Other methods for approximating the derivative function are acceptable.

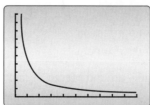

X	Y₁	Y₂
0	ERROR	45000
10	45	-4.5
20	22.5	-1.125
30	15	-.5
40	11.25	-.2813
50	9	-.18
60	7.5	-.125

X=0

$T(s) = $ Y₁:

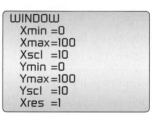

WINDOW
Xmin =0
Xmax=100
Xscl =10
Ymin =0
Ymax=100
Yscl =10
Xres =1

MORE *continued*

$T'(s) = Y_2$:

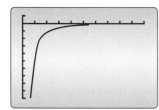

WINDOW
Xmin =0
Xmax=100
Xscl =10
Ymin =–10
Ymax=1
Yscl =1
Xres =1

Student responses may vary. Here is one possible response: The graph of $T'(s)$ is negative and increases toward 0 as the average speed increases. In addition, the graph of $T'(s)$ appears to be essentially 0 for average speeds greater than 50 mph. This suggests that there is very little difference in trip time for average speeds greater than 50 mph. When the average speed is slower than 20 mph, the graph of $T'(s)$ is very negative, which indicates that the greatest decrease in trip time occurs when the average speed increases from near 0 to about 20 mph.

6. **a.** $B(t) = 150(2^t)$

b. After 3 hours, there are 1,200 bacteria. After 6 hours, there are 9,600 bacteria. After 9 hours, there are 76,800 bacteria. After 12 hours, there are 614,400 bacteria.

c. Between 0 and 6 hr, the average rate of growth is $\frac{150(2^6) - 150(2^0)}{6 - 0} = 1{,}575$ bacteria/hr.

Between 6 and 12 hr, the average rate of growth is $\frac{150(2^{12}) - 150(2^6)}{12 - 6} = 100{,}800$ bacteria/hr.

d. Estimates will vary slightly depending on the strategy used. Here is one way to estimate the average growth rate. Other strategies should yield similar results.

At $t = 3$, the growth rate is approximately $\frac{150(2^{3.1}) - 150(2^{2.9})}{3.1 - 2.9} \approx 832$ bacteria/hr.

At $t = 6$, the growth rate is approximately $\frac{150(2^{6.1}) - 150(2^{5.9})}{6.1 - 5.9} \approx 6{,}660$ bacteria/hr.

At $t = 9$, the growth rate is approximately $\frac{150(2^{9.1}) - 150(2^{8.9})}{9.1 - 8.9} \approx 53{,}276$ bacteria/hr.

At $t = 12$, the growth rate is approximately $\frac{150(2^{12.1}) - 150(2^{11.9})}{12.1 - 11.9} \approx 426{,}211$ bacteria/hr.

e. The average growth rate between $t = 0$ and $t = 6$ is greater than the growth rate at $t = 3$ and less than the growth rate at $t = 6$. The graph shows these differences because the slope increases as time increases. One can see this in the way the graph curves upward. Thus, the slope of the line connecting the points when $t = 0$ and $t = 6$ is greater than the slope of the graph at $t = 3$ and less than the slope of the graph at $t = 6$. This continual increase in the slope of the graph (or rate of change) leads to similar differences between the average growth rate between $t = 6$ and $t = 12$ and the rate of growth at $t = 9$ and $t = 12$. The growth rate at the middle of the interval is closer to the rate at the lower x-values since the rate is increasing at an increasing rate.

f. The function is increasing at an increasing rate. You should expect an exponential rule for a function whose graph has this shape.

NOTE: Organizing Task 1 is an excellent problem to discuss with the entire class.

Organizing

1. **a.** ■ When $f'(x_0) > 0$, $f(x)$ is increasing.

   ■ When $f'(x_0) < 0$, $f(x)$ is decreasing.

   ■ When $f'(x_0) = 0$, $f(x)$ is at a maximum or a minimum. (Technically, the function could be constant horizontally at x_0.)

   b. ■ When $f'(x_0) > 0$, the graph will have a positive rate of change at this point. The greater the value of $f'(x_0)$, the faster $f(x)$ is increasing and the greater its rate of change.

   ■ When $f'(x_0) < 0$, the graph will have a negative rate of change at this point. The larger the absolute value of $f'(x_0)$, the faster $f(x)$ is decreasing and the more negative its rate of change.

   ■ When $f'(x_0) = 0$, the rate of change of the graph will be 0, and the function is (perhaps momentarily) neither increasing nor decreasing.

2. **a.** $\dfrac{f(x_2) - f(x_1)}{x_2 - x_1}$

   b. $\dfrac{f(x_0 + 0.1) - f(x_0 - 0.1)}{0.2}$ or $\dfrac{f(x_0) - f(x_0 - 0.1)}{0.1}$ or $\dfrac{f(x_0 + 0.1) - f(x_0)}{0.1}$

   Any of the above are acceptable. You could also replace 0.1 with a smaller positive number.

3. The graph of $g'(x)$ is shown at the right.

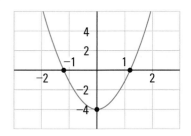

4. Since the minimum is at $x = 2$ and the function is a quadratic function, the graph must be symmetric across the line $x = 2$. Thus, since $f(0) = 3$ and $f(4) = 3$, the slope of the graph at $x = 0$ is −8 and at $x = 4$ is 8. Students need not compute the actual minimum value.

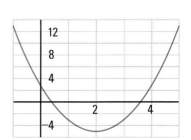

MORE *continued*

5. Student sketches should resemble $f(x) = -\sin x$.

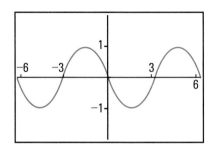

6. **a.** The rate of change of $f(x) = x^2$ at $x = 1$ is the same as the rate of change of $f(x) = x^2 + 5$ at $x = 1$.

■ The graph of $f(x) = x^2 + 5$ has the same shape as the graph of $f(x) = x^2$, but translated upward, so it makes sense that the graphs of the two functions have the same slope at $x = 1$.

■ The same will be true for all values of x, because the steepness of slope of the graph at any x-value is not changed by moving the graph vertically.

■ Consider the two functions $g(x)$ and $g(x) + k$. At any point x, the rate of change of the functions are approximated by $\dfrac{g(x + 0.01) - g(x - 0.01)}{0.02}$ and $\dfrac{g(x + 0.01) + k - [g(x - 0.01) + k]}{0.02}$.

But the second expression is equal to $\dfrac{g(x + 0.01) + k - g(x - 0.01) - k}{0.02} = \dfrac{g(x + 0.01) - g(x - 0.01)}{0.02}$.

Thus, for any value of x, the rate of change of $g(x)$ is the same as that of $g(x)$ translated by any vertical distance k.

b. The rate of change of $f(x) = x^2$ at $x = 4$ is approximately 8, but the rate of change of $h(x) = 3x^2$ at $x = 4$ is approximately 24. This demonstrates that the rates of change are not the same for given values of x for a function and a vertical stretch of that function. Students may conjecture that the rate of change of $h(x)$ is 3 times that of $f(x)$. They should test their conjectures at another point (other than $x = 4$). The proof should be provided in response to the last item for Part b.

■ This makes sense graphically because, for example, a graph that is stretched vertically reaches the function value of 10 faster than the unstretched function, and thus, has greater average rate of change. Students may want to consider a stretch (or shrink) by a factor between 0 and 1 to be sure that, in this case, the average rate of change from 0 to 10 is less than that of the original function.

■ This will be true at values of x except where the slope of the original function was 0. That x-value will still have a 0 slope for the stretched function.

MORE *continued*

■ Consider the rates of change of the functions $f(x)$ and $kf(x)$, where k is a real number. The rate of change of $f(x)$ is approximated by $\dfrac{f(x+0.01)-f(x-0.01)}{0.02}$ and that of $kf(x)$ is approximated by $\dfrac{kf(x+0.01)-kf(x-0.01)}{0.02} = \dfrac{k[f(x+0.01)-f(x-0.01)]}{0.02}$. These two expressions indicate that the rate of change of the stretched function will always differ from that of the original by a factor of k.

Reflecting

1. **a.** $F'(t) > 0$, because the temperature of the pizza is increasing.

    b. $F'(15)$ is the rate at which the temperature of the pizza is increasing after 15 min in the oven. The units will be in degrees Fahrenheit per minute.

    c. $F'(15) = 2$ indicates that after 15 minutes the temperature of the pizza is increasing at a rate of 2°F/min.

    d. $F'(t)$ may be 0 when the temperature of the pizza reaches the temperature of the air inside the oven. At that point, the pizza will not get any hotter. Students may also recall that oven temperature fluctuates slightly as the heat source is turned on and off, so it would be reasonable to expect the pizza temperature to fluctuate somewhat, making $F'(t) = 0$ at somewhat regular intervals.

2. Estimating the rate of change at a specific point gives a kind of snapshot of what is happening. The average rate of change gives a measure of what happened over the entire time interval. It provides information about what the net or overall change was, but does not say what happened at each instant in the time interval.

3. **a.** It says the upward velocity of the ball is 0 when it is at its maximum height. This is reasonable because when the ball is at its maximum height, it is neither going up nor coming down, though it may be moving sideways.

    b. Four hours after the earthquake 60 million people have heard about it and the news is spreading at a rate of 6.5 million people per hour.

    c. Five minutes after her ascent began, the diver has risen 25 ft to a depth of 150 ft. The depth is decreasing at a rate of 8 ft/min at that instant.

4. **a.** The vertical axis should be labeled, "Rate of change of fish population as a percent of maximum capacity per year".

    b. The derivative is maximum when t is approximately 4.3 years.

    c. The fish population was growing most rapidly at approximately 4.3 years.

    d. When t was approximately 4.3, the slope of the graph of $P(t)$ would be at its largest positive value. That is, the graph would be steepest when $t \approx 4.3$.

MORE *continued*

5. Zooming might give something like the image at the right for $f(x) = x^3$. The rate of change at $x = 0$ appears to be 0.

For the function $g(x) = |x|$, no matter how small you set the window, as long as both x and y are reduced (within the limits of the calculator), you get a graph with the same shape as the original, provided that the scales are in the same proportion.

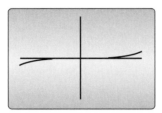

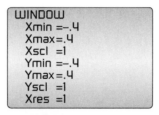

```
WINDOW
Xmin =-.4
Xmax=.4
Xscl =1
Ymin =-.4
Ymax=.4
Yscl =1
Xres =1
```

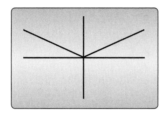

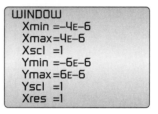

```
WINDOW
Xmin =-4E-6
Xmax=4E-6
Xscl =1
Ymin =-6E-6
Ymax=6E-6
Yscl =1
Xres =1
```

This seems to indicate that at 0 the rate of change switches immediately from a negative value to a positive value. There doesn't seem to be any way to determine what the rate of change is at $x = 0$.

6. **a.** Students will likely note that Leibnitz's notation is similar to the $\frac{\Delta y}{\Delta x}$ notation used to describe the slope of a line. Some students may have seen the notation $\frac{dy}{dx}$ or $f'(x)$ in a physics course when studying velocity.

b. When estimating $\frac{dy}{dx}$, x_1, and x_2 should be very close to x. (See the diagram at the right).

c. Responses will vary. Students may think it reminds them that the derivative is approximated by a difference quotient.

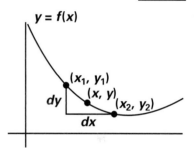

Extending

1. **a.** For $f(x) = a + bx$:

$f'(x) \approx \frac{f(x + 0.1) - f(x)}{0.1}$ Approximate rate of change at $(x, f(x))$

$= \frac{[a + b(x + 0.1)] - (a + bx)}{0.1}$ Substitution

$= \frac{0.1b}{0.1}$ Distributive property and subtraction

$= b$ Division

This result agrees with the work students have done with linear functions. The rate of change is constant and equal to the slope of the line.

b. For $f(x) = x^2$:

$f'(x) \approx \frac{f(x + 0.1) - f(x)}{0.1}$ Approximate rate of change at $(x, f(x))$

$= \frac{(x + 0.1)^2 - x^2}{0.1}$ Substitution

$= \frac{x^2 + 0.2x + 0.01 - x^2}{0.1}$ Distributive property

$= \frac{0.2x + 0.01}{0.1}$ Subtraction

$= 2x + 0.1$ Division

Unit 1

MORE *continue*

If 0.1 is replaced with smaller numbers, the estimates of $f'(x)$ get closer and closer to $2x$. Thus, $f'(x) = 2x$.

2. **a.** For $g(x) = ax^2$:

$$g'(x) \approx \frac{g(x + 0.1) - g(x)}{0.1}$$ — Approximate rate of change at $(x, g(x))$

$$= \frac{a(x + 0.1)^2 - ax^2}{0.1}$$ — Substitution

$$= \frac{0.2ax + 0.01a}{0.1}$$ — Distributive property and subtraction

$$= 2ax + 0.1a$$ — Division

If 0.1 is replaced with smaller numbers, the estimates of $g'(x)$ get closer and closer to $2ax$. Thus, $g'(x) = 2ax$.

b. For $h(x) = ax^2 + c$:

$$h'(x) \approx \frac{h(x + 0.1) - h(x)}{0.1}$$ — Approximate rate of change at $(x, h(x))$

$$= \frac{[a(x + 0.1)^2 + c] - (ax^2 + c)}{0.1}$$ — Substitution

$$= \frac{0.2ax + 0.01a}{0.1}$$ — Distributive property and subtraction

$$= 2ax + 0.1a$$ — Division

If 0.1 is replaced with smaller numbers, the estimates of $h'(x)$ get closer and closer to $2ax$. Thus, $h'(x) = 2ax$.

c. For $j(x) = ax^2 + bx$:

$$j'(x) \approx \frac{j(x + 0.1) - j(x)}{0.1}$$ — Approximate rate of change at $(x, j(x))$

$$= \frac{[a(x + 0.1)^2 + b(x + 0.1)] - (ax^2 + bx)}{0.1}$$ — Substitution

$$= \frac{0.2ax + 0.01a + 0.1b}{0.1}$$ — Distributive property and subtraction

$$= 2ax + 0.1a + b$$ — Division

If 0.1 is replaced with smaller numbers, the estimates of $j'(x)$ get closer and closer to $2ax + b$. Thus, $j'(x) = 2ax + b$.

d. For $k(x) = ax^2 + bx + c$:

$$k'(x) \approx \frac{k(x + 0.1) - k(x)}{0.1}$$ — Approximate rate of change at $(x, k(x))$

$$= \frac{[a(x + 0.1)^2 + b(x + 0.1) + c] - (ax^2 + bx + c)}{0.1}$$ — Substitution

$$= \frac{0.2ax + 0.01a + 0.1b}{0.1}$$ — Distributive property and subtraction

$$= 2ax + 0.1a + b$$ — Division

If 0.1 is replaced with smaller numbers, the estimates of $k'(x)$ get closer and closer to $2ax + b$. Thus, $k'(x) = 2ax + b$.

MORE *continue*

3. **a.**

Speed	b(s)	c(s)	d(s)
0	0	0	0
10	7.5	4	11.5
20	15	16	31
30	22.5	36	58.5
40	30	64	94
50	37.5	100	137.5
60	45	144	189
70	52.5	196	248.5
80	60	256	316
90	67.5	324	391.5
100	75	400	475

b. The second column, $b(s)$, says that as the speed increases, the stopping distance traveled before you press the brake pedal increases at a constant rate. The third column, $c(s)$, says that as the speed increases, the distance traveled from the time you press the brake pedal until you stop increases at a rate that gradually increases. The last column, $d(s)$, says that as the speed increases, the total stopping distance increases at the combined rate of increase.

c. The rate of change in total stopping distance is the sum of the rate of change in braking distance and the rate of change in distance traveled after braking.

d.

Speed	b'(s)	c'(s)	d'(s)
0	0	0	0
10	0.75	0.8	1.55
20	0.75	1.6	2.35
30	0.75	2.4	3.15
40	0.75	3.2	3.95
50	0.75	4.0	4.75
60	0.75	4.8	5.55
70	0.75	5.6	6.35
80	0.75	6.4	7.15
90	0.75	7.2	7.95
100	0.75	8.0	8.75

e. The fourth column, $d'(s)$, is the sum of the second and third columns. In other words, if $d(s) = b(s) + c(s)$, then $d'(s) = b'(s) + c'(s)$.

Unit 1

MORE *continue*

4. **a.** $g(x) = 5x$ and $h(x) = 3.5x$

x	f'(x)	g'(x)	h'(x)
–5	8.5	5	3.5
–4	8.5	5	3.5
–3	8.5	5	3.5
–2	8.5	5	3.5
–1	8.5	5	3.5
0	8.5	5	3.5
1	8.5	5	3.5
2	8.5	5	3.5
3	8.5	5	3.5
4	8.5	5	3.5
5	8.5	5	3.5

b. $g(x) = \sin x$ and $h(x) = \cos x$

x	f'(x)	g'(x)	h'(x)
–5	–0.674	0.283	–0.957
–4	–1.408	–0.653	–0.756
–3	–0.848	–0.988	0.141
–2	0.492	–0.416	0.908
–1	1.380	0.539	0.840
0	0.998	0.998	0
1	–0.301	0.539	–0.840
2	–1.323	–0.416	–0.908
3	–1.129	–0.988	–0.141
4	0.103	–0.653	0.756
5	1.241	0.283	0.957

MORE *continued*

c. $g(x) = x^2$ and $h(x) = 5x^2$

x	f'(x)	g'(x)	h'(x)
−5	−60	−10	−50
−4	−48	−8	−40
−3	−36	−6	−30
−2	−24	−4	−20
−1	−12	−2	−10
0	0	0	0
1	12	2	10
2	24	4	20
3	36	6	30
4	48	8	40
5	60	10	50

d. $g(x) = \sin x$ and $h(x) = x^2$

x	f'(x)	g'(x)	h'(x)
−5	−9.717	0.283	−10
−4	−8.653	−0.653	−8
−3	−6.988	−0.988	−6
−2	−4.415	−0.416	−4
−1	−1.461	0.539	−2
0	0.998	0.998	0
1	2.539	0.539	2
2	3.584	−0.416	4
3	5.012	−0.988	6
4	7.347	−0.653	8
5	10.283	0.283	10

Assessments 7–9

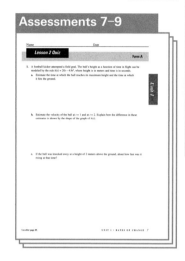

Assessments 10–12

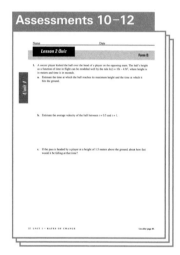

By comparing the results of Parts a–d, it can be seen that if $f(x) = g(x) + h(x)$, then $f'(x) = g'(x) + h'(x)$. This is the same result obtained in Extending Task 3. This result is reasonable because the slope of the graph of $f(x)$ is the slope of the graph of $g(x)$ plus the slope of the graph of $h(x)$.

5. Using the right-endpoint approximate derivative function from the lesson, the function $f(x) = g(x) + h(x)$,

$$f'(x) = \frac{f(x + 0.1) - f(x)}{0.1} = \frac{g(x + 0.1) + h(x + 0.1) - g(x) - h(x)}{0.1}$$

$$= \frac{g(x + 0.1) - g(x)}{0.1} + \frac{h(x + 0.1) - h(x)}{0.1}$$

$$= g'(x) + h'(x)$$

See Assessment Resources pages 7–12.

Unit 1

REVIEW AND PRACTICE individual task

▶**PUMP**

Answers

1. (a)   6. (b)

2. (c)   7. (c)

3. (c)   8. (b)

4. (e)   9. (b)

5. (a)   10. (c)

Lesson 3 Accumulation at Variable Rates

LESSON OVERVIEW The main focus of this lesson is to develop a meaning for the definite integral of a function and, in particular, to develop the idea that the definite integral of a rate function of some quantity is the net change in that quantity over the specified interval.

In Investigation 1, students return to the context of Investigation 1 ("Walk That Graph") in Lesson 1. This time they are asked to interpret the "walk" represented by a rate function. In particular, they are asked to develop a strategy to estimate the change in distance. The investigation then addresses the same ideas in a new context, the rate of flow of water. Investigation 2 introduces negative velocities and the idea of net change. The vocabulary and accompanying symbols that will formalize the foregoing concepts are introduced in Investigation 3, where estimation strategies are refined.

Lesson Objectives

- To estimate the net change in a quantity from its rate of change graph using systematic approximations and geometric ideas
- To describe the idea of a definite integral for a function and to estimate it in various ways

LAUNCH full-class discussion

Think About This Situation

See Teaching Master 22.
Students may find this graph difficult to interpret because it is the graph of a rate function. The previous two lessons examined how quantity A changed in relation to quantity B, and developed the idea of instantaneous rate of change in quantity A. For example, graphs showed quantity A, distance, on the vertical axis, and quantity B, time, on the horizontal axis. The graph of the derivative function then showed how the rate of change, velocity, related to quantity B, time. This "Think About This Situation" begins by asking students to consider a rate function. Take a few minutes to be sure that students can interpret the graph correctly and that they realize that there is another graph analogous to this one, telling the same story, but with

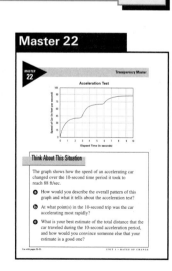

Master 22

LAUNCH *continued*

distance as the dependent variable instead of velocity. Any point on the distance-time graph will answer the question, "How much distance has been covered up to this point?" Getting that information from the graph of a rate function like the ones here is more involved.

a This graph is always increasing, but the rate of increase is not constant. The speed of the car continues increasing until it reaches about 88 ft/sec.

To shift gears the car has to stop accelerating, so the speed tends to become almost constant for a brief moment. This happens at about 2.5 and 5.5 seconds (or at approximately 55 and 73 ft/sec).

b The car was accelerating most rapidly during the first second, since it is there that the speed increases fastest (the graph is the steepest).

c Allow students some time to talk about their methods of trying to solve this part of the "Think About This Situation." Have students write down their estimates because later they will actually solve this problem.

Students might suggest that they try to estimate the car's speed in small intervals by means of constants, and then estimate distance traveled using those approximations in the formula *distance = speed · time*. Finally total distance traveled will be the sum of the distances traveled during those short periods. This would be a good estimate if the estimation intervals were small.

EXPLORE small-group investigation

INVESTIGATION 1 What's the Total?

This investigation gives students the opportunity to develop a strategy for estimating the total change in a set time, given a graph of a rate function. You may find it advantageous to build in a few brief class discussions. Be wary of students who settle on an estimation strategy very quickly. There are a number of erroneous ways of thinking about this task.

Because of their experience in Lessons 1 and 2, your students will probably want to divide the graphs where the rate is not constant into short time segments and use an average rate for each short time segment. As you observe them working on Activity 1, ask them if it matters whether they use a one-second or two-second-or-longer interval. (There is no advantage in using a short interval if the rate function is constant, that is, the velocity is constant, nor if the rate function is increasing or decreasing at a constant rate, that is, the velocity is changing, but the acceleration is constant.) If students don't come up with an approximation strategy, you might ask questions like "Can you put an upper or lower bound on the distance?" or "How would you calculate the distance if each walker's speed was constant?" However, don't be too quick to offer such hints. You may wish to draw the class together after the first activity to discuss their reasons for their strategies. You might consider having the distance function graphs that accompany these rate function graphs available, to facilitate discussion of accumulative change. (See Teaching Masters 23a–23b.)

EXPLORE *continued*

When it seems clear to you that an efficient strategy has been agreed upon, and students are making sense of the rate graphs and can connect them to the distance-time graphs, then assign Activity 2, where they will find that sometimes it is essential to use a short time interval to get an accurate estimate for change.

Masters 23a–23b

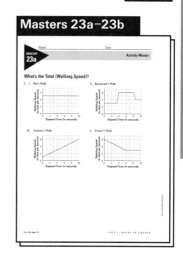

1. **See Teaching Masters 23a–23b.**

   i. Walk at a constant speed of 5 ft/sec for 10 seconds. The total distance covered will be 50 ft.

   ii. Walk at 3 ft/sec for the first 3.5 seconds, quickly accelerate to walk at 6 ft/sec for 4 seconds, and then walk 1.5 seconds at 4 ft/sec. Using an average speed of $4\frac{1}{2}$ ft/sec for the half-second Raymond was accelerating, and an average speed of 5 ft/sec for the half-second he was decelerating, the distance walked during the first 4 seconds will be 12.75 ft. During the next 4 seconds, Raymond walked 24 ft, and during the remaining 2 seconds, 8.5 ft, bringing the total distance walked to 45.25 ft.

   iii. You would need to accelerate for 10 seconds. At the start, your speed is about 1 ft/sec, but after 2 seconds it is already 2 ft/sec. After 4 seconds have elapsed, your speed should have climbed to 3 ft/sec and it will continue to increase at a constant rate. Six seconds into the walk, your speed should be about 4 ft/sec, and by the end of the walk your speed should be 6 ft/sec.

Time Elapsed (in seconds)	0	2	4	6	8	10
Speed (in feet per second)	1	2	3	4	5	6

Estimating (rather than calculating) the distance walked seems to be the only possibility. During the first 2 seconds, Annette's speed changes from 1 to 2 ft/sec. Her average speed is about 1.5 ft/sec. Thus, the distance covered during the first 2 seconds is about $1.5 \times 2 = 3$ ft. Similarly, during the next 2 seconds Annette's average speed is about 2.5 ft/sec, and so you can estimate the distance walked during these two seconds by $2.5 \times 2 = 5$ ft. During the next 2 seconds, her speed is about 3.5 ft/sec. You can estimate the distance walked during these two seconds by $3.5 \times 2 = 7$ ft. During the next 2 seconds, her speed is about 4.5 ft/sec, and the distance walked during these two seconds is $4.5 \times 2 = 9$ ft. During the final 2 seconds Annette's average speed is 5.5 ft/sec, and the distance walked is $5.5 \times 2 = 11$ ft. Thus, total distance walked will be about $3 + 5 + 7 + 9 + 11 = 35$ ft. (That this is the exact value is entirely beside the point.)

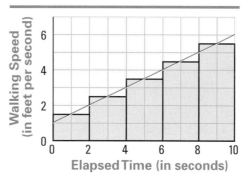

Annette's Walk

Unit 1

EXPLORE *continued*

The solution on the previous page is equivalent to approximating the distance really walked by means of the distance walked by someone who walks at constant speed for two seconds, then at a different constant speed for the next two seconds, and so on, as in the step graph on the previous page. But for this imaginary walker, the distance walked coincides with the sum of the areas of the rectangles.

Students may choose to use the smallest speed during the two-second period, or the largest instead of one "in the middle." They may also choose to estimate the walker's speed over intervals of length other than 2.

Whichever approach your students choose, they are replacing the actual speed of the walker by a reasonably close speed of the type found in the previous items. Student answers do not have to be exact.

Some students may notice that the distance traveled is equal to the total area under the graph, and they may calculate this by dividing the region into a rectangle and a triangle. The rectangle with base 10 and height 1 has an area of 10 representing 10 ft walked. The area of the triangle would be $\frac{1}{2} \cdot 10 \cdot 5$ or 25, representing 25 ft and giving a total of 35 ft walked. (This area can also be found by using the formula for the area of a trapezoid.)

iv. Start walking at 6 ft/sec and lower your speed (decelerate) by $\frac{1}{2}$ ft/sec per second for 6 seconds. Walk the remaining 4 seconds at a constant speed of 3 ft/sec. As before, an estimate for the distance walked can be found in different ways. During the first 2 seconds, Fraser's speed varies between 6 and 5 ft/sec. A reasonable estimate (not the best, though) is about 6 ft/sec. Thus, the distance covered during the first 2 seconds is about $6 \times 2 = 12$ ft. Similarly, during the next 2 seconds Fraser's speed is about 5 ft/sec, and so you can estimate the distance walked by $5 \times 2 = 10$ ft. During the next 2 seconds, his speed is about 4 ft/sec, and the distance walked is $4 \times 2 = 8$ ft.

During the final 4 seconds, his speed is exactly 3 ft/sec. The distance walked during these four seconds can be estimated by $3 \times 4 = 12$ ft.

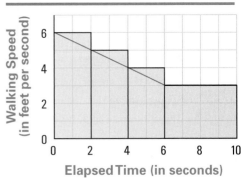

Fraser's Walk

The total distance walked is about $12 + 10 + 8 + 12 = 42$ ft. Again the speed of the walker is being approximated by simplifying the situation to a walker whose speed is constant and equal to 6 ft/sec over the first 2 seconds, constant and equal to 5 ft/sec over the next 2, and so on. So, in this case, the 42 ft is an overestimate of the actual distance walked.

EXPLORE *continued*

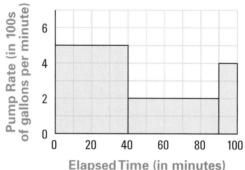

2. **See Teaching Master 24.**

    In this activity, the context has changed but students are investigating the same ideas. You can expect your students to begin to make the connection between area under the rate curve and change in a quantity. Students who do make this connection may estimate area using more exact geometric figures such as triangles, rectangles, or trapezoids, or they may count the squares in the region. You may wish to have students share their methods for Graph iii.

    i. During the first 40 minutes, water is pumped at a rate of 5 hundred gallons per minute. Therefore, 5 × 40 = 200 hundred gallons (20,000 gallons) were pumped during that period. During the next 50 minutes, water is pumped at 2 hundred gallons per minute. During those 50 minutes, 2 × 50 = 100 hundred gallons were pumped. Proceeding similarly, during the remaining 10 minutes, 4 × 10 = 40 hundred gallons were pumped.

    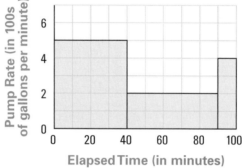

    A reasonable estimate is (5 × 40) + (2 × 50) + (4 × 10) = 340 hundred or 34,000 gallons. This is the same as calculating the areas of the rectangles on the graph above.

    ii. As before, there is more than one way to estimate the total amount of water pumped into the fields. One method uses 20-minute intervals and the value of the flow rate at the midpoint.

    This is the same as approximating the rate of the pump by the rate of a simpler pump that pumps at the same rate for 20 minutes as in the graph at the right.

    This gives a total amount pumped of (4 × 20) + (3 × 20) + (3 × 20) + (2 × 20) + (1 × 20) = 260 hundred gallons or 26,000 gallons.

    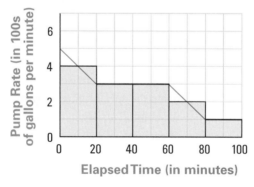

    iii. Using 10-minute intervals and estimating pump rate for the interval by using the rate at the midpoint:

Interval of 10 minutes	1st	2nd	3rd	4th	5th	6th	7th	8th	9th	10th
Est. Pump Rate (in 100s of gallons per minute)	1.5	2	2.5	3	5	5.5	4	3.5	1.5	0.4

    Proceeding as before, (1.5 × 10) + (2 × 10) + (2.5 × 10) + (3 × 10) + (5 × 10) + (5.5 × 10) + (4 × 10) + (3.5 × 10) + (1.5 × 10) + (0.4 × 10) = 289 hundred gallons. The total amount pumped is about 28,900 gallons.

Unit 1

Master 25

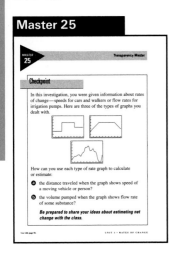

SHARE AND SUMMARIZE full-class discussion

Checkpoint

See Teaching Master 25.
Responses will vary, but these general ideas should be addressed during your class discussion of this Checkpoint. If students have not noticed that using the midpoint method when the rate of change is constant gives exactly the same result as finding the exact area (see Activity 1, Graph iii.), you may wish to pursue that idea here following the discussion. Students should notice graphically that the overestimate is equal to the underestimate for each rectangle.

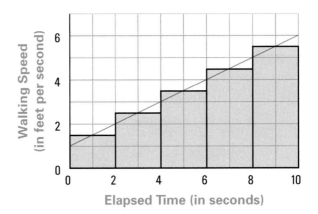

Elapsed Time (in seconds)

ⓐ In the first graph, you know that the speed is constant on each of three intervals. Assuming the horizontal axis is time, you can calculate distance traveled on each time interval multiplying *speed* × *time*, that is (*height of the speed function*) × (*length of interval*). This yields the area of the rectangle between part of the graph and the *x*-axis. Adding these distances will give total distance traveled.

In the next two graphs, divide the time interval into smaller subintervals and approximate the speed function by means of a function that is constant on each one of the small subintervals. Then calculate the distance traveled using an approximate speed value for each interval as in the first graph, adding the areas of the rectangles (or triangles or trapezoids) as in Graph ii between the graph and the *x*-axis.

ⓑ For volume pumped in the first graph: calculate volume pumped on each of the three time intervals for which the rate is constant multiplying *rate* × *time*. Again, volume pumped over each interval equals the area of the corresponding rectangle. Adding the three volumes gives the total volume pumped during that period.

In the second and third graphs, divide the interval into smaller subintervals as before, and approximate the rate function by means of a function that is constant on each one of these small subintervals. Then the estimate of the water volume pumped during that interval will be *rate* × *time*, using an approximate rate value for each interval as in the first graph. Adding all the volume estimates (that is, the areas of the rectangles between the graph and the *x*-axis) gives an estimate of total volume pumped. (Again, students may suggest using triangular or trapezoidal areas for Graph ii.)

APPLY individual task

▶**On Your Own**

a. Responses will depend on the intervals students use and how they estimate speed over each interval. At this point, students do not need to be systematic about this process.

Divide the first 6 seconds into small intervals of 1 second each and approximate, on each of them, the speed with a constant speed. One set of possible estimates is 220, 210, 200, 180, 160, and 140 ft/sec respectively.

The estimate for the distance traveled is $(220 \times 1) + (210 \times 1) + (200 \times 1) + (180 \times 1) + (160 \times 1) + (140 \times 1) = 1{,}110$ ft. Alternatively, you can divide the 6 seconds into intervals of 2 seconds each and approximate the speed during each of them with 215, 190, and 145 ft/sec respectively. The estimate obtained using this approximation is $(215 \times 2) + (190 \times 2) + (145 \times 2) = 1{,}100$ ft.

b. As in Part a, you can divide the 6 seconds in different ways and approximate the speed on the small intervals differently also. Here the interval is divided into three periods of 2 seconds each and the speed on them is approximated by 95, 60, and 45 ft/sec respectively. Using this approximation to estimate the distance traveled by the plane during those 6 seconds gives a total distance of $(95 \times 2) + (60 \times 2) + (45 \times 2) = 400$ ft.

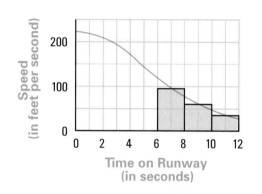

~~MORE~~
ASSIGNMENT *pp. 65–71*

Students can now begin Modeling Task 1 from the MORE assignment following Investigation 3.

EXPLORE small-group investigation

INVESTIGATION 2 Velocity and Net Change

Important ideas in this investigation are that rate of change can be negative, and that net change can be calculated by approximating and summing areas, paying attention to whether the area represents a gain or loss in the quantity.

EXPLORE *continued*

Since students have not dealt with negative velocities in this lesson, it is important to make sure they understand this. (You may remind them of work they did with negative velocity in Lessons 1 and 2.) You might stop the groups after Activity 1 to clarify the points in the following paragraphs if students are uncertain about what is happening. You may have students who are taking physics who could explain these ideas to their classmates. It might also be helpful to use the CBL to clarify this.

For somebody moving along the ray in front of the motion detector, it is quite natural to take velocity as the rate of change of the distance from the motion detector. Thus, when velocity is positive the distance from the motion detector grows (you move away from it), and when velocity is negative, this distance decreases (you move toward it). This is the expected relationship between a quantity and its rate of change.

In motion along a straight line, the choice of a "positive" direction is arbitrary. When an object moves in this positive direction, velocity is positive, when it moves in the opposite direction, velocity is negative. Another way of saying the same thing is that the half-line in front of the motion detector is the positive half of an axis, while the half behind it is the negative half axis and you measure position with respect to the origin situated at the motion detector. Thus, velocity is the rate of change of the position of the object in motion.

In this section, you may find it convenient to restrict all motion to the half-line in front of the motion detector. That will induce a fairly natural positive direction (away from the motion detector) and save you the choice of one that may be perceived as arbitrary and will give you a stronger interpretation for the quantity "distance to the motion detector."

Speed is the absolute value of velocity. The graph of speed is obtained by reflecting the part of the velocity graph that lies below the *x*-axis across it.

1. **a.** When the graph is negative, the distance to the motion detector decreases, so it means that the person is walking toward the motion detector.

   b. Walk away from the motion detector at 2 ft/sec for 3 seconds, then walk at a rate of 6 ft/sec for the next 5 seconds. Then, suddenly reverse direction and walk toward the motion detector at 4 ft/sec for 2 seconds.

   c. During the first 3 seconds, distance to the motion detector grows by $2 \times 3 = 6$ ft. During the next 5 seconds, distance to the motion detector grows by $6 \times 5 = 30$ ft. During the remaining 2 seconds, distance to the motion detector grows by $-4 \times 2 = -8$ ft, or decreases by 8 ft. Thus, net change in the distance to the motion detector is $(2 \times 3) + (6 \times 5) - (4 \times 2) = 28$. This means that the person is 28 ft further from the motion detector than at the beginning of the walk.

EXPLORE *continued*

2. **a.** Walk away from the motion detector at 3 ft/sec for 3 seconds. Continue walking in the same direction, at an increasingly slower pace for 2 seconds, then start walking toward the motion detector, accelerating, for 2 more seconds. During the last 3 seconds of the walk, continue walking toward the motion detector at a fixed velocity of 3 ft/sec.

b. During the first 3 seconds, the walker travels at 3 ft/sec to 9 ft away from the motion detector. During the following second the velocity decreases from 3 to 1.5 ft/sec. Take 2.25 ft/sec as an estimate of the velocity during that second. Similarly, take 0.75 ft/sec as an estimate of the velocity during the next second. Then, estimate the net change in the distance from the motion detector to be $(3 \times 3) + (2.25 \times 1) + (0.75 \times 1) = 12$ ft. The net change in distance is positive; therefore, the distance from the motion detector is 12 ft greater than at the starting position. (Some students may find the net change using a rectangular and a triangular region.)

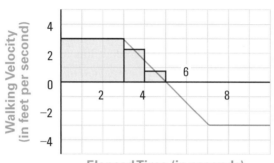

c. Some students may discover that during the last 5 seconds of the walk they have to reproduce the speeds of the first half (backwards) now walking toward the motion detector (since velocity is negative), and conclude without calculations that net change in distance to the motion detector is 0 ft. Others who choose to calculate, may realize that they have already worked out the first part of the walk and they only have to estimate net change in the second part and add the two results. They should obtain 0 ft (or something small, since it is an estimate). Others yet may start from scratch as in the graph at the right and calculate $(3 \times 3) + (2.25 \times 1) + (0.75 \times 1) - (0.75 \times 1) - (2.25 \times 1) - (3 \times 3) = 0$. It may be useful to have groups compare their methods.

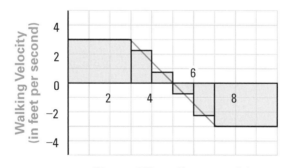

d. The walker started and ended at the same point since the net change in the walker's distance to the motion detector is 0 ft. However, you do not have any information about where the walk started.

e. The total distance traveled is 24 ft (12 ft away from the detector and 12 ft back toward it).

Master 26

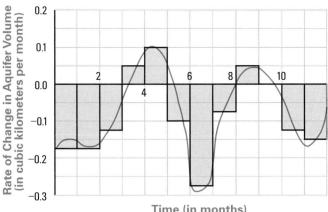

EXPLORE *continued*

3. The graph describes rate of change in the volume of water in the aquifer. Thus, when the rate is positive, the quantity (the volume) grows, and when the rate is negative, the volume decreases.

   a. During the first two months of the year the aquifer volume decreases at a rate of about 0.175 km³ per month, that is, the outflow is about 0.175 km³ per month more than the inflow. During March and early April the outflow is still greater than the inflow, but the difference between them is becoming smaller: the aquifer is still losing volume, but at a smaller rate. At some point in April, and until early June, the inflow is greater than the outflow, and the aquifer is gaining volume. From early June to late August the aquifer volume decreases again. For example, during July the aquifer loses volume at a rate of about 0.3 km³ per month, that is, the difference between inflow and outflow rates during July is about 0.3 km³ per month. During September and the first half of October, the aquifer gains volume at a low rate. From the middle of October until the end of the year, the aquifer loses volume: the outflow is again more than the inflow.

   b. No; perhaps the student is thinking that the graph is showing the volume of water in the aquifer, rather than the rate of change of the volume. Through March and April, the rate of change changes at a constant rate, but during March the volume in the aquifer was decreasing, and in mid-April the volume of water began to increase.

   c. Compare the areas between the *x*-axis and the function above and below the axis. If the area below the axis is greater than the area above it, then the aquifer lost water that year.

   d. **See Teaching Master 26.**
   One simple way is to estimate the number of grid squares above the *x*-axis and below the function, and subtract the number of grid squares below the *x*-axis and above the function. A negative number could indicate a net loss of water. Following is one sample count:

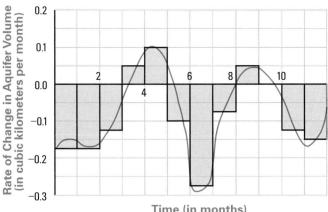

EXPLORE *continued*

Month	Est. Rate (in km³ per month)
January	−0.175
February	−0.175
March	−0.125
April	0.05
May	0.1
June	−0.1
July	−0.275
August	−0.075
September	0.05
October	0
November	−0.125
December	−0.15

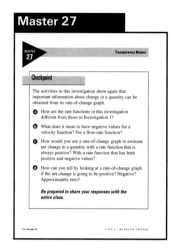

Master 27

The aquifer lost about 1 km³ of water during the year. Answers will vary depending on how estimates are made.

SHARE AND SUMMARIZE   full-class discussion

Checkpoint

See Teaching Master 27.

ⓐ In Investigation 1, the quantities had positive rate-of-change functions. In this investigation, the quantities have rate-of-change functions that have positive and negative values.

ⓑ When you walk in a straight line, the velocity function is the rate of change of the position with respect to an origin (in this case, the motion detector). Thus, when the velocity is negative, the coordinate of the position on the line decreases. Flow rate functions, which deal with inflow and outflow from a reservoir or container, are the rate-of-change functions for the volume of the liquid left in it. Thus, when a flow rate function is negative, the volume of the liquid is decreasing, that is, the outflow is greater than the inflow.

ⓒ When the rate function is always positive, divide the interval into small subintervals and approximate the rate of change by means of a simple function that is constant over each of these small subintervals. Net change in the quantity over each one of the small subintervals will be approximately the height of the simple function on that interval times the length of the interval, that is, the area of the rectangle. To estimate total net change, simply add those net changes by adding the areas of the rectangles. The estimate will be very close to the area of the region between the graph of the rate function and the *x*-axis.

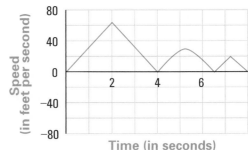
SHARE AND SUMMARIZE *continued*

CONSTRUCTING A MATH
TOOLKIT: Following the
Checkpoint discussion of
Parts c and d, students
should summarize their
understanding of informa-
tion about net change that
can be obtained from a rate
of change graph.

When the rate function has both positive and negative values, start in the same way: approximate the rate function by means of a simple function and estimate net change on that interval by multiplying the height of the simple function by the length of the time interval. Some of these results will be negative because the simple rate function will be negative on some intervals. More concretely, they will be the negative of the area of the rectangle. Then add these net changes to obtain an estimate of net change over the entire interval. The estimate will be close to a difference of areas between the graph of the rate function and the *x*-axis: areas above the *x*-axis minus areas below the *x*-axis.

d If the area bounded by the graph above the *x*-axis is greater than the area bounded by the graph below the *x*-axis, then the net change will be positive. If it is the other way around, the net change will be negative. If these areas are almost equal, the net change will be approximately 0.

APPLY   **individual task**

On Your Own

The velocity graph shows abrupt changes when the jumper reaches the end of the cord because the elasticity of the cord comes into play. The smooth change in the velocity graph represents the gradual velocity change due to gravity during the rebound.

a. Speed is the absolute value of the velocity. Therefore, to find the speed of the jumper at any given time, find the velocity and take its absolute value. One way to find out when the jumper is gaining speed is to use the graph of the velocity to obtain the graph of the speed.

Then, the speed increases between 0 and 2 seconds (when the
jumper is free-falling), between 4
and about 5.2 seconds (jumper
bouncing upward), and 6.5 and
about 7.2 seconds (free-falling
again). The jumper is motionless at
those times when speed is 0. This
happens at 4 seconds when she
stops falling and is about to start moving upward, at 6.5 seconds when the jumper stops moving up and is about to fall again, and at 8 seconds. The jumper stops falling and is about to bounce back upward at those times when her velocity changes from negative to positive.

The jumper gains speed moving upward, when her velocity is positive and increasing. She gains speed in her fall when the velocity is negative and decreasing.

APPLY *continued*

b. The area of the first shaded triangle is $\frac{4 \times 64}{2} = 128$. This means that net change in her distance to the water is –128 ft, so after 4 seconds, the jumper is $135 - 128 = 7$ ft above the ground.

After 6.5 seconds, the estimated net change in distance to the water is $\frac{2.5 \times 32}{2} - 128 = 40 - 128 = -88$, so the estimated height of the jumper is $135 - 88 = 47$ ft above the water.

After 8 seconds, the height is $47 - \frac{1.5 \times 20}{2} = 47 - 15 = 32$ ft.

c. The total distance traveled by the jumper is the sum of the absolute values of the distances. $D = 128$ ft (downward) + 40 ft (upward) + 15 ft (downward) = 183 ft

Velocity (in feet per second) — *Time (in seconds)* — values: 80, 40, 0, –40, –80; 128, 40, 15

MORE

ASSIGNMENT *pp. 65–71*

Students can now begin Modeling Task 2 or Extending Task 1 from the MORE assignment following Investigation 3.

EXPLORE small-group investigation

INVESTIGATION 3 Net Change, Areas, and Definite Integrals

In this investigation, students learn to use integral notation. The first activity uses a familiar context and a simple graph, to ease this transition. In Activity 1, students have to take care in interpreting their answers. The starting location is not given, so they can only determine the net change in distance, not the ending location.

Activities 2 and 3 refine the estimation method for definite integrals. Students might find it easier to see which method gives the better approximation of the area between the curve and the horizontal axis if they shade the rectangular blocks created by their method.

Before students work on the MORE tasks, you may wish to encourage them to find efficient technology methods to estimate integrals. One method would be to generate a sequence and store it in a list, L_1. Widths of intervals, even if they are not equal, could be stored in a second list, L_2. A third list, L_3, could be defined as the product of L_1 and L_2. Then find the sum of L_3. Students will likely suggest this method particularly if you prompt them with a question about efficient methods. You may wish to provide Technology Tips from Masters 28–31 to students once they experiment with Activity 2 Part d.

Masters 28–31

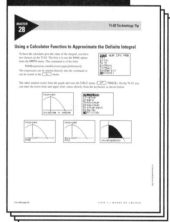

1. a. i. $\displaystyle\int_0^5 v(t)\, dt = 2 - 2 - 1.5 = -1.5$ m

This result shows that after 5 seconds, the walker is 1.5 m closer to the detector than at time 0 second.

EXPLORE *continued*

ii. $\int_{5}^{10} v(t)\,dt = -\frac{1}{2} + \frac{1}{2}(3 \cdot 3) + 1(3) = -0.5 + 4.5 + 3 = 7$ m

This result shows that after 10 seconds of the walk, this walker was 7 m farther from the detector than he was at 5 second.

iii. $\int_{0}^{10} v(t)\,dt = -1.5 + 7 = 5.5$ m

This result shows that after the entire 10-second trip, the walker ended up 5.5 m farther from the detector than his position at time 0 second.

b. If you consider the total area between $v(t)$ and the x-axis, using the absolute value of $v(t)$ (or considering all areas positive), you will have the total distance the walker moved in the 10-second walk.

$$\text{Distance walked} = 2 + 2 + 2 + 4.5 + 3 = 13.5 \text{ m}$$

(Be sure that students recognize that this is not the same as $\left|-1.5\right| + \left|7\right|$.)

2. a. The separate terms in the sum each represent the area of one rectangle. The width of each rectangle is 0.5. The numbers 4.4, 4.9, 4.9, 4.4, 3.4, and 1.9 represent the heights of the six rectangles. These values are determined by substituting the midpoint value of x for each rectangle into the function. For example, $f(0.25) \approx 4.4$ and $f(0.75) \approx 4.9$.

b. Some students may say that the estimate will be larger than the actual value because the triangular areas above the curve appear to be slightly larger than those below the curve, but other students may have different ideas. It is highly unlikely that this approximation is exactly equal to the integral.

c. A more accurate approximation could be determined by dividing the area into more rectangles. For example, the width of each rectangle could be 0.25 or 0.1.

d. A calculator or computer routine gives a value of 12, compared to the estimated value of 11.95. (See Technology Tips 28–29.)

3. a. The strategy explored in Activity 2 is the midpoint method, so the students are likely to use that one, probably after partitioning the interval into five subintervals. Again, there are other possibilities like the left- or right-endpoint values, using trapezoids, or intervals of different length. (Note that between $x = 3$ and $x = 5$ the function is almost constant.)

Using the midpoint method:

Interval	0 to 1	1 to 2	2 to 3	3 to 4	4 to 5
h(x)	$h(0.5) = 2.67$	$h(1.5) = 1.6$	$h(2.5) = 1.14$	$h(3.5) = 0.89$	$h(4.5) = 0.73$

EXPLORE *continued*

$$\int_0^5 h(x)\, dx \approx 2.67 + 1.6 + 1.14 + 0.89 + 0.73 = 7.03$$

Using the right-endpoint method:

$$\int_0^5 h(x)\, dx \approx (2 \times 1) + (1.33 \times 1) + (1 \times 1) + (0.8 \times 1) + (0.67 \times 1) = 5.8$$

Using the left-endpoint method:

$$\int_0^5 h(x)\, dx \approx 4 + 2 + 1.33 + 1 + 0.8 = 9.13$$

Masters 32a–32b

b. The approximation using the right-endpoint method is smaller than the exact integral because the sum of the areas of the rectangles formed using the method is smaller than the area of the region between the graph and the *x*-axis. With the left-endpoint method, the approximation is greater than the integral. The midpoint case would almost be exact.

c. As before, differences may appear as a result of partitioning the interval into different subintervals or because the methods chosen (right-endpoint, left-endpoint, or midpoint) were not the same.

d. Responses will vary. Some students might keep the right-endpoint method and partition each of the five intervals to form a total of 10 or more intervals. Others might choose to keep the same five subintervals and switch to the midpoint method, which in this case will be closer to the actual value of the integral.

SHARE AND SUMMARIZE full-class discussion

Checkpoint

See Teaching Masters 32a–32b.

a The definite integral gives the difference of the areas of the regions between the graph of the function and the *x*-axis. It is equal to the sum of the areas of the regions above the *x*-axis minus the sum of the areas of the regions below it.

b The integral of a rate function between two moments in time is the net change in the quantity over that period.

c You can divide the interval into small subintervals and use the left-endpoint, right-endpoint, or midpoint method to estimate the integral.

d To approximate the integral over a specific interval, you calculate the area under the curve to be approximately equal to the sum of a series of rectangles. The smaller the width of the rectangles, the better the approximation of the integral. This is because the smaller the interval, the more linear the function appears. This means that the rectangular estimate is very close to the actual area.

CONSTRUCTING A MATH TOOLKIT: Students should explain the meaning of a definite integral in terms of areas and net change in a quantity.

APPLY individual task

On Your Own

a. The intervals when the ball is going upward (velocity positive) or downward (velocity negative) are identified on the graph at the right. The ball reaches a highest point (stops going up and starts going down) at 1 and about 2.5 seconds and some other time after 3 seconds. The steep ascending segments correspond to those moments when the ball touches the ground and compresses and decompresses violently.

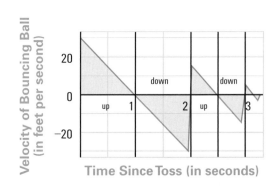

b. The net change after 1 second (the area of a triangle with base 1 and height 30) is 15 ft.

The net change after 2 seconds is the difference of the areas of two triangles with the same base lengths and heights. The estimate is 0 ft.

The net change after 2.5 seconds is net change in the first 2 seconds plus net change between 2 and 2.5. The former is 0 ft. The latter is approximately the area of a triangle with base 0.5 and height 15, or approximately 3.75 ft.

The net change after 3 seconds is net change before 2.5 seconds plus net change between 2.5 and 3. The latter will be around –3.75 ft. Thus, the overall net change is approximately 0 ft.

c.   i. $\displaystyle\int_0^2 v(t)\, dt = 0$ ft

   ii. $\displaystyle\int_0^3 v(t)\, dt = 0$ ft

   iii. $\displaystyle\int_1^3 v(t)\, dt = -15$ ft

MORE independent assignment

Modeling

1. a. The skier starts the race moving at a constant speed of 6 mph and maintains that speed for the first half hour. During the next quarter of an hour, she skis at a pace of 3 mph, perhaps corresponding to a steep hill. Then she goes back to her pace of 6 mph for another quarter of an hour. Over the following half hour her speed steadily decreases in such a way that at the end of that half hour she finds herself skiing at 4 mph. This may correspond to a long slow rise in the trail. Then she skis at a pace of $\frac{1}{4}$ mph for one-quarter hour. Finally, she skis the rest of the trip (three-quarters of an hour more) at a constant speed of 5 mph. The trail is most likely fairly flat for the last 45 minutes.

b. Calculations for the first hour are shown below.

Interval (in hours)	0 to 0.5	0.5 to 0.75	0.75 to 1
Area Under Graph (in miles per hour)	$6 \times 0.5 = 3$	$3 \times 0.25 = 0.75$	$6 \times 0.25 = 1.5$

The distance skied during the first hour was 5.25 mi.

For the second hour the calculations are

Interval (in hours)	1 to 1.5	1.5 to 1.75	1.75 to 2
Area Under Graph (in miles per hour)	$\frac{4+6}{2} \times 0.5 = 2.5$	$0.25 \times 0.25 \approx 0.06$	$5 \times 0.25 = 1.25$

Thus, the distance skied during the second hour was approximately 3.8 mi.

c. In the last half hour, the skier went $5(0.5) = 2.5$ mi. Thus, the distance skied during the 2.5 hour trip was $5.25 + 3.8 + 2.5$ or approximately 11.55 mi.

ASSIGNMENT *pp. 65–71*

Modeling: 1, 2, and 3 or 4*
Organizing: 1, 2, and 4
Reflecting: 2 and 3
Extending: 1 and choice of one*

When choice is indicated, it is important to leave the choice to the student.
NOTE: *It is best if Organizing tasks are discussed as a whole class after they have been assigned as homework.*

2. a. Students can use the midpoint method to first partition the 10 seconds into periods of 1 second, then estimate the velocity at the midpoint of each interval, express the velocity in feet per second rounding to the nearest integer, finally determine the sum of the areas of all of the rectangles. (Since each rectangle has a base of 1, the total distance in feet is the sum of the velocity values.) The estimate is approximately 638 feet.

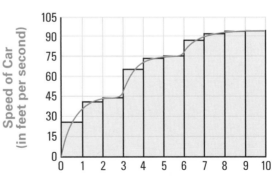

Interval (in seconds)	0–1	1–2	2–3	3–4	4–5	5–6	6–7	7–8	8–9	9–10
Midpoint Speed (in feet per second)	23	38	41	58	68	70	80	85	87	88

MORE *continued*

b. You could proceed in the same fashion (midpoint method) after partitioning the 10 seconds into 20 intervals of half a second each. In most cases, the resulting approximation will be better.

3. a. You can take advantage of the symmetry and estimate the area of the right half only. Using estimates from the graph or the rule at the midpoint of the interval gives the table below:

Interval (in feet)	0 to 5	5 to 10	10 to 15	15 to 20
Height of Midpoint (in feet)	29	24	14	0

The estimate for half the area is 335 ft². The estimate for the area of the figure is 670 ft². To improve the accuracy, use a finer grid. (If students use only the grid, they may say that the area under the parabola is approximately 28 squares, where each square has an area of 25 ft². This gives a total area of approximately $28 \times 25 = 700$ ft².)

b. The *x*-intercepts of the graph are $\pm \sqrt{\frac{30}{0.1}} \approx \pm 17.3$, so you should integrate from -17.3 to 17.3.

$$\int_{-17.3}^{17.3} (30 - 0.1x^2)\, dx = 692.8 \text{ ft}^2$$

4. a.

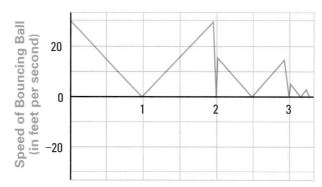

MORE *continued*

b.   i. $\int_0^2 s(t)\,dt = 30$ ft

The total distance traveled in the first bounce is 30 ft.

ii. $\int_2^3 s(t)\,dt = 7.5$ ft

The total distance traveled in the second bounce is 7.5 ft.

iii. $\int_0^3 s(t)\,dt = 37.5$ ft

The total distance traveled in the first two bounces is 37.5 ft.

c.

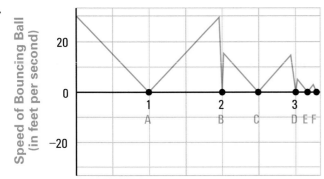

Point	Time	Flight Position
A	1 sec	The ball is at its maximum height.
B	2 sec	The ball hits and bounces off the ground.
C	2.5 sec	The ball is at the turning point after the first bounce.
D	3 sec	The ball bounces off the ground.
E	3.2 sec	The ball is at the turning point after the second bounce.
F	3.4 sec	The ball is caught.

d.

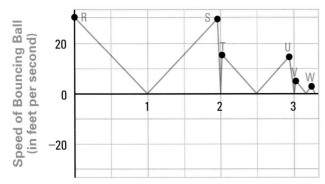

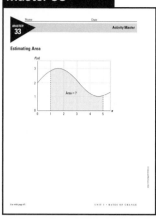

MORE *continued*

Point	Time	Flight Position
R	Initial Time	The ball has just been hit.
S	2 sec	Just before the first bounce
T	2.1 sec	Just after the first bounce
U	3 sec	Just before the second bounce
V	3.1 sec	Just after the second bounce
W	3.4 sec	Just before the third bounce

Organizing

1. **See Teaching Master 33.**

   a. By sketching rectangles and determining the sum of the areas of the rectangles, you can approximate the area between the *x*-axis and the graph of $f(x)$ for $1 \le x \le 5$. One possibility is shown at the right.

   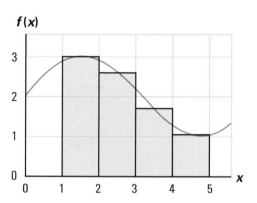

   $$\text{Area} = 1(3.0) + 1(2.6) + 1(1.7) + 1(1.1)$$
   $$= 8.4$$

   b. ■ If the midpoint of each interval is used, the calculation would be $A \approx 1(f(1.5)) + 1(f(2.5)) + 1(f(3.5)) + 1(f(4.5))$.

   ■ Technology methods will vary. To get a calculator or computer integration tool to estimate the area, the function formula, and the endpoints of the integration interval, in this case 1 and 5, must be entered. The command for the TI-83 is fnInt(f(x),x,1,5). (See Technology Tips (Masters 28 and 29) for this method and a graphical method of evaluating integrals.)

2. a. Using the midpoint of each interval, the approximation is
   $$\int_0^3 f(x)\,dx \approx (0.5)(f(0.25)) + (0.5)(f(0.75)) + (0.5)(f(1.25)) + (0.5)(f(1.75)) + (0.5)(f(2.25)) + (0.5)(f(2.75))$$
   $$= 9.0625$$

MORE *continued*

b. $\int_0^3 f(x)\,dx \approx 9$

The estimate from Part a should be very close to this value.

c. The value will be larger. Since the graph of $f(x)$ has the y-axis as an axis of symmetry, the area between $f(x)$ and the x-axis, from -2 to 0, will be above the x-axis and so $\int_{-2}^3 f(x)\,dx$ will be larger than $\int_0^3 f(x)\,dx$.

d. The value will be smaller because the graph from 3 to 10 falls below the x-axis, so that area will be subtracted from $\int_0^3 f(x)\,dx$.

3. a. Using the midpoint method,

$$\int_{-2}^2 f(x)\,dx \approx 1(f(-1.5)) + 1(f(-0.5)) + 1(f(0.5)) + 1(f(1.5)) = 19.$$

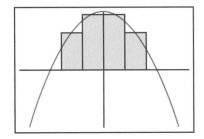

b. You can get a better approximation by using narrower rectangles.

c. $A = \int_0^{\sqrt 6} f(x)\,dx + \left| \int_{\sqrt 6}^4 f(x)\,dx \right|$

4. Responses will vary. These are examples.

a. $y = 2x - 6$

Any line with x-intercept of 3 will have this property.

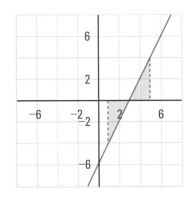

MORE *continued*

b. $y = x$

Any line through the origin will have this property.

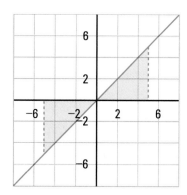

c. $y = -\sin x$

Any function of the form $y = a \sin x$ will have this property.

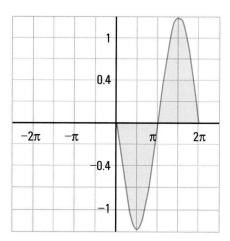

d. $y = \frac{2}{9}x - \frac{2}{9}$

This equation was derived by finding the coordinates of point B in the diagram using the area formula for the triangle whose area is 1 square unit.

Area $= \frac{1}{2} \cdot 3 \cdot b = 1$ square unit

$b = \frac{2}{3}$

The equation of the line through (1, 0) and $\left(4, \frac{2}{3}\right)$ is $y = \frac{2}{9}x - \frac{2}{9}$.

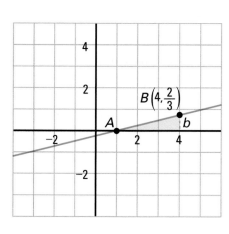

MORE *continued*

Reflecting

1. Integration estimates net change in quantities described by nonlinear functions using functions that are linear.

2. In the case of differentiation, you take differences of values of the distance function over small intervals (divided by differences of values of x). In the case of integrals, you put together (integrate) "little bits" of change (change over small periods) to obtain net change.

3. To convince someone who has not studied calculus ideas that the rate of change/net change/integral connection makes sense, it is probably best to start with a very simple example.

    A car traveling 60 mph for 3 hours goes 180 miles. This makes sense for most people. The rate of change function $g(t)$ in this case is a constant, $g(t) = 60$, so the graph of $g(t)$ is a horizontal line.

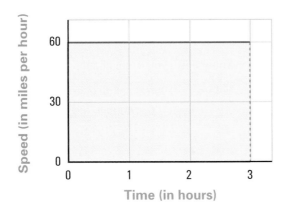

If you look at the area between the graph and the time axis, it is a 3 hour by 60 mph rectangle, whose area is 180 miles. Thus, the area agrees with what a person understands to be the net change in position of the car (the distance traveled). A calculus name for this area is the definite integral from 0 to 3.

Now look at a car that is not traveling at a constant speed. How could you determine how far this car has traveled after a length of time? A person who understands speed and distance traveled will see that estimates must be made. Making estimates with numerical calculations is equivalent to approximating the area under a nonconstant graph using a rectangle method. Thus, it makes sense to use the integral idea to find the net change in the position of a car traveling at a varying rate of speed.

4. **a.** Speedometers in cars measure in miles per hour.
    Tachometers in cars measure in revolutions per minute.
    Stationary bikes measure in calories burnt per hour.

    b. Total distance
    Total revolutions
    Total calories burned

MORE *continued*

Extending

1. **a.** When the rate of change in the volume is negative, the volume decreases. The factors that affect the volume are evaporation and inflow. Evaporation must be greater than inflow, that is, the rate at which the lake loses water due to evaporation is higher than the rate at which the lake receives water from its tributaries (inflow rate).

    b. In this task, there may be small discrepancies due to differences in the perceived values of the rate function (in addition to those emanating from the choice of strategy). One method is to divide the interval between 0 and 6 (corresponding respectively to 1960 and 1966) into intervals of length 1 and use the right-endpoint method.

Right Endpoint	1	2	3	4	5	6
Rate Function (Approx.)	−20	−24	−15	1	−28	−15

    The estimate of the net change in volume is then −101 km^3, that is, the Aral Sea effectively lost about 101 km^3 of water between 1960 and 1966.

    c. Volume in 1966 = Volume in 1960 + net change ≈ 1,066 + (−101) = 965 km^3.

    d. Volume in 1972 = Volume in 1966 + net change between 1966 and 1972. Our estimate for the former is 965 km^3. To estimate the net change, use the same strategy as before:

Right Endpoint	7	8	9	10	11	12
Rate Function (Approx.)	−19	−14	22	−20	−34	−33

    Volume in 1972 ≈ 965 + (−98) = 867 km^3

Right Endpoint	13	14	15	16	17	18
Rate Function (Approx.)	−16	−44	−44	−42	−42	−36

    Volume in 1978 ≈ 867 + (−224) = 643 km^3

Right Endpoint	19	20	21	22	23	24
Rate Function (Approx.)	−43	−25	−28	−30	−29	−25

    Volume in 1984 ≈ 643 + (−180) = 463 km^3

Right Endpoint	25	26	27	28	29	30
Rate Function (Approx.)	−21	−20	−12	−20	−19	−24

    Volume in 1990 ≈ 463 + (−116) = 347 km^3

    e. You have estimates of several values of a function $V(t)$ giving the volume of the Aral Sea as a function of years elapsed since 1960. Both a linear function and a qua-

MORE *continued*

dratic function fit reasonably well. The linear model predicts that in the year 2000, the volume of the Aral will be approximately 90 km³. The quadratic model predicts a negative volume for the year 2000. Yes, the data gathered supports the contention that the Aral Sea will have practically disappeared by the year 2000.

2. **a.** For instance, $\int_0^2 (x^3 - 5x)\, dx = -6$ and $\int_2^5 (x^3 - 5x)\, dx = 99.75$. Also $\int_0^5 (x^3 - 5x)\, dx = -6 + 99.75 = 93.75$.

    b. $\int_a^b f(x)\, dx$ is the difference between the darker shaded area above and the area below the *x*-axis. $\int_b^c f(x)\, dx$ is the lighter shaded area. $\int_a^c f(x)\, dx$ is the sum of the darker shaded area plus the lighter shaded area above minus the area below the *x*-axis, but this is the sum of the other two integrals. Something similar will occur when the student analyzes positive

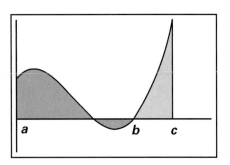

functions, negative functions, functions that are positive between *a* and *b* and negative between *b* and *c*, or functions that change sign on both intervals. Thus, the conjecture seems to be true.

    c. $\int_a^b f(x)\, dx$ would be net change in the quantity between *a* and *b*, $\int_b^c f(x)\, dx$ would be net change in the quantity between *b* and *c*, $\int_a^c f(x)\, dx$ would be net change in the quantity between *a* and *c*. This is the sum of net change between *a* and *b* plus net change between *b* and *c*, or the sum of the other two integrals.

3. **a.** The conjecture is true. Use any of the estimation methods on the functions $f(x)$ and $f(x) + 5$ in the graph to estimate the integrals. If you approximate $f(x)$ and $f(x) + 5$ with constant functions in each subinterval, the constant for $f(x) + 5$ will be 5 units more than the constant for $f(x)$, and the contribution of the area toward the estimated integral will be 5 × (length of the subinterval), greater for $f(x) + 5$ than it is for $f(x)$.

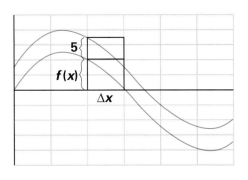

Assessments 13—15

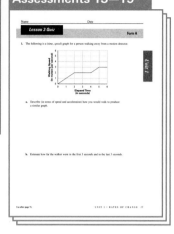

Assessments 16—18

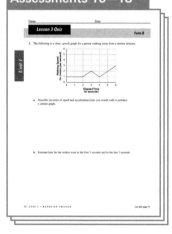

MORE *continued*

This will occur on all the subintervals. When you add up all these approximations to obtain the integral of $f(x) + 5$, the estimate for the integral of $f(x) + 5$ will be the same as the estimate for the integral of $f(x)$ plus additional terms, each of which is 5 times the length of one of the small intervals. The sum of the latter will be 5 times the length of the entire interval, which coincides with the integral of 5 over the big interval.

b. The reasoning is not dependent on the constant being 5. It is true for every constant.

4. a. Using the trapezoid method, the height of each trapezoid is 0.5 and the lengths of the parallel sides will be the values of the left and right endpoints of the interval. If a is the beginning of the interval and b is the end of the interval, the area of each trapezoid is $1\left(\dfrac{f(a) + f(b)}{2}\right) = 0.5[(f(a) + f(b)]$.

a	b	f(a)	f(b)	0.5(f(a) + f(b))
0	1	1	5	3
1	2	5	7	6
2	3	7	7	7
3	4	7	5	6
4	5	5	1	3
			Total Area	**25**

b. Using the calculator: $\displaystyle\int_0^5 f(x)\,dx \approx 25.83$.

Using rectangles and the right-endpoint method:

$$\int_0^5 f(x)\,dx \approx 1(f(1)) + 1(f(2)) + 1(f(3)) + 1(f(4)) + 1(f(5)) = 25.$$

Using rectangles and the midpoint method:

$$\int_0^5 f(x)\,dx \approx f(0.5) + f(1.5) + f(2.5) + f(3.5) + f(4.5) = 26.25.$$

Both the right-endpoint rectangle and trapezoid methods give 25, which is a little smaller than the calculator answer. The midpoint rectangle method gives 26.25, which is a little more than the calculator answer.

See Assessment Resources pages 13–18.

REVIEW AND PRACTICE individual task

▶PUMP

Answers

1. (b)

2. (c)

3. (c)

4. (d)

5. (b)

6. (d)

7. (a)

8. (c)

9. (d)

10. (e)

Lesson 4 *Looking Back*

SYNTHESIZE UNIT IDEAS small-group activity

1. a. The table below uses the approximation $\dfrac{d(t+0.01)-d(t-0.01)}{0.02}$ for the derivative $d'(t)$. Students might choose to use a different increment.

Time t	$d'(t)$ Estimates	$s(t)$ Values
0	−0.50	0
0.5	12.22	12.67
1	23.60	24
1.5	33.78	34.14
2	42.88	43.2
2.5	51.02	51.31
3	58.31	58.56
3.5	64.82	65.05
4	70.64	70.85
4.5	75.86	76.04
5	80.52	80.68
5.5	84.68	84.83
6	88.41	88.54
6.5	91.75	91.86
7	94.73	94.83
7.5	97.40	97.49
8	99.78	99.87
8.5	101.92	101.99
9	103.83	103.89
9.5	105.53	105.59
10	107.06	107.12

The small difference between the results is explained because the slope of the line through the points $(t, d(t-0.01))$ and $(t, d(t+0.01))$ was calculated for each of the values of t in the table. This line has almost the same slope as the curve, but it is not exactly the same. To improve the estimate, choose a smaller increment h for the estimate $\dfrac{d(t+h)-d(t-h)}{2h}$.

SYNTHESIZE *continued*

b. Since $d(t)$ is always increasing, $s(t)$ will always be positive. The rate of change of $d(t)$ seems to be approaching a constant and this is reflected in the leveling off of the graph of $s(t)$.

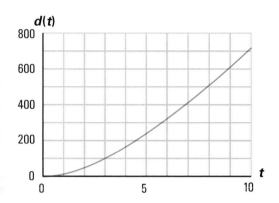

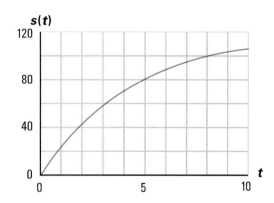

c. ■ From $t = 0$ to $t = 10$: The distance (in feet) fallen during each of these ten seconds can be estimated using the speed in feet per second at the beginning of each second.

Second	Approximated Speed
First	$s(0) = 0$
Second	$s(1) = 24$
Third	$s(2) = 43.2$
Fourth	$s(3) = 58.56$
Fifth	$s(4) = 70.85$
Sixth	$s(5) = 80.68$
Seventh	$s(6) = 88.54$
Eighth	$s(7) = 94.83$
Ninth	$s(8) = 99.87$
Tenth	$s(9) = 103.89$

The distance fallen from $t = 0$ to $t = 10$ can be estimated by summing the approximated speed column, since the length of each interval is 1 second. The distance is approximately 664.42 ft.

■ From $t = 1$ to $t = 5$: $24 + 43.2 + 58.56 + 70.85 = 196.61$ ft

■ From $t = 5$ to $t = 9$: $80.68 + 88.54 + 94.83 + 99.87 = 363.92$ ft

■ From $t = 9$ to $t = 10$: 103.89 ft

d. Distance fallen:

between $t = 0$ and $t = 10$ is $d(10) - d(0) = 717.98$ ft

between $t = 1$ and $t = 5$ is $d(5) - d(1) = 236.95 - 12 = 224.95$ ft

between $t = 5$ and $t = 9$ is $d(9) - d(5) = 612.48 - 236.95 = 375.53$ ft

between $t = 9$ and $t = 10$ is $d(10) - d(9) = 717.98 - 612.48 = 105.5$ ft

Unit 1

SYNTHESIZE *continued*

The exact values are all larger than the estimates, which is reasonable since on every period of 1 second the speed estimated was its lowest value (the speed at the beginning of that period). The estimates would be more accurate if shorter periods (of say $\frac{1}{2}$ second) were used with the same method (left-endpoint), or if the midpoint method were used.

e. Calculate net change in distance fallen as the integral of the rate function $s(t)$:

between $t = 0$ and $t = 10$: $\int_0^{10} s(t)\, dt = \int_0^{10} 120(1 - 0.8^t)\, dt = 719.97$ ft

between $t = 1$ and $t = 5$: $\int_1^5 s(t)\, dt = \int_1^5 120(1 - 0.8^t)\, dt = 226$ ft

between $t = 5$ and $t = 9$: $\int_5^9 s(t)\, dt = \int_5^9 120(1 - 0.8^t)\, dt = 375.96$ ft

between $t = 9$ and $t = 10$: $\int_9^{10} s(t)\, dt = \int_9^{10} 120(1 - 0.8^t)\, dt = 105.56$ ft

These results are very close to the results from Part d, but not as close to the results from Part c.

2. a.

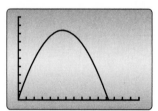

```
WINDOW
 Xmin =0
 Xmax=15
 Xscl =1
 Ymin =0
 Ymax=100
 Yscl =10
 Xres =1
```

The ball reached its maximum height about 5.56 seconds after it was hit and returned to the Moon's surface about 11.11 seconds after it was hit.

b. At the beginning, the ball is gaining height, that is, its distance to the Moon's surface increases, so the rate of change of this distance, the ball's vertical velocity, will be positive. As the ball gets higher, its vertical velocity decreases and 5.56 seconds after it was hit, when it reaches its maximum height, its velocity is 0. Then the ball starts to fall, and its velocity becomes negative and the distance to the Moon's surface decreases. As it falls down, the ball gains speed, that is, its velocity (which is negative) decreases (its absolute value becomes larger).

SYNTHESIZE *continued*

c. Using $\dfrac{h(t + 0.01) - h(t - 0.01)}{0.02}$ for the approximation of $h'(t)$ gives the following table.

Time t	Estimate for $h'(t)$	Time t	Estimate for $h'(t)$
0	30.0	6	−2.4
0.5	27.3	6.5	−5.1
1	24.6	7	−7.8
1.5	21.9	7.5	−10.5
2	19.2	8	−13.2
2.5	16.5	8.5	−15.9
3	13.8	9	−18.6
3.5	11.1	9.5	−21.3
4	8.4	10	−24.0
4.5	5.7	10.5	−26.7
5	3.0	11	−29.4
5.5	0.3		

The pattern of values is linear and the velocity decreases at a rate of −2.7 ft/sec per half-second, that is, −5.4 ft/sec per second.

d. The moment when the ball reaches its maximum height, its velocity is 0, so in either the graph or the table of the velocity, look for the time t when $h'(t) = 0$. In both the table and the graph, this will happen when t is slightly larger than 5.5 seconds.

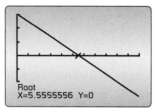

Root
X=5.5555556 Y=0

e. Since the slope is −5.4 and the y-intercept is 30, the rule for $h'(t)$ is $h'(t) = -5.4t + 30$. The graph of this function is a straight line with slope −5.4. For each 1-unit increment of t in the table, the $h'(t)$ value decreases by 5.4.

3. The speed of the skydiver grows all the time without returning to 0. Thus, the skydiver falls all the time (actually you can only say that he moves in the same direction all the time). On the other hand, the ball's velocity tells that it moves in one direction (up) at the beginning and in the opposite direction at the end. The moment when it changes direction (about 5.5 seconds after being hit) is the moment when it reaches its maximum height.

SYNTHESIZE *continued*

4. **a–b.** In Graph i, the news spreads slowly at first, which suggests a few informed students spreading the news person to person. Since few know at the beginning, they can tell the news to only a small number of new students and the growth is sluggish. As the number of informed students increases, they have the capability of spreading the news to more people, which explains faster growth about 7 hours after the decision. A few hours later, most students already know the news and it is difficult to find a student who is not informed. This explains why the growth rate decreases.

   In Graph ii, a large number of students learn the news almost immediately, which suggest the radio/TV scenario. Here too, after most students know the news, finding somebody to tell who does not know becomes increasingly difficult, which explains the slow rate of growth after several hours.

   c. Student methods for matching graphs to equations may vary. $f(t)$ is an exponential decay function which has been reflected across the horizontal axis and then translated up 500 units. Thus, the shape matches Graph ii. Another approach students might take is to estimate each function as this example shows: since $f(2) = 255$ and $g(2) = 6.17$, $f(t)$ matches Graph ii and $g(t)$ matches Graph i.

   d. Students' estimation methods will vary but should entail using either the left-endpoint, right-endpoint, or midpoint estimation methods. The function $f(t)$ grows quite rapidly, so the derivative of $f(t)$ is large at the beginning (near $t = 0$). As time passes, the function $f(t)$, which has a decreasing rate of change, moderates its growth, so $f'(t)$ becomes smaller.

   The derivative of $g(t)$ is small near 0 (which means $g(t)$ grows slowly). Then $g'(t)$ increases suddenly. These high values of $g'(t)$ correspond to the steep growth in $g(t)$. Then, the derivative becomes smaller and the function's growth becomes moderate. Finally, near the 12-hour mark, the rate of change is small again, which means that the function $g(t)$ moderates its growth.

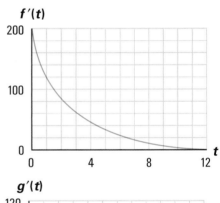

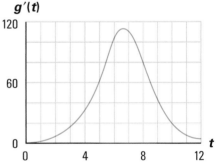

SYNTHESIZE *continued*

e. One method of estimating the net change using the graph is to sum the areas of rectangles. To use the midpoint method with several intervals, first divide the interval from 2 to 6 into smaller intervals. Then, find the value of the function at the midpoint of each interval and multiply each value by the width of the interval. Finally, find the sum of these products. This sum is an estimate of the number of

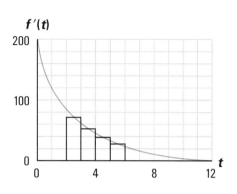

students who heard about the school closing between $t = 2$ and $t = 6$. To check the estimate for $f(t)$, evaluate $f(6) - f(2)$. (For $f'(t)$: net change $\approx 70 + 50 + 48 + 23 =$ 191 students. Check by evaluating $f(6) - f(2) \approx 186$. Using the midpoint method for $g'(t)$, the net change is approximately $5 + 14 + 22 + 43 + 79 = 163$. Check by evaluating $g(6) - g(2) \approx 158$.)

f. The integrals are $\int_2^6 \frac{f(t + 0.01) - f(t - 0.01)}{0.02}\ dt$ and $\int_2^6 \frac{g(t + 0.01) - g(t - 0.01)}{0.02}\ dt$.

5. a. The path is a semicircle with radius 15 ft, so its length, using the formula for the length of the circumference, is equal to 15π or about 47.1 ft.

b. If the starting point is at one end of the semicircle, the graph is shown below.

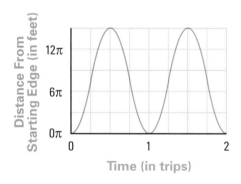

c. The velocity graph is the graph of the derivative of the function "distance to the initial point." The velocity is positive when the skateboarder is moving away from the initial point (the function is increasing) and negative when he is moving toward the initial point (the function is decreasing).

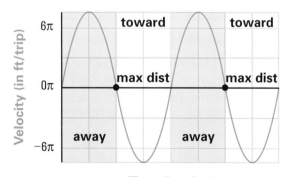

Masters 34a–34b

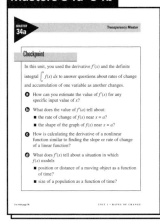

SHARE AND SUMMARIZE full-class discussion

Checkpoint

See Teaching Masters 34a–34b.

ⓐ An estimate of $f'(x)$ can be found using $f'(x) \approx \dfrac{f(x + 0.01) - f(x - 0.01)}{0.02}$ or a similar expression. Another possibility is $f'(x) \approx \dfrac{f(x + 0.01) - f(x)}{0.01}$. Other increments can also be used.

ⓑ ▪ The rate of change of $f(x)$ near a is approximately $f'(a)$.

▪ The graph of $f(x)$ near a looks very much like a straight segment with slope $f'(a)$.

ⓒ In both cases, you use a quotient of the type discussed in Part a above. In the case of a nonlinear function, the smaller the increment the better. In the case of a linear function, the exact rate of change can be obtained with any size increment.

ⓓ ▪ In the case when $f(x)$ represents position or distance of a moving object, $f'(x)$ is the function that gives its velocity relative to the starting position specified by $f(x)$.

▪ When $f(x)$ is the size of a population as a function of time, $f'(x)$ is the rate of growth of that population.

ⓔ $\displaystyle\int_a^b f(x)\, dx$ gives a difference of areas bounded by the graph of $f(x)$:

(areas above the x-axis) – (areas below the x-axis).

ⓕ ▪ When $f(x)$ models the velocity of a moving object as a function of time, $\displaystyle\int_a^b f(x)\, dx$ is the net change in the position or distance of the object from time a to time b.

▪ When $f(x)$ models the rate of change in a population as a function of time, $\displaystyle\int_a^b f(x)\, dx$ is the net change in population during the period between time a and time b.

ⓖ With the aid of the rule for $f(x)$, you can compute $\dfrac{f(x + 0.01) - f(x - 0.01)}{0.02}$ or a similar expression to obtain an estimate of the derivative. To estimate an integral, you could subdivide the interval of integration into small intervals. On each subinterval you could approximate the function value. If you know the formula for the function, you can find the value of the function at the midpoint of each small interval. Then you can estimate net change in the system by finding the area bounded by the simpler approximating function and the x-axis.

ⓗ To improve the estimates of derivatives, you can calculate $\dfrac{f(x + h) - f(x - h)}{2h}$ for smaller values of h. To improve the estimates of integrals, you can divide the interval into smaller subintervals (divide each subinterval in two) and estimate the integral with the new set of rectangles.

APPLY individual task

▶ On Your Own

See Teaching Master 35a–35c.

Responses will vary. Above all, this should be something that is useful to the individual student. You may wish to have students use Teaching Masters 35a–35c "Rates Of Change" Unit Summary, to help them organize the information.

See Assessment Resources pages 19–35.

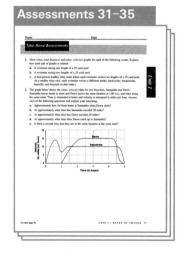

Looking Back, Looking Ahead

▶Reflecting on Mathematical Content

One central theme in the *Contemporary Mathematics in Context* development of algebraic concepts, skills, and problem solving has been study of relationships among quantitative variables. The core idea is the mathematical concept of function, and students have been guided to develop a repertoire of function families that can be applied to model and study the most important patterns of variation.

Using function tables, graphs, and symbolic rules, students have been asked to determine especially interesting characteristics of linear, quadratic, exponential, rational, and trigonometric functions. They have also been asked to look for significant patterns of change in each function family and specific example. Linear functions are those that model constant additive change. Exponential functions are those that model constant multiplicative change. Quadratic, inverse, and periodic models each have different but characteristic patterns of change shown in their tables and graphs.

In one sense, this first unit in *Contemporary Mathematics in Context* Course 4 is a review of the important function families that students have studied in prior courses. However, in another very important sense this "Rates of Change" unit is a bridge from algebraic perspectives on change to the notion of instantaneous change that is the heart of differential and integral calculus. In the first lesson of "Rates of Change," students compared average and instantaneous rates of change and related those ideas to patterns in tables and graphs of familiar functions. In the second lesson, they developed techniques for approximating instantaneous rates of change (derivatives) of functions and some rules for derivatives of simple functions. In the third lesson, they looked at the inverse question of calculating areas between a function graph and the x-axis.

By studying the "Rates of Change" unit, students now have a strong conceptual foundation for future study of calculus. This unit is not intended to be a quick survey of that deep and broad subject. The idea here is to highlight once again the importance of studying ways that variables change in relation to each other, to introduce the new idea of instantaneous rate of change, and to build student intuitions about the numerical, graphic, and symbolic representations of such change.

Unit 1 Assessment

Modeling Motion

UNIT OVERVIEW Motion is an essential element in our lives. It is natural to ask if motion can be modeled mathematically. Two mathematical tools are introduced in this unit that help students model motion. The first is the vector, which is introduced initially as a free vector that is drawn wherever it may be needed and later as a position vector attached to a specific point. It is the position vector representation that leads to the introduction of the second tool, which is parametric representation of locations specified by vectors. The set of these locations forms the graph of the motion as a function of a third variable, usually time. The parametric representations and a graphing calculator or computer graphing software allow students to see linear, projectile, circular, and elliptical motions of objects and to analyze the resulting paths.

Unit 2 Objectives

- ■ To describe and use the concept of vector in mathematical, scientific, and everyday situations
- ■ To represent vectors geometrically and to operate on geometric vectors
- ■ To describe, represent, and use vector components synthetically and analytically
- ■ To use vector concepts to represent linear, projectile, circular, and elliptical motions in a plane parametrically
- ■ To analyze motions using parametric models

Note: If you are teaching this unit to students planning to concentrate in the humanities in college, you may wish to omit the parametric material in order to allow time to study other units in the text. (See p. xix of this *Teacher's Guide*.)

Unit 2 Planning Guide

Lesson Objectives	Assignments	Suggested Pacing	Materials
Lesson 1 *Modeling Linear Motion* • To represent vectors as line segments with both direction and magnitude • To describe and illustrate the scalar multiple of a vector • To describe and illustrate the opposite of a vector • To describe and illustrate the components of a vector • To add two vectors geometrically and by using components • To describe and illustrate the relationship between the coordinates of the terminal point of a position vector and its components • To model linear motions and forces with vectors	**MORE** **after page 86** Students can begin Modeling Task 1 or Reflecting Task 1 or 2 from p. 99. **after page 91** Students can begin Reflecting Task 4 or Extending Task 2 from p. 99. **after page 94** Students can begin Modeling Task 2 or 3, Organizing Task 1, or Extending Task 3 or 4 from p. 99. **page 99** **Modeling:** 1, 2 or 3, and 4* **Organizing:** 1, 2 or 3, and 4 or 5* **Reflecting:** 1, 2, and 3 **Extending:** 2, 4, and choice of one* **PUMP** **pages 106–107**	**Path A:** 10 days **Path B:** 13 days	• Globe (optional) • Nautical mile rulers (see Master 39) • Protractors • Centimeter rulers • Compasses • Teaching Resources 37–47 • Assessment Resources 42–49
Lesson 2 *Simulating Linear and Nonlinear Motion* • To write parametric equations for linear motion • To simulate linear motion using technology • To write parametric equations for projectile motion • To simulate projectile motion using technology • To identify important forces affecting motion • To write a parametric representation of a circle • To use both radian and degree measurements to describe angular velocity • To use technology to simulate the path of a point on a rotating circle • To describe the location of a point on a rotating circle in terms of its initial location and the angular velocity • To use technology to simulate the motion of an object in an elliptical orbit	**MORE** **after page 115** Students can begin Organizing Task 1 or 4 or Reflecting Task 3 from p. 127. **after page 119** Students can begin Modeling Task 1, 2, 3, or 4; or Reflecting Task 2 from p. 127. **after page 122** Students can begin Organizing Task 5 or Reflecting Task 5 from p. 127. **page 127** **Modeling:** Choose two from 1–4, and 5* **Organizing:** 1, 4, and 5 **Reflecting:** 2, 3, and 5 **Extending:** 3 or 4, and 5* **PUMP** **pages 134–135**	**Path A:** 11 days **Path B:** omit	• Chalk or tape • Teaching Resources 48–56 • Assessment Resources 50–55
Lesson 3 *Looking Back* • To review and test the major objectives of the unit		**Path A:** 3 days **Path B:** 2 days	• Teaching Resources 57–58 • Assessment Resources 56–71

When choice is indicated, it is important to leave the choice to the student.
Note: *It is best if Organizing tasks are discussed as a whole class after they have been assigned as homework.*

Lesson **1** *Modeling Linear Motion*

LESSON OVERVIEW Lesson 1 introduces the idea of a vector as a directed quantity that is represented geometrically by an arrow or directed line segment. The context that is used is marine navigation, in which vectors represent courses or paths (distance and direction) boats may take. In the first investigation, students develop the concepts of vector, scalar multiple of a vector, and opposite of a vector, all in the navigation context.

The second investigation introduces the sum or resultant vector in the context of course change. A special case occurs when the addend vectors are horizontal and vertical. The lengths of these vectors can be calculated exactly using the length of the resultant, its direction, and the sine and cosine functions. This work forms the basis for component analysis and parametric representation.

In Investigation 3, students investigate the effect of two or more forces such as wind and currents on a linear course. Component analysis is used to model such situations and to locate the modified course needed to steer so that the planned course is actually traversed. Position vectors (vectors placed with their initial points on the origin of a coordinate system) are introduced in the last investigation of this lesson. The components of the position vectors give the coordinates of the terminal point of the position vector that represents the location of a moving point.

The "Nautical Chart Scales" transparency master in the *Teaching Resources* can be used to make nautical mile rulers that will be sturdy and will be transparent, to allow for accurate measurement. These rulers should be copied on the same copier and at the same settings as the "Nautical Chart" activity master so that they will match.

Lesson Objectives

- ■ To represent vectors as line segments with both direction and magnitude
- ■ To describe and illustrate the scalar multiple of a vector
- ■ To describe and illustrate the opposite of a vector
- ■ To describe and illustrate the components of a vector
- ■ To add two vectors geometrically and by using components
- ■ To describe and illustrate the relationship between the coordinates of the terminal point of a position vector and its components
- ■ To model linear motions and forces with vectors

Unit 2

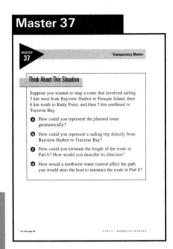

Master 37

MASTER
37   Transparency Master

Think About This Situation

Suppose you wanted to map a route that involved sailing
3 km west from Bayview Harbor to Presque Island, then
6 km south to Rudy Point, and then 5 km southeast to
Traverse Bay.

a How could you represent the planned route
geometrically?

b How could you represent a sailing trip directly from
Bayview Harbor to Traverse Bay?

c How could you estimate the length of the route in
Part b? How would you describe its direction?

d How would a northwest water current affect the path
you would steer the boat to maintain the route in Part b?

Use with page 80.   UNIT 2 • MODELING MOTION

LAUNCH   full-class discussion

Think About This Situation

See Teaching Master 37.

a A route could be represented geometrically by drawing connecting segments on the map.

b Draw a segment that connects the two locations.

c The length of the trip could be determined by using the map's scale or by using properties of geometric figures and trigonometry. The direction might be described by giving degree deviation from either north, south, east, or west.

d Since a northwest water current would push the boat to the north and to the west, to compensate you would want to sail towards a destination that was to the south and east of Traverse Bay.

EXPLORE   small-group investigation

INVESTIGATION 1 ▶ Navigation: What Direction and How Far?

A vector is defined here as a quantity that is characterized by its magnitude and direction. Thus, any physical phenomenon that needs a number and a direction to describe it can be modeled with vectors. Force and displacement are two examples. The advantage of this definition is that vectors can be represented in various ways, one of which is geometrically by arrows. Thus, since a vector is characterized by its magnitude and direction, arrows in various locations represent the same vector whenever they have equal magnitudes and directions.

You will need to provide copies of the nautical chart (Master 38) and make nautical mile rulers on transparencies from Master 39 for student use since much of the investigation deals with routes on that chart. Students will also need protractors.

Activity 1 is straightforward, but you may want to do this together as a class, because familiarity with the chart markings and measurements is essential for several investigations. A globe is useful in pointing out how the lines of latitude divide Earth by slices of equal width, and that a nautical mile is based on this idea. By contrast, the lines of longitude are closer together as a pole is approached.

Activity 2 establishes the meaning of "heading," and Activity 3 introduces vectors. Activities 4 and 5 introduce scalar multiples of vectors and opposite vectors. All of these activities should be accessible to students working in small groups. Be sure to check that students are measuring headings correctly and that they understand and are using the terms "heading" and "vector" correctly.

EXPLORE *continued*

1. See Teaching Masters 38 and 39.

    The questions in Parts a–e are nonmathematical, but are included to help students become familiar with the nautical chart. Students should work with Master 38 and the nautical mile rulers (same scale), rather than the reduced copy of this chart in the student text.

    The chart gives angle measurements in degrees and minutes. You may wish to review this system of measurement with your students.

    a. "3" has a bell; "GP" has a bell; "SH" has a gong.

    b. "2" has a flashing red light that flashes every 4 seconds.
        "3" has a 4-second flashing green light.
        "6" has a 4-second flashing red light.
        "SH" has a 6-second flashing light. (It will be white since no color is indicated.)
        "GP" has a 2.5-second flashing green light.
        SM "2" has a 2.5-second flashing red light.

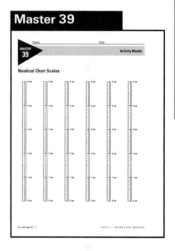

        (Note: Channel lights are colored to indicate the safe path to shore. Red flashing lights should be kept on the right of the boat when returning to harbor ("red, right, returning"). Green flashing lights should be kept on the left of the boat when returning to shore. White flashing lights are used when it is safe to pass on either side, usually to mark a channel or harbor entrance.)

    c. A circle with a dot at its center marks a landmark. A stack (a smokestack or pipe, labeled STK), a tank, a cupola (a dome-like structure), and a stone tower are shown on the chart.

    d. The dotted lines outline shallow water. A boat could run aground if it ignored the hazard.

    e. Using the ruler provided, the distance is about 1.9 nautical miles (nm).

    f. The top scale is longitude, the right-hand scale is latitude.
        The scales on the chart may be difficult for students to interpret. You may wish to have a globe available for students to examine. The scale marked off on a parallel of latitude (horizontal lines on the chart) gives the angles of longitude east and west from the prime meridian, the 0° line that passes through Greenwich, England. Have students think about a coordinate axis on grid paper. The scales on the *x*-axis

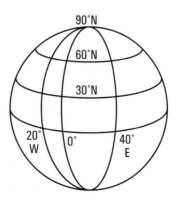

Unit 2

EXPLORE *continued*

mark off distance between the vertical grid lines. In a similar manner, the scale on the *y*-axis marks off the distance between horizontal lines. On a navigational chart, the scale marked off on a line of longitude (vertical lines on the chart) gives the latitude north or south from the equator. Latitude lines are the horizontal circles around the globe. The angles of latitude are measured from the center of Earth.

g. The right-hand scale can also be used as a scale for nautical miles. Think of the latitude measures as distances from the equator, rather than angle measures. 10° N latitude is $\frac{1}{9}$ of the distance from the equator to the North Pole. You can also think of 1° latitude as $\frac{1}{360}$ of the circumference of Earth. A nautical mile represents $\frac{1}{60}$ of 1° or 1 minute of latitude. Latitude measure is used because 1 minute of latitude represents the same distance anywhere on the globe.

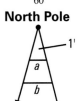

On the other hand, 1 minute of longitude marks off a shorter distance the closer you are to the poles. It is like measuring segments joining the sides of an angle that are different distances from the vertex.

h. Since a statute mile is 5,280 ft, a nautical mile is about 1.15 statute miles.

2. a. Check students' drawings. The "SH" buoy is the nearest to *P*.

b. The heading is 340° and the distance is 1.7 nm.

c. The heading is about 180° and the distance is about 2.2 nm.

d. The heading is about 48°. The distance from the easterly end of the public launching ramp to the "SH" buoy is about 1.5 nm.

e. Since water craft are able to move in roughly straight paths, the distance traveled is represented by the length of the arrow, and the direction of the path is represented by the heading of the arrow.

3. This activity will alert students to the use of vectors to represent speeds and forces.

a. ■ $\frac{1}{2}$ cm in drawing = 1 cm   ■ $\frac{1}{2}$ cm in drawing = 1 cm

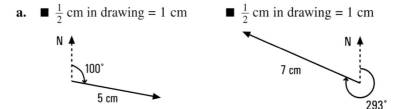

■ N

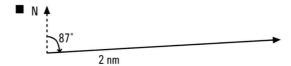

EXPLORE *continued*

b.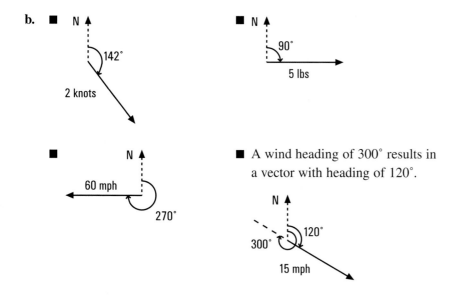

The arrows representing each vector quantity may differ in length from student to student, but the headings ought to be identical. It would be worthwhile to note that for wind, the heading is the direction from which it is blowing, that is, a west wind has heading 270°.

c. The arrows in Part a should all be the same. The arrows in Part b may have various lengths depending on the scale choice. Thus, if a pound is represented by 1 cm, then 5 pounds is represented by a 5 cm arrow. Students should realize, however, that the vectors are equal because each arrow represents the given magnitude and direction.

d. The test works because if *PQSR* is a parallelogram, then $\overline{PQ}$ and $\overline{RS}$ are both parallel and congruent. Since they are parallel and both arrows point to the left and upward, the directions are the same. Since they are congruent, the lengths are the same. Thus, vector *PQ* equals vector *RS*. (You can press students to note that the arrows they draw are in different places, but as long as the magnitudes and directions are equal, the arrows represent the same vector.)

Whenever students consider vector problems, you should help them decide whether a rough sketch or a more precise drawing is needed. The student text suggests this by using the words "sketch" and "draw". You need to encourage students to sketch as often as possible since accurate drawing takes much more time.

4. a. See students' sketches. The location is determined by drawing a vector 1.5 nm on heading 25°. The actual location may vary from student to student depending on the starting point they used, but it should be between the "6" and "SH" buoys.

b. Use the same heading and make the vector 3 times as long. In each case, start with the 1-hour vector and multiply its length by the stated number of hours.

EXPLORE *continued*

    c. The two 5-cm vectors sketched by students could be equal, but they need not be. The heading of the first vector drawn must be the same as that of the original. However, the second vector can have any heading.

    d. Draw a vector with the same heading and length *n* times that of the given vector. The headings of the two vectors are the same, but their lengths differ by a factor of *n*.

5. a. Student drawings, which should be on the nautical chart, should extend 2 nm into the channel at 20° to the right of the north vector.

    b. The return vector starts at the ending point of the previous vector and is drawn to the start of the previous vector. The magnitude is 2 nm and the heading is 200°.

    c. The vectors have the same length, but opposite headings; they differ by 180°.

    d. Students should draw a vector from the "3" bell with magnitude 2 nm and heading 200°. This vector is equal to the one drawn in Part b, only with a different starting point.

Master 40

NOTE: You may want to tell students that college mathematics and physics textbooks often use single lowercase boldface roman letters, such as **u** or **a**, to denote vectors, rather than the notation in their textbook.

SHARE AND SUMMARIZE   full-class discussion

Checkpoint

See Teaching Master 40.

ⓐ Two arrows represent the same vector if the arrows have the same length and point in the same direction.

This idea is sometimes hard to grasp because you can draw as many arrow representations of a vector as you wish. A more accurate way to think about it mathematically is that equality is an equivalence class of vectors with the same direction and magnitude. (In the world of numbers, a similar idea is that all sums that add to, say, 15 are equivalent. Modular arithmetic, introduced in Unit 9, "Informatics," is another example of the equivalence class idea.)

ⓑ A vector and a multiple of that vector have the same direction (opposite directions when the multiplier is negative), and their magnitudes are the given multiple of each other.

ⓒ Opposite vectors have equal magnitudes; the absolute value of the difference in the directions is 180°.

Between the Checkpoint and "On Your Own" for this investigation, the student text introduces important vocabulary and notation for vectors and scalars. Be sure that students understand the difference between vectors and scalars.

CONSTRUCTING A MATH TOOLKIT: Students should write a definition of vector in their own words, as well as an explanation of scalar multiple of a vector and of opposite vectors. Examples labeled with the new notation will help them get started using this new idea.

APPLY individual task

▶On Your Own

See Teaching Master 41.

Master 41

a. Magnitude ≈ 70 mi; heading about 100°

b. Magnitude ≈ 70 mi; heading about 280°
Beginning at Charlevoix, $-\vec{v}$ should end partially across the lake towards Escanaba, Michigan.

c. Magnitude ≈ 100 mi; heading about 290°

d. Magnitude ≈ 50 mi; heading about 290°

MORE
ASSIGNMENT   *pp. 99–105*

Students can now begin Modeling Task 1 or Reflecting Task 1 or 2 from the MORE assignment following Investigation 4.

EXPLORE small-group investigation

INVESTIGATION 2 Changing Course

You may wish to quickly launch this investigation with the following activity:
Pick a location on the map of the Massachusetts coast used in Investigation 1 between Oak Island and Hog Island, out of sight of the "GP" bell. Ask how a boat located near the "GP" bell could get to this location. Have different students draw their routes on an overhead transparency of the map. Have a brief discussion about the different routes. Which is shortest? What is the result of them all? Suppose your mode of transport was a helicopter, not a boat? Label the vectors with student names $\vec{a}_{Pete} + \vec{b}_{Pete}$, $\vec{a}_{Val} + \vec{b}_{Val}$, *and so on. You can tell your students they are about to find out what it means to add vectors.*

EXPLORE *continued*

Students will again need copies of the map, nautical mile rulers, and protractors to make accurate drawings. Activities 1–3 are straightforward. Draw the class together briefly after these are complete to ensure that everyone has understood that the resultant vector is the sum of two or more vectors. Some students may have understood that $\vec{a} + \vec{b} = \vec{b} + \vec{a}$, but do not realize that $\vec{r} = \vec{a} + \vec{b}$ (where $\vec{r}$ is the resultant vector) is also true. It may be that they are equating lengths of paths, not results. If students do not understand this, they will see Activity 4 as only a "draw the path" activity, and not give the heading and length for the result. One way you can emphasize this is to refer back to the different routes drawn in the introduction. Thus, $\vec{r} = \vec{a}_{Pete} + \vec{b}_{Pete} = \vec{a}_{Val} + \vec{b}_{Val}$ and so on.

1. a. See students' charts. The lengths are measured in nautical miles. The lengths are 2 nm and 0.5 nm.

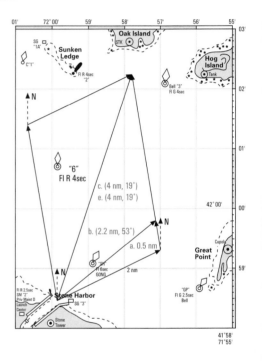

  b. Keith needs to travel approximately 2.2 nm at a heading of 53° from the channel mouth. Students are expected to use measurement to determine both the distance and the course heading.

  c. Keith needs to travel approximately 4.0 nm at a heading of approximately 19°.

  d. For each trip, the initial point of the resultant vector is the same as the initial point of the first vector of the trip. The terminal point of the resultant vector is the same as the terminal point of the second vector of the trip.

  e. See students' charts. The resultant vector for this route is 4 nm with a heading of approximately 19° which is equal to the vector in Part c.

EXPLORE *continued*

2. Scale: ⊢——⊣; $\frac{1}{2}$ cm represents 1 cm for all diagrams.

   a. 8.6 cm, 40°

   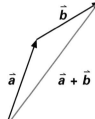 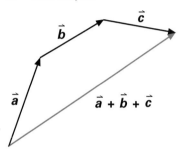

   b. 2 cm, 20°

   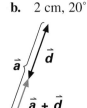

   c. 10.8 cm, 55°

   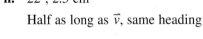

   d. 8.8 cm, 70°

   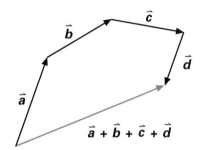

3. **a.** The resultant vectors are equal.

   b. This is similar to the commutative property of addition for real numbers.

   c. See student drawings. The shape formed is a parallelogram with one diagonal (the resultant). It is a parallelogram because the representations of both $\vec{a}$ and $\vec{b}$ are parallel and equal in length.

4. **Note that students will need to define a direction for north.**

   a. **i.** 253°, 8 cm

   Twice as long as $\vec{u}$, same heading (scalar multiplication)

   ii. 22°, 2.5 cm

   Half as long as $\vec{v}$, same heading

   iii. Cannot be done by inspection

   iv. Cannot be done by inspection

   v. Cannot be done by inspection

   vi. Cannot be done by inspection

   vii. 202°, 10 cm

   Twice as long as $\vec{v}$, heading differs by 180°

   viii. Cannot be done by inspection

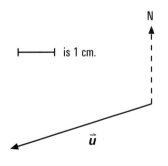

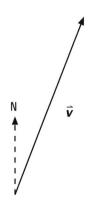

EXPLORE *continued*

     ix. Cannot be done by inspection

     x. Cannot be done by inspection

b. **iii.**

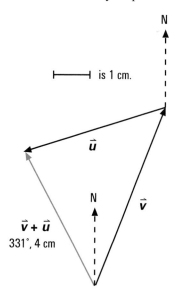

     iv. Same magnitude and heading as Part iii: 331°, 4 cm

     v. Same heading as Part iii, but three times as long: 331°, 12 cm

     vi. Same heading as Part iii, but three times as long: 331°, 12 cm

     viii.

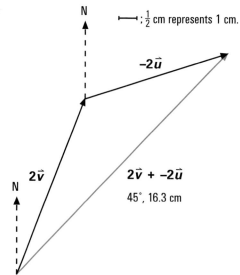

EXPLORE *continued*

ix.

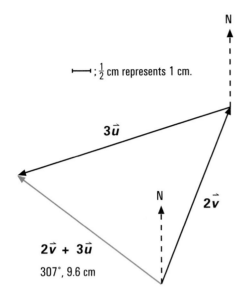

; $\frac{1}{2}$ cm represents 1 cm.

3$\vec{u}$

2$\vec{v}$

2$\vec{v}$ + 3$\vec{u}$

307°, 9.6 cm

x. 151°, 8 cm

It is twice as long as the resultant vector in Part iii and differs in direction by 180°.

c. The general rule is that the sum of scalar multiples of two vectors is the scalar multiple of the sum of the vectors. In symbols, $n\vec{a} + n\vec{b} = n(\vec{a} + \vec{b})$. This rule may be stated as, "Scalar multiplication is distributive over vector addition."

5. a. There are an infinite number of other routes represented by two (or more) vectors. Student work will vary.

b. The resultant vector for each of the alternative routes is the same as the one in Activity 1 Part c.

c. ■ True; the starting point and the ending point are determined by the starting point of the first vector in the sum and the ending point of the second vector in the sum. There is only one such vector.

■ False; there are infinitely many pairs of vectors with the same resultant vector.

NOTE: Students should connect these statements to their knowledge of real number addition.

6. a. The vector with heading 0° has magnitude approximately 1.3 nm. The vector with heading 90° has magnitude approximately 1.8 nm. The resultant forms the hypotenuse of a right triangle. By the Pythagorean Theorem, the length of the resultant vector is $\sqrt{1.8^2 + 1.3^2} = \sqrt{4.93} \approx 2.2$ nm.

b. There is another pair of arrows (going north first, then east), but they represent the same two vectors. Thus, the vectors are unique, but there are two arrow representations.

EXPLORE *continued*

c. **Students may benefit from some review of the trigonometric functions and the use of the calculator to compute angle measures.**
The tangent of the angle at the Stone Harbor vertex of the diagram is $\frac{1.3}{1.8} \approx 0.72$. Thus, the angle is $\tan^{-1}(0.72) \approx 36°$, and the heading is about 54° (since $90° - 36° = 54°$). If students use the alternate sketch, going north first, they will calculate $\tan^{-1}(1.4) \approx 54°$. The computed and measured angle measures should be quite close.

7. a. Either use the 12° angle or the 78° angle in the right triangles below. In either case, the horizontal component has length 0.42 nm and the vertical component has length 1.96 nm.

$\sin 12° = \frac{b}{2}$, so $b \approx 0.42$ nm.

$\cos 12° = \frac{a}{2}$, so $a \approx 1.96$ nm.

or

$\cos 78° = \frac{b}{2}$, so $b \approx 0.42$ nm.

$\sin 78° = \frac{a}{2}$, so $a \approx 1.96$ nm.

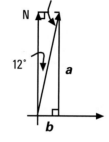

b. ■ The triangle is a right triangle, and the two acute angles have measures 35° and 55°.

■ The magnitudes are approximately 1.64 nm (north/vertical) and 1.15 nm (west/horizontal). (Students can calculate these in more than one way. For instance, the north magnitude is 2 cos 35° or 2 sin 55°.)

■ The heading for the north vector is 0° and the heading for the west vector is 270°.

c. The vertical component has magnitude 1 nm and heading 180° (south). The horizontal component has magnitude approximately 1.73 nm and heading 90 (east).

d. One way to approach this task is to find the measure of the angle formed by the *x*-axis and the vector. This measure is found by subtracting the heading from 270°. Call this angle measure θ. Another way to think about it is to consider the angle formed by the vector and the *y*-axis. This angle has measure equal to the heading minus 180°. Call this angle measure α. Then the horizontal component has magnitude 2 cos θ or 2 sin α and heading 270°. The vertical component has magnitude 2 sin θ or 2 cos α and heading 180°. For a vector with magnitude 5 nm, the magnitudes change to 5 cos θ = 5 sin α (vertical) and 5 sin θ = 5 cos α (horizontal). The headings stay the same, 270° and 180°. Students do not need to describe both approaches.

NOTE: Some students may use the 30°-60°-90° relationship here, but do not expect them to do so. This concept will be introduced in Unit 7.

EXPLORE *continued*

Some students may note that for any heading of φ, multiplying the magnitude of the vector by sin φ gives the horizontal component, with heading 90° for a positive value and heading 270° for a negative value. Likewise, multiplying by cos φ gives the vertical component, with heading 0° for a positive value and heading 180° for a negative value. It is not necessary to push for this understanding at this time, but some students may discover it themselves.

If students discover this generalization, they may find it confusing that here sin φ is associated with the *horizontal* component and cos φ with the *vertical* component, if they have previously learned the unit circle definitions of the trigonometric functions. You can explain that the reason that sine and cosine seem to be reversed here is that angles are measured in a different way. When using headings, angles are measured clockwise from the vertical, rather than counterclockwise from the horizontal. Students will go back to measuring angles counterclockwise from the *x*-axis in Investigation 4. (See Reflecting Task 5, page 104.)

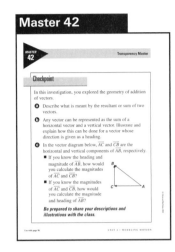

Master 42

SHARE AND SUMMARIZE full-class discussion

Checkpoint

See Teaching Master 42.

ⓐ The resultant of two vectors, when the second begins at the terminal point of the first, is the vector determined by the initial point of the first vector and the terminal point of the second vector. A second representation of the resultant is the diagonal of the parallelogram determined by the two addend vectors, when the addends and the diagonal begin at the same point.

ⓑ Start with a diagram of the vector, including the north (vertical) direction. Then draw a horizontal (east-west) line going through the terminal or initial point of the vector. Then draw a perpendicular to either the vertical or horizontal line that goes through the other endpoint of the vector. The horizontal and vertical components are the legs of the right triangle formed, with terminal and initial points matching where the components are in contact with the original vector. At the 90° angle, the two component vectors are placed terminal point to initial point.

ⓒ ▪ Use the heading of $\overrightarrow{AB}$ to calculate the measure of angle A (in the given diagram, $m\angle A = $ heading $- 270°$). Then $AC = AB \cos A$ and $CB = AB \sin A$.

▪ To find the magnitude of $\overrightarrow{AB}$, use the Pythagorean Theorem: $AB = \sqrt{AC^2 + CB^2}$. The heading of $\overrightarrow{AB}$ is $270° + m\angle A = 270° + \tan^{-1}\left(\frac{CB}{AC}\right)$.

CONSTRUCTING A MATH TOOLKIT: Students should explain what a resultant vector is. Have them draw an example and write a vector equation. Students should also explain how to calculate horizontal and vertical components of a vector given heading and magnitude of the vector, either by an example or with a general procedure.

ASSIGNMENT   pp. 99–105

Students can now begin Reflecting Task 4 or Extending Task 2 from the MORE assignment following Investigation 4.

APPLY individual task

On Your Own

a. Keith should set a heading of about 335°; the distance is about 3 nm.

b. The horizontal (west) component has a length of about 1.2 nm and the vertical (north) component has a length of about 2.8 nm.

c. Using 3 nm and 65°, the calculated values are 1.27 nm for the horizontal component and 2.72 nm for the vertical component. The calculated values should be very close to those obtained by measurement.

EXPLORE small-group investigation

INVESTIGATION 3 ▶ Go with the Flow

This investigation extends the vector model of plotting navigational routes to those for which there are additional forces that affect the path of the boat or plane. Students who are familiar with navigation or aviation may be willing to share their knowledge. They may know how to plan a course to counteract the effect of a current. Ask students when a sailor would have to know how much to adjust a set course. (Answer: Whenever landmarks are not used as guides to continuous adjustment, such as in foggy conditions, or night sailing, or long-distance travel)

You may want students to see the effect of movement of the medium (air or water) on the path traversed. Keep this introduction brief, but be sure that students enter the investigation with an intuitive idea about the effect of the combination of forces. This can be done by demonstrating what happens if the intended course is due east, but the wind is from the east, or from the west, or from the north, or from the south. Consider having students "walk" the courses that result from the combination of forces.

Other ways to demonstrate the effect of a sum of forces are possible. One way to do this is to have one student be the boat and another the water. The boat uses a pencil to draw the route on the water (a piece of paper). The boat traces a path from top to bottom. Now the boat follows the same course, but the paper is slowly moved perpendicular to the course. In this case, the boat (pencil) traces a path that moves more diagonally across the paper. The course in moving water will then be evident. Another way to show this is to slowly roll a table tennis ball across a desk. It will traverse a straight path. Now send the ball across the desk in the same manner, but another student gently blows perpendicularly to the original path. The ball will be diverted from its original path. This again illustrates the effect of a moving medium on the path of an object moving in it.

This investigation also expands the use of vectors to other situations in which forces are applied. Examples include trying to move an object by pulling with two constant forces or trying to block a volleyball with enough force to keep it on the opponent's side of the net. Two ideas are key. First, the combined force acting on

EXPLORE *continued*

an object is the sum of the individual force vectors, regardless of the number of forces. Second, vector diagrams putting tail to head for several force vectors models the situation, even when conceptually all the force is applied at one point.

In Activities 1 and 2, students learn how to sketch and calculate the components of the sum of vectors. The end result of Activities 1 and 2 is a "one-hour sketch," showing the boat's path after one hour of travel. The effect of the boat engine and current forces would be a continuous adjustment, but it is convenient to think of this as if the forces acted consecutively. Since there is no expected variation in the outcome of these activities, you may wish to do this as a large group. If you do that, be sure to pause after everyone has completed a sketch and calculations to discuss how this "one-hour sketch" could be used to calculate the position after any number of hours. You may wish to ask your students to describe in their own words the steps that were taken in order to reach this result.

Activity 3 generalizes the process of using components to add two vectors. Activity 4 is similar to Activities 1 and 2 but uses a different context.

Activities 5 and 6 introduce different settings for which vector models are appropriate. In Activity 5, help students see that they can add two vectors with a common tail by translating one vector and using a "head-to-tail" diagram.

Activity 7 returns to a navigational setting. With the work on component analysis and other techniques, students should be able to handle the idea of finding an unknown vector.

You may wish to have students compare and summarize solution methods. At this point, some students will see that a quick sketch will tell them whether to add or subtract lengths of components of vectors to get the components of the desired vector. They will be able to use general relationships: If $\vec{r} = \vec{b} + (-\vec{c})$, then $\vec{r}_{vertical} = \vec{b}_{vertical} + (-\vec{c}_{vertical})$ and $\vec{r}_{horizontal} = \vec{b}_{horizontal} + (-\vec{c}_{horizontal})$. Other students will remain more dependent on the visual cues in the drawing to add lengths. You can emphasize again that this strategy finds a solution by considering one-hour vectors. The effect is continuous, but it is easier to consider the effect as a result of one force after another.

1. You may wish to review the Law of Sines and the Law of Cosines with your class since they are used in this activity.

   a. The diagram is accurate.

   b. ■ Measuring the diagram gives approximately 14.4 nm in one hour.

   ■ The vector diagram produces the triangle on the next page. (One way to calculate the measure of the 150° angle is to assume the two north direction lines are parallel and use alternate interior angles.)

   Use the Law of Cosines:
   $$r^2 = 10^2 + 5^2 - 2(10)(5) \cos 150°$$
   $$\approx 211.60$$
   $$r \approx 14.55 \text{ nm}$$

Unit 2

EXPLORE *continued*

c. For the first hour, the boat traveled at a rate of 14.55 knots with a heading of about 40°. Students may measure the angle that determines the heading or use the Law of Sines as follows:

$$\frac{\sin \alpha}{5} = \frac{\sin 150°}{14.55}$$

$$\sin \alpha = \frac{5 \sin 150°}{14.55}$$

$$\alpha \approx 10°$$

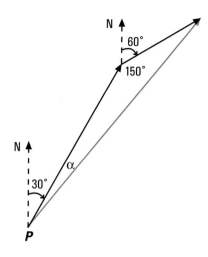

Therefore the heading is approximately 30° + 10° = 40°. The boat will continue at this rate and heading if all conditions remain the same, because for each additional hour you would repeat the calculations in Part b, starting with the location of the boat at the end of the previous hour.

2. a. After one hour, the planned course vector has magnitude 10 nm and heading 30°. It has horizontal component 10 sin 30° = 5 nm and vertical component 10 cos 30° ≈ 8.66 nm.

   b. After one hour, the current vector has magnitude 5 nm and heading 60°. The horizontal component is 5 sin 60° ≈ 4.33 nm. The vertical component is 5 cos 60° = 2.5 nm. The new sketch looks like this:

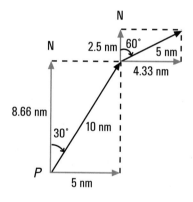

EXPLORE *continued*

    c. The horizontal component of the resultant vector is 5 + 4.33 = 9.33 nm, and its vertical component is 8.66 + 2.5 = 11.16 nm. The magnitude of the resultant vector is then $\sqrt{9.33^2 + 11.16^2} \approx 14.55$ nm, with a heading of $\tan^{-1}\left(\frac{9.33}{11.16}\right) \approx 39.9°$. Students may prefer to calculate the heading as $90° - \tan^{-1}\left(\frac{11.16}{9.33}\right) \approx 39.9°$. You must assume that vector addition is commutative and associative to complete this.

    d. The speed and magnitude found in this activity are the same as those in Activity 1.

3. **a–c.** See the diagram at the right.

    d. The sums of the component vectors give the components of the vector that represents $\vec{v} + \vec{u}$. The sum of the two resultant vectors is equal to $\vec{v} + \vec{u}$.

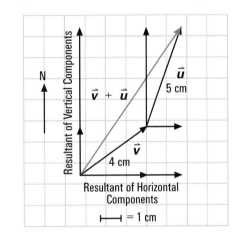

    e. Given the horizontal and vertical components of two (or more) vectors, the sum of the vectors can be found by first adding the horizontal components and then adding the vertical components to get the horizontal and vertical components of the sum. Adding these components will then give the sum of the original vectors.

4. **a.**

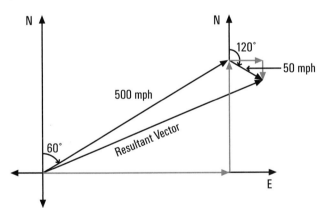

    b. Using right-triangle trigonometry, components for the planned-course velocity:

        Horizontal (east) = 500 sin 60° = 500 cos 30° ≈ 433 mph

        Vertical (north) = 500 cos 60° = 500 sin 30° = 250 mph

    Components for the wind velocity:

        Horizontal (east) = 50 sin 60° = 50 cos 30° ≈ 43.3 mph

        Vertical (south) = –50 cos 60° = –50 sin 30° = –25 mph

NOTE: Students should realize that to obtain the correct resultant vector they will need to think of the south and west vectors as negative.

EXPLORE *continued*

Components for the actual route:

Horizontal (east) ≈ 433 + 43.3 ≈ 476.3 mph

Vertical (north) = 250 + (–25) = 225 mph

The distance the airplane traveled in one hour is $\sqrt{(476.3)^2 + (225)^2} \approx 526.8$ mi. The heading is $90° - \tan^{-1}\left(\frac{225}{476.3}\right) \approx 64.7°$.

c. The ground speed is $\frac{526.8 \text{ mi}}{1.0 \text{ hr}} = 526.8$ mph.

d. Students could make a drawing to scale and measure the distance and heading, or they could use the Law of Cosines to determine the length of the resultant vector in the diagram in Part a.

5. a.

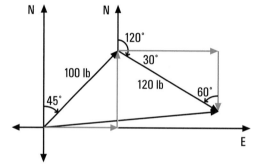

b. Components for 100 lb, 45° vector:

Horizontal (east) = 100 cos 45° ≈ 70.71 lb

Vertical (north) = 100 sin 45° ≈ 70.71 lb

Components for 120 lb, 120° vector:

Horizontal (east) = 120 sin 60° = 120 cos 30° ≈ 103.92 lb

Vertical (south) = –120 cos 60° = –120 sin 30° = –60 lb

Components of the resultant vector:

Horizontal (east) = 70.71 + 103.92 ≈ 174.63 lb

Vertical (north) = 70.71 + (–60) ≈ 10.71 lb

The heading is $90° - \tan^{-1}\left(\frac{10.71}{174.63}\right) \approx 86.49°$.

c. The resultant force has magnitude $\sqrt{174.63^2 + 10.71^2} \approx 174.96$ lb. If the doghouse weighs 150 lb, the force of 174.96 lb will move it.

d. Jerame must ensure that his north component exactly cancels Thad's. That means that if Jerame pulls with heading *x*:

$$120 \cos x \approx -70.71$$
$$\cos x \approx -\frac{70.71}{120}$$
$$x \approx 126.1°$$

EXPLORE *continued*

6. a.

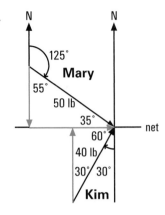

b. Mary's components:

Horizontal (east) = 50 sin 55° = 50 cos 35° ≈ 40.96 lb

Vertical (south) = –50 cos 55° = –50 sin 35° ≈ –28.68 lb

(Again, students should realize that to obtain the correct resultant vector, they will need to think of the south vector as negative.)

Kim's components:

Horizontal (east) = 40 sin 30° = 40 cos 60° = 20 lb

Vertical (north) = 40 cos 30° = 40 sin 60° ≈ 34.64 lb

The components of the resultant force on the ball:

Horizontal (east) = 40.96 + 20 ≈ 60.96 lb

Vertical (north) = (–28.68) + 34.64 ≈ 5.96 lb

The north component indicates that the ball is propelled in a positive or north direction, so it lands on Mary's side.

c. Mary's north component must neutralize or cancel Kim's north component. Thus, if *x* is Mary's new heading, 50 cos *x* must be less than or equal to –34.64 lb (since Kim's side is the negative north direction). Thus,

$$50 \cos x \le -34.64$$
$$\cos x \le \frac{-34.64}{50}$$

Since $\cos^{-1} x$ is a decreasing function, reverse the inequality to get $x \ge \cos^{-1}\left(\frac{-34.64}{50}\right)$ or $x \ge 133.85°$. Thus, the heading must be at least 133.85°. (Students may prefer to work with equality, and then use reasoning to determine that the heading angle would need to be greater to put the ball on Kim's side of the net.)

7. Solutions will vary. Students may make a scale drawing and measure, or they may use component analysis and add the opposite of the current vector to the desired course vector. The heading is about 6.2° and the magnitude is about 6.2 knots. A component analysis solution follows on the next page.

EXPLORE *continued*

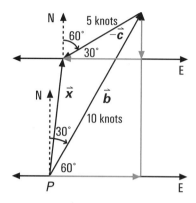

Boat path components for $\vec{b}$:

  Horizontal (east) = 10 sin 30° = 10 cos 60° = 5 knots

  Vertical (north) = 10 cos 30° = 10 sin 60° ≈ 8.66 knots

Current components for $-\vec{c}$:

  Horizontal (west) = –5 sin 60° = –5 cos 30° ≈ –4.33 knots

  Vertical (south) = –5 cos 60° = –5 sin 30° = –2.5 knots

Components for the adjusted vector $\vec{x}$:

  Horizontal (east) = 5 + (–4.33) ≈ 0.67 knots

  Vertical (north) = 8.66 + (–2.5) ≈ 6.16 knots

The course heading is $\tan^{-1}\left(\frac{0.67}{6.16}\right) \approx 6.2°$, which is the path of the boat. The magnitude of the vector is $\sqrt{(0.67)^2 + (6.16)^2} \approx 6.2$ knots.

Master 43

MASTER
43   *Transparency Master*

Checkpoint

In this investigation, you examined how vectors can be used to model situations in which more than one force is acting on an object.

a Describe how vector models can be used to model linear motion in moving air or water.

b Explain how the horizontal and vertical components of vectors can be used to determine heading and speed of a boat or airplane that is moving in water or air that is also moving.

Be prepared to share your descriptions and thinking with the entire class.

Use with page 94   UNIT 2 • MODELING MOTION

SHARE AND SUMMARIZE **full-class discussion**

Checkpoint

See Teaching Master 43.

a When an object moves in a medium (air or water) that is in motion, the two motions combine to form a new linear motion (as long as both motions have constant speed). The sum of the two vectors gives the new course.

b The components, along with a diagram, can be used to find the magnitude by adding the horizontal components of all vectors and the vertical components of all vectors. (South

SHARE AND SUMMARIZE *continued*

and west components are negative.) Using the Pythagorean Theorem, the magnitude is simply the square root of the sum of the squares of the sums of the resulting horizontal and vertical components.

The heading of the motion can be determined by using the inverse tangent of the ratio of either the vertical component over the horizontal component or the reciprocal of that ratio, depending on the placement of the angle. The resulting angle may need to be adjusted to represent the heading from the north.

CONSTRUCTING A MATH TOOLKIT: Students should define the components of a vector, and explain how to use them to add two vectors and to get the magnitude and direction of the resultant vector. Including an example would be helpful.

APPLY | **individual task**

▶**On Your Own**

a. A wind from the northwest has a heading of 135°. Student sketches should look like this:

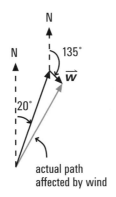

$\vec{w}$ is the wind vector.

b. The sketch below shows the new vector equal to the planned course minus the wind vector.

Desired route components:
　Horizontal (east) = 600 sin 20° ≈ 205.2 mi
　Vertical (north) = 600 cos 20° ≈ 563.8 mi

Wind vector components for $-\vec{w}$:
　Horizontal (west) = −70 cos 45° ≈ −49.5 mi
　Vertical (north) = 70 sin 45° ≈ 49.5 mi

Adjusted route components:
　Horizontal (east) = 205.2 + (−49.5) ≈ 155.7 mi
　Vertical (north) = 563.8 + 49.5 ≈ 613.3 mi

The heading is $\tan^{-1}\left(\frac{155.7}{613.3}\right) \approx 14°$.

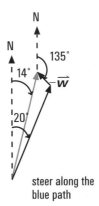

steer along the blue path

c. The still air speed is $\sqrt{155.7^2 + 613.3^2} \approx 632.8$ mph. This speed is needed in order for the planned course vector to have a magnitude of 600 mph.

MORE
ASSIGNMENT *pp. 99–105*

Students can now begin Modeling Task 2 or 3; Organizing Task 1, 2, or 3; or Extending Task 3 or 4 from the MORE assignment following Investigation 4.

EXPLORE small-group investigation

INVESTIGATION 4 Coordinates and Vectors

The central purposes of this investigation are to introduce the position vector on a coordinate system, and the relation between the coordinates of the terminal point of a position vector and the expressions for the components. These ideas will be used extensively in the remaining two lessons when nonlinear motion is analyzed.

In the beginning of this investigation, students switch from heading to the more standard way of measuring the direction of vectors (counterclockwise from the positive x-axis). There are practical reasons why sailors use headings based on a north direction that can always be established, and there are equally-practical reasons why mathematicians prefer directions using an angle determined by a base ray. (An important reason is to draw on the definition of trigonometric functions based on the unit circle.) This will not be immediately apparent to your students, but you can tell them that they should be on the lookout for generalizations that work when the standard mathematical direction angle is used.

Before assigning activities, you can discuss the differences between heading and direction, illustrating each with specific examples. Review equality of vectors, and introduce vectors with a fixed initial point. You may wish to discuss Activities 1 and 2 as a class before going on to Activity 3. Check for accuracy of group conclusions. Emphasize that the direction angle will be measured from a base ray. The positive x-axis will be used as the base ray.

Activity 3 can be done in small groups or as a large group. Copies of Teaching Master 44 will be helpful. Your students will be able to find the components of the given vectors, but they will probably use sketches that result in finding the sine and cosine of the reference angles for the directions given, although students may not call them reference angles. This will result in equations like $x = -4 \cos 35°$ or $x = -4 \cos(180° - 145°)$ for the horizontal coordinate of the second vector. The sketch makes it clear why the negative sign is essential. This is perfectly correct. However, if you see your students doing this, you can ask them why they did not just use $x = 4 \cos 145°$. They will probably say that $145°$ is not the angle inside the triangle they have drawn. You can ask them to evaluate $4 \cos 145°$ anyway. They will find that it's the opposite of $4 \cos 35°$! Ask them why. Similar questions can be asked about the other vectors.

Following Activity 3, you may wish to discuss as a class the two ideas that come out of this activity. The first is the connection between coordinates and component vectors. The second is that the direction angle θ can be used in the same equations, $x = a \cos \theta$ and $y = a \sin \theta$, to give the coordinates for every position vector $\vec{a}$. If your students have not noticed that they can use the direction angle directly, then you can draw this to their attention, and point out how conveniently the calculations create positive and negative answers that mirror the positions of the coordinates. In preparation for this discussion, have a graph of $y = \sin x$ and $y = \cos x$ on the board. Identifying where $145°$ and $35°$ are located on the x-axis will allow students to see that $\sin 35°$ and $\sin 145°$ are equal. (Likewise they can see that $\cos 35°$ and $\cos 145°$ are opposites, $\sin 41°$ and $\sin 221°$ are opposites, $\cos 60°$ and $\cos 240°$

EXPLORE *continued*

are opposites, sin 315° and sin 45° are opposites, and cos 315° and cos 45° are the same.)

In small groups, students should be able to tackle the rest of the activities, using their equations to find the components/coordinates.

1. **a.** The direction of $\vec{v}$ is 10°.

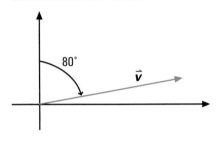

b. The heading of $\vec{p}$ is 10°.

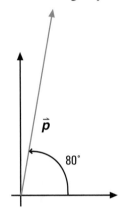

c. The heading of $\vec{m}$ is 320°.

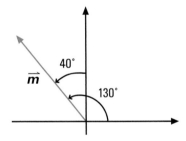

d. The direction of $\vec{n}$ is 320° or −40°.

2. $\vec{u}$ is a vector with direction 200° and $\vec{v}$ is a vector with heading 200°.

$\vec{u}$ makes a 20° angle with the negative *x*-axis and $\vec{v}$ makes a 70° angle with that same axis.

There is an angle of 50° between vectors $\vec{u}$ and $\vec{v}$.

The heading and direction are identical if the angle is 45° or 225°.

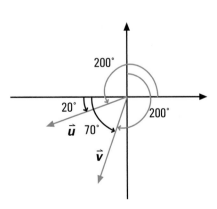

Unit 2

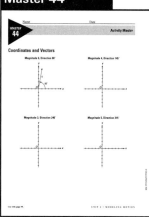

Master 44

NOTE: Either here or at the Checkpoint, students should recognize that coordinates can be found using direction angles larger than 90°. See the introduction on page T122.

EXPLORE *continued*

3. **See Teaching Master 44.**

   a. There should be one vector in each quadrant with coordinates as listed in Part b.

   b. Estimates will vary. The coordinates of the "parent" vectors are approximately (1.0, 5.9), (−3.3, 2.3), (−1.5, −2.6), and (3.5, −3.5).

   The *x*-coordinate of the terminal point of the horizontal component is the *x*-coordinate of the terminal point of the parent vector. Similarly, the *y*-coordinate for the terminal point of the vertical component is the *y*-coordinate of the terminal point of the parent vector.

   c. 6 cos 80° is the *x*-coordinate of the terminal point of the vector. It is also the length of the *x*-component.

   6 sin 80° is the *y*-coordinate of the terminal point of the vector, and is the magnitude of the *y*-component.

   Evaluate these expressions and take the absolute value to get the magnitude.

   d. The calculated values should be close to the estimates.

   ■ $x = 4 \cos 145° \approx -3.3$
   $y = 4 \sin 145° \approx 2.3$

   ■ $x = 3 \cos 240° \approx -1.5$
   $y = 3 \sin 240° \approx -2.6$

   ■ $x = 5 \cos 315° \approx 3.5$
   $y = 5 \sin 315° \approx -3.5$

4. a. Student one-hour vectors will vary in length. (18 knots = 18 nm/hr)

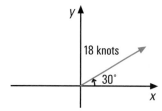

   b. Each point should be on the vector with direction 30°. The distance from the initial point to the boat's position after 1 hour is 18 nm. Thus, using their chosen scale, students should locate points on the vector that are 9, 18, and 36 nm from the initial point.

EXPLORE *continued*

The coordinates after $\frac{1}{2}$ hour are $x = 18(0.5) \cos 30° \approx 15.59(0.5) = 7.80$ nm and $y = 18(0.5) \sin 30° = 9(0.5) = 4.5$ nm.

The coordinates after 1 hour are $x = 15.59$ nm and $y = 9$ nm.

The coordinates after 2 hours are $x = 31.18$ nm and $y = 18$ nm.

c. The coordinates after *t* hours are $x = 15.59t$ nm and $y = 9t$ nm. The general vector components are $x = 18t \cos 30° \approx 15.59t$ nm and $y = 18t \sin 30° = 9t$ nm.

5. a. The distances along the vector will be the same as in Activity 4, Part b, but the vector has a direction of 120°.

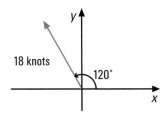

b. $\frac{1}{2}$ hour: *x*-component: $9 \cos 120° = -4.5$ nm

                  y-component: $9 \sin 120° \approx 7.79$ nm

    1 hour: *x*-component: $18 \cos 120° = -9$ nm

                  y-component: $18 \sin 120° \approx 15.59$ nm

    2 hours: *x*-component: $36 \cos 120° = -18$ nm

                  y-component: $36 \sin 120° \approx 31.18$ nm

c. $x = 18t \cos 120° = -9t$ nm, $y = 18t \sin 120° \approx 15.59t$ nm

d. $x = 18t \cos 210° \approx -15.59t$ nm, $y = 18t \sin 210° = -9t$ nm

    $x = 18t \cos 330° \approx 15.59t$ nm, $y = 18t \sin 330° = -9t$ nm

e. The rules are the same except for the measure of the angles.

6. a. Student vectors will vary in length.

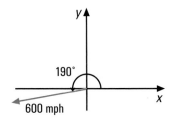

b. The *x*-coordinate is $x = 600t \cos 190°$, and the *y*-coordinate is $y = 600t \sin 190°$. Thus, when $t = 0.25$, $(x, y) = (-147.72, -26.05)$; when $t = 1.3$, $(x, y) = (-768.15, -135.45)$, and when $t = 3.2$, $(x, y) = (-1,890.83, -333.40)$.

EXPLORE *continued*

c. $t = \frac{d}{r} = \frac{2,000}{600} = \frac{10}{3}$

$x = 600\left(\frac{10}{3}\right) \cos 190° \approx -1,970$

$y = 600\left(\frac{10}{3}\right) \sin 190° \approx -347$

The coordinates after traveling 2,000 mi are approximately $(-1,970, -347)$.

7. a. Student vectors will vary in length.

b. First family: $x = 0.8 \cos 31° \approx 0.686$ mi
    $y = 0.8 \sin 31° \approx 0.412$ mi

Second family: $x = 1.1 \cos 42° \approx 0.817$ mi
    $y = 1.1 \sin 42° \approx 0.736$ mi

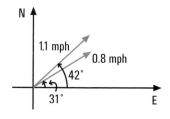

They are $\sqrt{(0.817 - 0.686)^2 + (0.736 - 0.412)^2} \approx 0.349$ mi apart.

NOTE: Students should be able to explain how this result occurs when applying the distance formula.

c. Each hour, the distance increases by 0.349 mi, so after 2 hours they are $2 \cdot 0.349 = 0.698$ mi apart and after 3 hours they are $3 \cdot 0.349 = 1.047$ mi apart.

d. $D = 0.349t$

The change in distance is constant; each hour the distance increases by 0.349 mi.

e. $3 = 0.349t$, so $t \approx 8.6$ hours.

8. a.

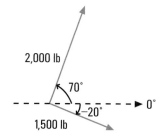

b. One way to proceed is to compute the component vectors and add them to find the components of the resultant:

$x' = 1,500 \cos (-20°) \approx 1,409.54$ lb

$y' = 1,500 \sin (-20°) \approx -513.03$ lb

$x'' = 2,000 \cos 70° \approx 684.04$ lb

$y'' = 2,000 \sin 70° \approx 1,879.39$ lb

The resultant components are

$$x = 1,409.54 + 684.04 = 2,093.58$$
$$y = -513.03 + 1,879.39 = 1,366.36.$$

EXPLORE *continued*

Thus, the magnitude is $\sqrt{2{,}093.58^2 + 1{,}366.36^2} \approx 2{,}500$ lb.

The direction is $\tan^{-1}\left(\frac{1{,}366.36}{2{,}093.58}\right) \approx 33.1°$.

SHARE AND SUMMARIZE **full-class discussion**

Checkpoint

See Teaching Master 45.

ⓐ The length of $\overrightarrow{OB}$ is 5. The sides of the 135° angle are the vector $\overrightarrow{OB}$ in the second quadrant and the positive *x*-axis.

ⓑ A vector is the sum of its component vectors. When the initial point of the vector is at the origin, the coordinates of the terminal point of the vector of magnitude *r* and direction θ are (*r* cos θ, *r* sin θ). The length of the horizontal component is the absolute value of the *x*-coordinate of the terminal point, and the length of the vertical component is the absolute value of the *y*-coordinate of the terminal point.

CONSTRUCTING A MATH TOOLKIT: Students should sketch examples of position vectors, one in each quadrant, with the direction angle shown. Under each example, students should write how to find the components/coordinates. They should also provide an example showing the three ways to represent a vector, that is, as a position vector with coordinates (*x*, *y*), with coordinates [*r*, θ], and as a free vector not placed on a coordinate system.

Master 45

APPLY **individual task**

▶ On Your Own

a. 4 hours × 35 knots = 140 nm

b. (140 cos 110°, 140 sin 110°) = (−47.88 nm, 131.56 nm)

c. The distance from (−75 nm, 75 nm) is
$\sqrt{[-75 - (-47.88)]^2 + (75 - 131.56)^2} = 62.73$ nm.

The distance from (25 nm, 125 nm) is
$\sqrt{[25 - (-47.88)]^2 + (125 - 131.56)^2} = 73.17$ nm.

The ship is closest to the port located at (−75 nm, 75 nm).

d. Responses may vary. Some factors that the pilot might consider are the quality of repair facilities, their availability, and the nature of the route to the ports.

MORE
ASSIGNMENT *pp. 99–105*

Modeling: 1, 2 or 3, and 4*
Organizing: 1, 2 or 3, and 4
or 5*
Reflecting: 1, 2, and 3
Extending: 2, 4, and choice
of one*

When choice is indicated, it is important to leave the choice to the student.
NOTE: *It is best if Organizing tasks are discussed as a whole class after they have been assigned as homework.*

Master 46

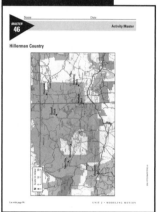

MORE independent assignment

Modeling

When students work on maps that have been copied, results will vary slightly from these solutions because copiers sometimes shrink print slightly, and the horizontal and vertical shrink may not have the same factor. For the same reason, scales may be slightly off. Student results should agree with those of their classmates.

Point out to students that if a problem statement uses headings, they should solve the problem using headings. If no system is indicated, they should use a coordinate system, with the positive x-axis used as the 0° ray.

You can provide students with copies of Master 46 for Modeling Task 1. This map is larger than the one in the student text.

1. See Teaching Master 46.

    a. To go from the town of Shiprock to Tuba City, Jim should head 250° for approximately 95 mi.

    b. To go from Tuba City to Flagstaff, Jim should head 200° for about 45 mi. This would give a trip time of about 0.45 hour or 27 minutes.

    c. Shiprock to Round Rock: about 245°; 30 mi
    Round Rock to Window Rock: about 160°; 40 mi
    Window Rock to Standing Rock: about 76°; 26 mi
    Standing Rock to Shiprock: about 345°; 45 mi

2. **a.** The skipper should set a heading of approximately 147°.

    b. The trip is approximately 4 nm, so it would take about $\frac{4 \text{ nm}}{6 \text{ knots}} = \frac{2}{3}$ hour, or 40 minutes, in still water.

    c.

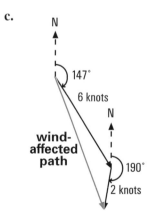

MORE *continued*

d. Components of boat vector:

$e' = 6 \cos 57° = 6 \sin 33° \approx 3.3$ knots

$n' = -6 \sin 57° = -6 \cos 33° \approx -5.0$ knots

Components of wind vector:

$e'' = -2 \sin 10° = -2 \cos 80° \approx -0.35$ knots

$n'' = -2 \cos 10° = -2 \sin 80° \approx -1.97$ knots

Actual route components:

$e = 3.3 - 0.35 = 2.95$ knots

$n = -5.0 + (-1.97) = -6.97$ knots

Heading $= \tan^{-1}\left(\frac{6.97}{2.95}\right) + 90° \approx 67° + 90° = 157°$

e. The skipper must add the opposite of the wind vector to his planned course vector to get the desired course.

The opposite of the wind vector is

$e''' = 2 \sin 10° = 2 \cos 80° \approx 0.35$ knots

$n''' = 2 \cos 10° = 2 \sin 80° \approx 1.97$ knots

Thus, the new route vector has components

$e' + e''' = 3.3 + 0.35 \approx 3.65$ knots

$n' + n''' = -5.0 + 1.97 \approx -3.03$ knots

The heading of this route is $\tan^{-1}\left(\frac{3.03}{3.65}\right) + 90° \approx 39.7° + 90° = 129.70°$.

3. a. His heading should be about 244°.

b. The trip is about 75 mi, so it will take about 45 minutes at 100 mph. His arrival time will be approximately 10:45 A.M.

c. This solution assumes the origin is located at Shiprock.

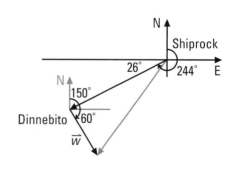

Position due to helicopter velocity (100 mph, 244°):

Horizontal (east): $-100t \cos 26° \approx -89.88t$ mi

Vertical (north): $-100t \sin 26° \approx -43.84t$ mi

Position change due to wind velocity (20 mph, 150°):

Horizontal (east): $20t \cos 60° = 10t$ mi

Vertical (north): $-20t \sin 60° \approx -17.32t$ mi

Wind-affected coordinates:

Horizontal (east): $-89.88t + 10t = -79.89t$ mi

Vertical (north): $-43.84t - 17.32t = -61.16t$ mi

Since his estimated time of arrival gives 45 minutes or $\frac{3}{4}$ hour of flying time, his coordinates at 10:45 A.M. will be

Horizontal (east): $-79.89\left(\frac{3}{4}\right) = -59.92$ mi

Vertical (north): $-61.16\left(\frac{3}{4}\right) = -45.87$ mi.

MORE *continued*

With the origin at Shiprock, the coordinates of Dinnebito are

Horizontal (east): $-75 \cos 26° \approx -67.41$ mi

Vertical (north): $-75 \sin 26° \approx -32.88$ mi

Therefore, the distance between the two locations is

$$\sqrt{(-67.41 + 59.92)^2 + (-32.88 + 45.87)^2} \approx 15 \text{ mi.}$$

d. Jim wants his position at 10:45 A.M. to be at Dinnebito. The wind-adjusted position vector can be expressed as $\vec{v}t = \vec{D} - \vec{w}t$, where $\vec{v}$ is the velocity vector for the actual path, $\vec{w}$ is the wind velocity vector, and $\vec{D}$ is the position vector of Dinnebito, for t in hours.

$\vec{v}t$ components:

Horizontal (east): $-67.41 - 10t$ mi

Vertical (north): $-32.88 + 17.32t$ mi

Since Jim wants to arrive in 45 minutes, $t = 0.75$.

east: $0.75\vec{v} = -67.41 - 10(0.75) = -74.91$ mi

north: $0.75\vec{v} = -32.88 + 17.32(0.75) = -19.89$ mi

east: $\vec{v} = -99.88$ mph

north: $\vec{v} = -26.52$ mph

Thus, Jim's heading should be $\tan^{-1}\left(\frac{-99.88}{-26.52}\right) + 180° \approx 75.13° + 180° = 255.13°$. (Note that Jim's ground speed (resultant speed) will then be $\sqrt{99.88^2 + 26.52^2} \approx 103.34$ mph, which will get him to Dinnebito in 45 minutes.)

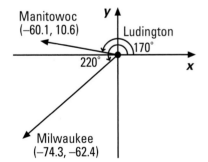

Manitowoc (−60.1, 10.6)
Ludington 170°
220°
Milwaukee (−74.3, −62.4)

4. a. Using a standard coordinate system with the positive y-axis as 90° and changing to directions rather than headings, the coordinates in miles are

Manitowoc: $x = 61 \cos 170°$ and $y = 61 \sin 170°$, thus $(x, y) = (-60.1, 10.6)$.

Milwaukee: $x = 97 \cos 220°$ and $y = 97 \sin 220°$, thus $(x, y) = (-74.3, -62.4)$.

b. For the boat going to Manitowoc, $x = 8t \cos 170°$ and $y = 8t \sin 170°$. For the boat going to Milwaukee, $x = 10t \cos 220°$ and $y = 10t \sin 220°$. For $t = 1$, the locations of the two boats are approximately $(-7.9, 1.4)$ and $(-7.7, -6.4)$. Their distance apart at 8:00 A.M. is $\sqrt{(-0.2)^2 + (7.8)^2} \approx 7.8$ mi. The boats will continue to move away from each other at 7.8 mph. Thus, at 11:00 A.M., they are about $3(7.8)$ or 23.4 mi apart. Students could also find the coordinates of the two boats after 3 hours using the distance formula.

c. They lose radio contact when they are 50 mi apart. Since they move apart at 7.8 mph, the solution to the equation $50 = 7.8t$ will give the time they have traveled when they first lose contact. If $50 = 7.8t$, then $t \approx 6.4$ or 6 hours and 24 minutes. Thus, they lose contact at approximately 2:24 P.M.

MORE *continued*

d. The boat heading toward Manitowoc is 61 – 6.4 · 8 = 9.8 mi from Manitowoc. The boat heading to Milwaukee is 97 – 6.4 · 10 = 33 mi from Milwaukee.

Organizing

1. a. To subtract one number from another, add its opposite (additive inverse).

b. To subtract $\vec{b}$ from $\vec{a}$, add the opposite of $\vec{b}$ to $\vec{a}$.

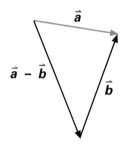

c. $\vec{a} + (-\vec{b})$

d. $\vec{a} - \vec{b} + \vec{b}$ is $\vec{a}$.

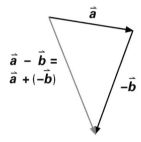

2. a. 90°

b. Draw $\overrightarrow{OP}$, starting at point O. Then complete the rectangle with $\overrightarrow{OP}$ as a diagonal and sides multiples of $\vec{a}$ and $\vec{b}$. Measure these sides to find $m\vec{a}$ and $n\vec{b}$. Note that either m or n (or both) may be less than 1. If $\overrightarrow{OP}$ is not in the interior of the angle formed by $\vec{a}$ and $\vec{b}$, then the opposite of $\vec{a}$, $\vec{b}$, or both may need to be used. Here is one specific example:

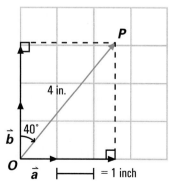

$m \approx 2.57$
$n \approx 2.04$

MORE *continued*

c. Yes; methods will vary. One way would be to complete the rectangle with $\overrightarrow{OQ}$ as a diagonal, measure $m\vec{a}$ and divide by 1 (the length of $\vec{a}$) to find the absolute value of m. Measure $n\vec{b}$ and divide by 1.5 to find the absolute value of n. Then assign the appropriate sign to each value.

d. If $\overrightarrow{OQ}$ has the same direction as $\vec{a}$, then $n = 0$. If $\overrightarrow{OQ}$ has the same direction as $\vec{b}$ then $m = 0$. If Q coincides with O, then $m = n = 0$.

3. **Each of the true statements could be explained in various ways. Students may choose to draw general sketches that illustrate the situations or to assign general coordinates and manipulate them. Be sure that students are not using one specific example to justify their reasoning. It is important to expect them to give more sophisticated explanations.**

a. True: $m(n\vec{a})$ is a vector m times the length of the vector $n\vec{a}$, while $n\vec{a}$ is a vector n times the length of $\vec{a}$. Thus, $(mn)\vec{a}$ is a vector mn times the length of $\vec{a}$. Thus, $m(n\vec{a})$ and $(mn)\vec{a}$ have the same magnitude. If m and n have the same sign, then $m(n\vec{a})$ and $(mn)\vec{a}$ have the same direction. Similarly, if m and n have opposite signs, then $m(n\vec{a})$ and $(mn)\vec{a}$ have the direction opposite to that of $\vec{a}$. Thus, for all real numbers m and n, $m(n\vec{a}) = (mn)\vec{a}$.

b. True: If the coordinates of the position vector $\vec{a}$ are (x, y) then

$$(m + n) \cdot (x, y) = ((m + n)x, (m + n)y)$$
$$= (mx + nx, my + ny)$$
$$= (mx, my) + (nx, ny)$$
$$= m(x, y) + n(x, y)$$
$$= m\vec{a} + n\vec{a}.$$

c. True: If $\vec{a}$ and $\vec{b}$ are position vectors with $\vec{a} = (x_a, y_a)$ and $\vec{b} = (x_b, y_b)$, then

$$m(\vec{a} + \vec{b}) = m(x_a + x_b, y_a + y_b)$$
$$= (mx_a + mx_b, my_a + my_b)$$
$$= m(x_a, y_a) + m(x_b, y_b)$$
$$= m\vec{a} + m\vec{b}.$$

d. False: If either m or n is negative, then $|m + n| \neq |m| + |n|$. Thus, the lengths are not equal.

4. **a.** The components of $\overrightarrow{OA}$ are $x = r \cos \theta$ and $y = r \sin \theta$.

The components of $\overrightarrow{OB}$ are $x = b \cos \phi$ and $y = b \sin \phi$.

b. A has coordinates of $(r \cos \theta, r \sin \theta)$ and B has coordinates of $(b \cos \phi, b \sin \phi)$.

c. Components of $\overrightarrow{OA} + \overrightarrow{OB}$: $x = r \cos \theta + b \cos \phi$, $y = r \sin \theta + b \sin \phi$

MORE *continued*

d. The direction of $\overrightarrow{OA}$ is $(\theta + 180°)$. This means that the endpoint of the vector $-\overrightarrow{OA}$ is a reflection through the origin of the endpoint of $\overrightarrow{OA}$, so $x = -r\cos\theta$ and $y = -r\sin\theta$.

e. $\overrightarrow{OB} - \overrightarrow{OA} = \overrightarrow{OB} + (-\overrightarrow{OA})$ which has components $x = b\cos\phi - r\cos\phi$ and $y = b\sin\phi - r\sin\theta$.

5. **a.** Length of $\vec{u}$ $= \sqrt{(2-0)^2 + (3-0)^2}$

$$= \sqrt{4 + 9}$$

$$= \sqrt{13} \approx 3.6$$

Length of $\vec{v}$ $= \sqrt{(-1-0)^2 + (4-0)^2}$

$$= \sqrt{1 + 16}$$

$$= \sqrt{17} \approx 4.1$$

From the given coordinates, $\vec{u}$ is in Quadrant I and $\vec{v}$ is in Quadrant II. Thus, the directions are between 0° and 90° and between 90° and 180°, respectively.

Direction of $\vec{u}$: $\theta = \tan^{-1}\left(\frac{3}{2}\right) \approx 56.31°$

Direction of $\vec{v}$: The measure of the angle that $\vec{v}$ makes with the negative x-axis is $\tan^{-1}\left(\frac{4}{1}\right) \approx 76°$. So the direction of $\vec{v}$ is approximately $180° - 76° = 104°$.

b. $\vec{u} + \vec{v}$ can be found by adding x-coordinates to x-coordinates and y-coordinates to y-coordinates. Thus, $\vec{u} + \vec{v} = (2, 3) + (-1, 4) = (1, 7)$.

c. ■ $\vec{u} + \vec{v} = (x_1, y_1) + (x_2, y_2) = (x_1 + x_2, y_1 + y_2)$; x-coordinates are added to each other, as are y-coordinates.

■ $m\vec{u}$ has magnitude m times the magnitude of $\vec{u}$. But this means the x-component of $m\vec{u}$ is m times the x-component of $\vec{u}$, likewise for the y-component. Thus, the coordinates of the terminal point of $m\vec{u}$ are (mx_1, my_1).

d. ■ $\vec{v} + \vec{u} = (x_2, y_2) + (x_1, y_1) = (x_2 + x_1, y_2 + y_1)$ by definition of vector addition
$= (x_1 + x_2, y_1 + y_2) = (x_1, y_1) + (x_2, y_2)$ by commutative property of addition of real numbers and by definition of vector addition

$= \vec{u} + \vec{v}$

■ $m(\vec{v} + \vec{u}) = m[(x_2 + y_2) + (x_1 + y_1)] = m(x_2 + x_1, y_2 + y_1)$

by definition of vector addition

$= (mx_2 + mx_1, my_2 + my_1) = (mx_2, my_2) + (mx_1, my_1)$

by distributive property of a scalar over vector addition and by definition of vector addition

$= m(x_2, y_2) + m(x_1, y_1) = m\vec{v} + m\vec{u}$ by definition of scalar multiplication over a vector

MORE *continued*

Reflecting

1. **a.** Students should show sketches.

   ■ Vectors with the same length that are not parallel or collinear are not equal.

   ■ Parallel or collinear vectors that do not have the same length are not equal.

   b. The arrows are identical.

   c. The arrows are parallel or collinear, point in the same direction, and are congruent.

2. **a.** A vector can be drawn from a point on figure F to the corresponding point on figure G. The length and direction of the vector would represent the direction and magnitude of the translation. Note that vectors drawn from any point on F to the corresponding point on G will be equal.

   b. Yes, every translation can be described by a vector. In a translation, each point (x, y) moves to $(x + h, y + k)$, so h and k can be seen respectively as the horizontal and vertical components of the vector describing the translation.

3. **a.** length $= \sqrt{a^2 + b^2}$

   b. The signs tell you in which quadrant the terminal point lies. For a and b both negative, the terminal point (a, b) lies in Quadrant III, so that is where the vector would be drawn.

   c. Use a calculator to find $\tan^{-1}\left(\frac{b}{a}\right)$. Then use a diagram and the angle measure to determine the direction of the vector. $\tan^{-1}\left(\frac{b}{a}\right)$ will always lie in Quadrant IV or Quadrant I and the absolute value of $\tan^{-1}\left(\frac{b}{a}\right)$ will be the measure of the angle made by the x-axis and the vector. If the terminal point lies in Quadrants II or III, you will have to add $180°$ to $\tan^{-1}\left(\frac{b}{a}\right)$. For example, for the point $(-2, -3)$, the vector is in Quadrant III and $\tan^{-1}\left(\frac{b}{a}\right) \approx 56.3°$. Here, $180°$ must be added to get the direction of the vector: $56.3° + 180° = 236.3°$.

   For any point in Quadrant I, the direction of the vector is $\tan^{-1}\left(\frac{b}{a}\right)$.

   For any point in Quadrant II, the direction of the vector is $180° + \tan^{-1}\left(\frac{b}{a}\right)$.

   For any point in Quadrant III, the direction of the vector will be $180° + \tan^{-1}\left(\frac{b}{a}\right)$.

   For any point in Quadrant IV, the direction of the vector will be $360° + \tan^{-1}\left(\frac{b}{a}\right)$.

   ($360°$ is added because the angle given by $\tan^{-1}\left(\frac{b}{a}\right)$ is in Quadrant IV, but is negative, and the direction of a vector is always measured as a positive angle.)

4. **a.** $\vec{b} - \vec{u} = \vec{v}$

   b. $\vec{w} - \vec{a} = \vec{u}$

   c. $\vec{v} + \vec{u} - \vec{b} = \vec{0}$

   d. $\vec{b} + \vec{a} - \vec{v} - \vec{w} = \vec{0}$

MORE *continued*

5.

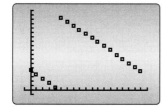

L1	L2	L3
0	90	-----
20	70	
40	50	
60	30	
80	10	
100	350	
120	330	

L1(1)=0

L1	L2	L3
140	310	
160	290	
180	270	
200	250	
220	230	
240	210	
260	190	

L1(8)=140

L1	L2	L3
260	190	
280	170	
300	150	
320	130	
340	110	
360	90	
-----	-----	

L1(14)=260

```
WINDOW
 Xmin =-20
 Xmax=380
 Xscl =20
 Ymin =-20
 Ymax=380
 Yscl =20
 Xres =1
```

The scatterplot is composed of two parts, each with slope –1. In the lower left corner, you have the relation modeled by $y = -x + 90°$. The other points have model $y = -x + 450°$. No one linear or nonlinear equation will work for both parts of the scatterplot.

Since the relationship between the heading and direction coordinate systems is a reflection across the 0° line and a rotation of 90°, the expression $90° - H = D$ will convert headings to directions, and likewise $90° - D = H$ will convert directions to headings. If you add 360° to negative values, this matches the plot.

Extending

1. All properties that hold for addition of 2×2 matrices also hold for addition of vectors. The following are some of the properties that your students might investigate.

Commutative Property: $\vec{u} + \vec{v} = \vec{v} + \vec{u}$

Associative Property: $(\vec{u} + \vec{v}) + \vec{w} = \vec{u} + (\vec{v} + \vec{w})$

Additive Identity: $\vec{v} + \vec{0} = \vec{v}$, (where $\vec{0} = (0, 0)$)

Additive Inverse: $\vec{v} + (-\vec{v}) = \vec{0}$

Unit 2

MORE *continued*

2. **a.** The proof is valid. $XY = \frac{1}{2}AB$ follows from the fact that the equal vectors $\frac{1}{2}\overrightarrow{AB}$ and $\overrightarrow{XY}$ have equal magnitudes. Likewise, $\overrightarrow{XY} \parallel \overrightarrow{AB}$ follows because equal vectors $\overrightarrow{XY} = \frac{1}{2}\overrightarrow{AB}$ have the same direction; you know from the figure that these vectors are not collinear, so they must be parallel.

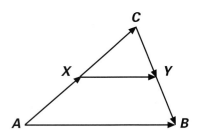

b. The argument would not need to be modified since all of the statements hold for an obtuse triangle.

3. **a.**

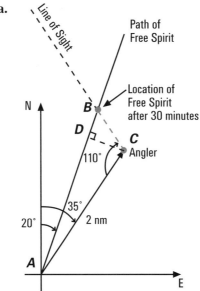

b. In the diagram above, *BC* (distance between the boats) is a little more than $\frac{1}{2}$ nm.

c. No; the components of the *Angler* are easily determined, but since the distance *Free Spirit* traveled and her speed are unknown, a crucial piece of information that would allow you to determine the components of *Free Spirit's* position is missing.

d. Note that m$\angle BAC = 15°$ and m$\angle ABC = 55°$. Using the Law of Sines:

$\frac{2 \text{ nm}}{\sin 55°} = \frac{BC}{\sin 15°}$ or $BC = \frac{2 \sin 15°}{\sin 55°} \approx 0.63$ nm, which is close to the result in Part b.

To find the distance *AB* that the *Free Spirit* has traveled in 30 minutes, apply the Law of Sines again: $\frac{2}{\sin 55°} = \frac{AB}{\sin 110°}$ or $AB = \frac{2 \sin 110°}{\sin 55°} \approx 2.3$ nm.

Since this occurs in $\frac{1}{2}$ hour, the speed is approximately 4.6 knots.

MORE *continued*

4. Since the 10,000-newton vector is the diagonal of a parallelogram, the opposite angles are equal. Therefore, the measure of each angle marked θ is $\frac{360° - 2(75°)}{2} = 105°$. Let y represent the magnitude of $\vec{y}$. Since opposite sides of a parallelogram are equal, you can work with a triangle with sides of length $1.5y$ and y, and included angle of $105°$. Applying the Law of Cosines:

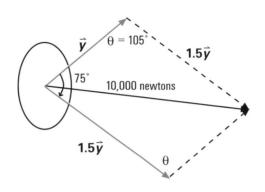

$$10,000^2 = (1.5y)^2 + y^2 - 2(1.5y)(y) \cos 105°$$
$$10,000^2 = 3.25y^2 - 3y^2 \cos 105°$$
$$10,000^2 = y^2(3.25 - 3 \cos 105°)$$
$$y^2 = \frac{10,000^2}{3.25 - 3 \cos 105°}$$
$$y^2 \approx 24,835,729$$
$$y \approx 4,984 \text{ newtons}$$
$$1.5y \approx 7,475 \text{ newtons}$$

5. a.

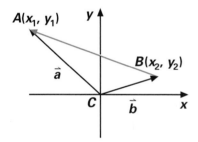

$$AB = \sqrt{(x_1 - x_2)^2 + (y_1 - y_2)^2}$$

Using the Law of Cosines, $AB^2 = AC^2 + BC^2 - 2AC \cdot BC \cos C$.

$$(x_1 - x_2)^2 + (y_1 - y_2)^2 = (x_1^2 + y_1^2) + (x_2^2 + y_2^2) - 2\sqrt{x_1^2 + y_1^2} \cdot \sqrt{x_2^2 + y_2^2} \cdot \cos C$$
$$-2x_1x_2 - 2y_1y_2 = -2\sqrt{x_1^2 + y_1^2} \cdot \sqrt{x_2^2 + y_2^2} \cdot \cos C$$
$$\cos C = \left(\frac{x_1x_2 + y_1y_2}{\sqrt{x_1^2 + y_1^2} \cdot \sqrt{x_2^2 + y_2^2}} \right)$$
$$C = \cos^{-1} \left(\frac{x_1x_2 + y_1y_2}{\sqrt{x_1^2 + y_1^2} \cdot \sqrt{x_2^2 + y_2^2}} \right)$$

b. Since $\cos 90° = 0$, if the angle is $90°$ then the value of the inner product, $x_1x_2 + y_1y_2$, is 0.

Masters 47a–47d

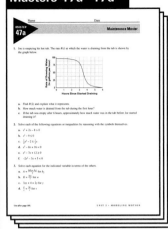

MORE *continued*

c. ■ Angle between (2, 3) and (4, –3):
$$C = \cos^{-1}\left(\frac{(2)(4) + 3(-3)}{\sqrt{2^2 + 3^2} \cdot \sqrt{4^2 + (-3)^2}}\right) = \cos^{-1}\left(\frac{-1}{\sqrt{13} \cdot \sqrt{25}}\right) \approx 93.2°$$

■ Approximate angle between (–2, 1) and (3, –5): 147.5°

■ Angle between (–1, –5) and (–3, –2): 45°

■ Approximate angle between (1, 2) and (3, 4): 10.3°

See Teaching Masters 47a–47d for maintenance tasks that students can work on following Lesson 1.

See Assessment Resources pages 42–49.

Assessments 42–45

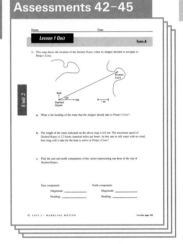

REVIEW AND PRACTICE individual task

▶ **PUMP**

Answers

1. (e)	6. (d)
2. (a)	7. (b)
3. (e)	8. (d)
4. (c)	9. (c)
5. (c)	10. (d)

Assessments 46–49

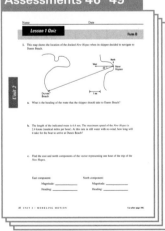

Unit 2

Lesson 2 *Simulating Linear and Nonlinear Motion*

LESSON OVERVIEW   Much of the work in this lesson deals with motion of a projectile. Three fundamental ideas from physics will be used:

1.   An object at rest stays at rest until some force is applied to make it move.

2.   The fundamental motion of an object is linear. If an object begins to move, it will continue to move in the same direction if no other force is operating on it.

3.   Motion can be decomposed into its horizontal and vertical components and these components are independent of each other. This means that a force can affect one component while having no effect on the other. (Aristotle thought that they were not independent and that a change in one caused a change in the other. It was Galileo who discovered the independent nature of the components.)

In this lesson, the vector component analysis of linear motion is used to introduce parametric equations, $x = At \cos B$, $y = At \sin B$, of a line passing through the origin, at an angle of B with the positive x-axis and such that the velocity of the moving object is A units per unit of time t. Special cases of the parametric representation when $B = 0°$, and when $B = 90°$ and A is negative, are used to model racing boats and gravity respectively. In the second investigation, parametric representation of nonlinear motion is investigated by adding other forces to a projectile such as a slow-pitch softball pitch. In some sense, you have followed Newton's laws of motion by beginning with the examination of linear motion with no other forces involved and gradually add new forces and other constraints to develop better models for familiar motions.

Investigation 3 examines circular motion and its parametric representation. Even though the parametric equations are similar to those for linear motion, the results are quite different. The idea of angular velocity is key to understanding this motion. In all of this work, the graphing calculator is an important tool for representing motion and carrying out computations. It assists students in developing a robust understanding of motion.

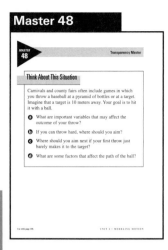

Master 48

Lesson Objectives

- ■ To write parametric equations for linear motion
- ■ To simulate linear motion using technology
- ■ To write parametric equations for projectile motion
- ■ To simulate projectile motion using technology
- ■ To identify important forces affecting motion
- ■ To write a parametric representation of a circle
- ■ To use both radian and degree measurements to describe angular velocity
- ■ To use technology to simulate the path of a point on a rotating circle
- ■ To describe the location of a point on a rotating circle in terms of its initial location and the angular velocity
- ■ To use technology to simulate the motion of an object in an elliptical orbit

LAUNCH full-class discussion

Think About This Situation

Ask students to think about situations in which they impart motion to objects. Use this as a lead-in to the questions in the "Think About This Situation."

See Teaching Master 48.

ⓐ There are many variables such as the weight of the ball, the size of the target, the thrower's skill and strength, environmental factors such as wind, light, and so on.

ⓑ If you can throw hard, you should aim only a little above the target. This is reasonable because the ball will get to the target rapidly, with little time for gravity to bring it down.

ⓒ Throw the ball upward at some angle so that it rises and hits the target on its downward path. The proper release angle depends on the thrower's strength and other factors.

ⓓ There are many factors, such as gravity, the initial velocity, the angle of delivery, movement of the air, and height of release.

EXPLORE small-group investigation

INVESTIGATION 1 Parametric Models for Linear Motion

You can introduce this lesson by telling your students that they are going to learn ways to represent linear, parabolic, and circular motion, both symbolically and graphically. You may want to briefly review work they have done previously relating to these kinds of motion. The equation $y = ax$ represents a linear path through the origin, with a given slope.

- You can ask how $y = ax$ connects to the idea of an object traveling in a straight line at a constant speed. What do you know about the *y*-coordinate/component? What do you know about the *x*-coordinate? (The *x*-coordinate represents time and the *y*-coordinate represents distance. The speed is "*a*".)

- What graph would you expect for $y = ax^2 + bx + c$? (a parabola) You have seen this equation used in connection with projectiles. What did *y* represent? What did *x* represent? (Students have seen this type of equation used to represent the height of a projectile, such as the path of a football. Notice that *x* represents time and not a position, while *y* represents the height at time *x*. The equation does not represent the actual path of the projectile.)

- What about $y = a \sin x$? What shape is this graph, what motion have you associated with this, what did *y* represent, and what did *x* represent? (This is a periodic graph. You used this equation to model how the height above the center line of a Ferris wheel changed over time as the Ferris wheel rotated. Notice that *x* again represented time in this equation. The sine curve does not represent the actual path of a point on the Ferris wheel.)

You can let your students know that they are going to connect what they know about components of a vector to write new equations for the path of each kind of motion, starting with linear motion in Investigation 1.

The first activity uses a familiar context to introduce parametric representation of linear motion: the path of a boat. Copies of Teaching Master 49 will be helpful for student work on this activity. At the end of Lesson 1, students found that they could represent the components of any constant velocity vector with equations that took into account the direction of the vector, θ, and the constant speed A, $x = At \cos \theta$, and $y = At \sin \theta$. In fact, the equations they have generated are parametric equations since both *x*- and *y*-components depend on a third variable *t*. Activities 1–3 help students make the transition to graphing the path of (*x*, *y*) by using parametric equations. Activities 4–8 introduce special cases, where either the *x*- or *y*-component is constant, or where there are adjustments in starting values of *t*. Activity 9 extends the idea of parametric equations to non-constant velocity, where one component (*x*) is constant. This activity may require some large group discussion. Emphasize that the path is linear, although the equation for *y* is not.

EXPLORE *continued*

1. **See Teaching Master 49.**

   a.

   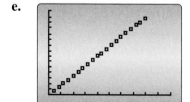

   b. $x = 8t \cos 60°$

   $y = 8t \sin 60°$

Elapsed Time t (hours)	Horizontal Component x	Vertical Component y
0.0	0.0	0.00
0.1	0.4	0.69282
0.2	0.8	1.3856
0.3	1.2	2.0785
0.4	1.6	2.7713
0.5	2.0	3.4641
0.6	2.4	4.1569
0.7	2.8	4.8497
0.8	3.2	5.5426
0.9	3.6	6.2354
1.0	4.0	6.9282
1.1	4.4	7.621
1.2	4.8	8.3138
1.3	5.2	9.0067
1.4	5.6	9.6995
1.5	6.0	10.392
1.6	6.4	11.085
1.7	6.8	11.778
1.8	7.2	12.471
1.9	7.6	13.164
2.0	8.0	13.856

   c. Students can use the rules from Part b and the **List** capability of a calculator or computer software to efficiently complete the table. You may wish to remind them that they can use the sequence command on their calculators to fill in the column for elapsed time. On the TI calculators, **seq(** is located under the LIST/OPS menu. The command **seq(A,A,0,2,.1)→L₁** will properly fill **L₁** with the indicated *t*-values. To complete the other two columns, let **L₂ = 8L₁ cos 60°** and **L₃ = 8L₁ sin 60°**.

   d. The variable *t* is increasing in increments of 0.1. The variable *x* is increasing in increments of 0.4 for each 0.1 increase in *t*. The variable *y* is increasing in increments of 0.69282 for each 0.1 increase in *t*. The variables *x* and *y* are both measured in nautical miles.

   e.

   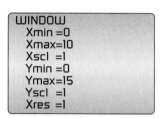

   The points all seem to lie on a line. The scatterplot displays positions of the boat, which is traveling at a speed of 8 knots along a straight line that makes a 60° angle with the *x*-axis.

EXPLORE *continued*

NOTE: If students are using either a TI-89 or TI-92, they will need to put a multiplication sign after the **T** in both equations; otherwise, the calculator interprets **Tcos** and **Tsin** as variables.

2. a. The two sets of equations are equivalent, since 8 cos 60° = 4 and 8 sin 60° ≈ 6.92820323.

   b. This table should be identical (for **T** = 0 to **T** = 2) to the one in Part c of Activity 1. The patterns continue.

3. a. The students' displays should match the one shown in the textbook.

   b. One point is displayed for **T** = **Tmin** and then one more for each value of **T** less than or equal to **Tmax**. (If any point falls on the *x*- or *y*-axis, then it will not be visible. Tracing the points would allow students to see when there is a point on either axis.) As soon as **T** is larger than **Tmax**, the graphing stops. Twenty-one points will be shown for **Tmin** = 0, **Tmax** = 2, **Tstep** = 0.1 or **Tmin** = 0, **Tmax** = 1, **Tstep** = 0.05. There are infinitely many possibilities for 21 points, not all beginning at the origin. A **Tmin** value other than 0 will start the graph at a point different from the origin. The screen size is determined by the **X** and **Y** settings. To ensure that all points are shown on the screen, make sure the *x* and *y* values corresponding to **Tmin** and **Tmax** are on the screen. (This test will not work for nonlinear situations. Also, a point corresponding to **Tmax** may not be shown if **Tstep** is such that **T** never takes the value of **Tmax**.)

   c. The values of **T**, **X**, and **Y** shown on the screen should be the same as those in the table.

4. a. $X_T = 600T \cos 15°$, $Y_T = 600T \sin 15°$

   b. East: 600(2.5) cos 15° ≈ 1,449 mi
   North: 600(2.5) sin 15° ≈ 388 mi

   c. Graphs may vary somewhat. Be sure that the window is scaled so that **Xmax** > 3,100, **Ymax** > 831, and **T** increases in increments of 0.5. One graph and appropriate window screen are below, followed by a squared window that more clearly demonstrates the 15° angle.

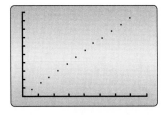
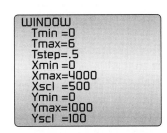
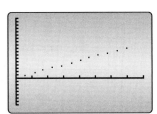

   d. Change **Tstep** to $\frac{12}{60}$ or 0.2 to show the location every 12 minutes.

5. a. Since the direction angle is 0°, the parametric equations are $X_T = 8T \cos 0°$ and $Y_T = 8T \sin 0°$, which simplify to $X_T = 8T$ and $Y_T = 0$. In order to display the graph,

EXPLORE *continued*

either turn off the axes or show the graph off the *x*-axis by making Y_T be a nonzero constant such as $Y_T = 0.2$.

b. To travel 50 nm, X_T must be 50. Therefore $50 = 8T$ or $T = 6.25$ hours. See Part d for a graph of the path of the *Charlotte Rose*.

c. Assuming that $T = 0$ at noon, the equations could be $X_T = 10(T - 1)$ and $Y_T = 0.6$. The Y_T value should be 0.4 greater here than it was in Part a.

d. Choose values of *y* that differ by 0.4. One possible display follows.

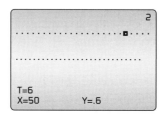 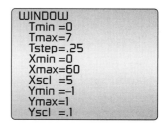

e. The *Lady Anna* reaches 50 nm when $T = 6$. At that time, the *Charlotte Rose* has traveled only 48 nm. To determine these T values, use the $\boxed{\text{TRACE}}$ feature, examine the tables, or solve $10(T - 1) = 50$ for T and $8T = 50$ for T and compare.

The two boats will have traveled the same distance when $T = 5$. This can be found by solving $8T = 10(T - 1)$ for T.

Master 50

Name _____ Date _____

MASTER 50 — Activity Master

Graphs of Parametric Equations

Use with page 111. — UNIT 2 • MODELING MOTION

TECHNOLOGY NOTE: When tracing parametric graphs, the right-arrow key moves the cursor to the point corresponding to the next higher T value and the left-arrow key moves the cursor to the point corresponding to the next lower T value. Depending on the parametric equation, the cursor may move to the left or down, rather than to the right and up, when pressing the right-arrow key to trace the graphs in Activity 5 Part f or Activity 6 Parts b, d, f, and h.

f. The parametric equations for the *Charlotte Rose* could be $X_{1T} = -8T$ and $Y_{1T} = 0.2$. The parametric equations for the *Lady Anna* could be $X_{2T} = -10(T - 1)$ and $Y_{2T} = 0.6$. The window will need to be changed so that $Xmin = -50$ and $Xmax = 0$.

6. See Teaching Master 50.

It is important that all students sketch all of these graphs. They can draw their graphs on copies of the activity master.

a.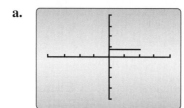

b.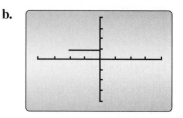

EXPLORE *continued*

c.

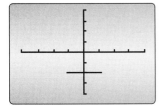

d.

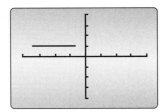

e.

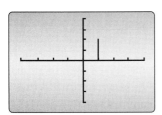

f.

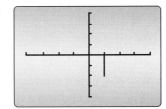

g.

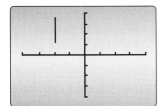

h.

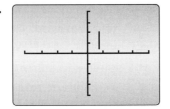

7. **a.** The graph is a horizontal line if the parameter *t* appears with degree one in the equation for *x* and not at all in the equation for *y*. The graph is a vertical line if *t* appears only in the *y*-equation, and only with degree one.

b. Students should use constants and linear expressions involving *t* as done in Activity 6. Otherwise, they will have difficulty predicting the shape of the graph.

c. $5t \cos 0° = 5t$ and $5t \sin 0° + 8 = 8$

d. $5t \cos 90° + 10 = 10$ and $5t \sin 90° = 5t$

e. All of the remaining pairs of parametric equations in Activity 6 match this form. When $\theta = 0°$, the equations reduce to $x = At + B$ and $y = D$. When $\theta = 90°$, the equations reduce to $x = B$ and $y = At + D$.

8. **a.** See student sketches. The origin of the coordinate system could be at the place the *Sawatdee* starts.

b. If the *Sawatdee* begins at the origin, the parametric equations for the *Sawatdee's* location are $X_{1T} = 8T$ and $Y_{1T} = 1$. The parametric equations for the *Delhi Dhaba* could be $X_{2T} = -10T + 60$ and $Y_{2T} = 2$.

c. The boats will meet at 3:20 P.M. and will be approximately 26.67 mi from where the *Sawatdee* began. If students think about what the equations mean, they can

EXPLORE *continued*

determine that the boats will meet when $8T = -10T + 60$, or when $T = 3\frac{1}{3}$ hours. If $T = 3\frac{1}{3}$ hours, the boats will meet at 3:20 P.M. Substituting $T = 3\frac{1}{3}$ into the equation X_{1T} will give the location with respect to the *Sawatdee's* starting location. They will meet after the *Sawatdee* has traveled $\frac{80}{3}$, or approximately 26.67 mi.

By tracing the graphs, students should be able to determine that they will meet between 3:00 and 3:30 P.M. after the *Sawatdee* traveled approximately 26.67 mi.

On the table, students may look for the T value that makes $X_{1T} = X_{2T}$. The value of X_{1T} (or X_{2T}) will give the location.

9. **Students who are aware of the gravitational constant but have not taken physics may wonder why the coefficient of the t^2 term is not 9.8 in this situation. If some do ask, the following explanation may be helpful:**

   If the dropped object is in a vacuum (where there is no air resistance) the object accelerates at a rate of -9.8 m/sec^2. The acceleration is negative since the force of gravity is downward. Acceleration multiplied by time gives the speed of an object, since $\frac{m}{s^2} \cdot s = \frac{m}{s}$, which are units of speed. In a vacuum, an object will fall at a speed of -9.8 m/sec$^2 \cdot t$ seconds $= -9.8t$ m/s. When an object is moving at a constant rate of speed, the distance traveled is that speed multiplied by time. Here, though, the rate is variable. In one second the change would be from 0 m/s to $-9.8t$ m/s for an average speed of $\frac{0 - 9.8t}{2}$ m/s $= -4.9t$ m/s. Thus, the distance an object falls due to gravity is given by $\frac{-9.8t}{2}$ m/s $\cdot$ t seconds $= -4.9t^2$ m.

   a. The equation $X = 1$ moves the path of the object off the *y*-axis. The equation $Y = -4.9T^2 + 200$ indicates that when $T = 0$, the object is 200 m above Earth. The $-4.9T^2$ term accounts for the force of gravity acting on the object.

   b. $Tmin = 0$, $Tmax = 7$, $Tstep = 0.3$ will work well for T.

   $0 \le X \le 3$ and $-20 \le Y \le 200$ will work well for the display.

   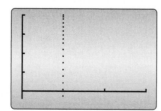

   c. The Y value tells you the height of the object above the ground.

   d. The distance it falls per second increases with time. This can be observed by the larger spaces between dots on the graph or larger differences in consecutive *y* values in a table.

   e. Students can solve $-4.9T^2 + 200 = 0$ to get $T \approx 6.39$ seconds. Using TRACE or the table of values, they can determine that the object hits Earth after about 6.4 seconds.

   f. It could be any number. It simply provides a "column" in which the graph can be drawn.

   g. $X = 1$, $Y = -16T^2 + 150$

SHARE AND SUMMARIZE full-class discussion

Checkpoint

See Teaching Master 51.

a Parametric equations for *x* and *y* are rules that describe both *x* and *y* in terms of another variable such as time (which is called the parameter).

b A vector shows you where an object is located at a fixed time. Parametric equations allow you to see the locations sequentially over some time period. The parametric equations are the rules giving the components of the terminal point of the vector for any time *t*.

c ■ For a horizontal linear path, choose *y* to be constant and *x* to be a linear function of *t*, specifically $x = At$ where *A* is the velocity.

■ For a vertical linear path, choose *x* to be constant and *y* to be a linear function of *t*, specifically $y = At$ where *A* is the velocity.

■ If the angle that the line makes with the *x*-axis is θ, then the equations for the line are $x = At \cos\theta$ and $y = At \sin\theta$, where *A* is the velocity.

The Checkpoint questions cover the basic situations of linear motion at a constant rate. Some students may benefit from additional discussion of Activity 9. Why is the equation for *y* quadratic? (Because the velocity is not constant) Why is the graph not a parabola? (If you graphed $y = -4.9t^2 + 200$ on (*t*, *y*)-axes, you would have a parabola. You are graphing values for (*x*, *y*) where both of these are position coordinates.) Take time to be sure that students understand that the parametric graph really does model position.

CONSTRUCTING A MATH TOOLKIT: Students should describe parametric equations and write examples of each type of equation mentioned in Part c of the Checkpoint. You may also wish to have students record the general parametric equations for linear motion with a constant velocity.

Unit 2

APPLY individual task

▶ **On Your Own**

a. For motion on Earth: $x = 1$, $y = -4.9t^2 + 100$
     the Moon: $x = 2$, $y = -0.83t^2 + 100$
     Jupiter: $x = 3$, $y = -11.44t^2 + 100$

b. Using dot mode and graphing equations simultaneously provides an informative display.

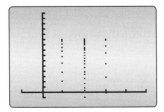

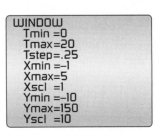

```
WINDOW
 Tmin =0
 Tmax=20
 Tstep=.25
 Xmin =-1
 Xmax=5
 Xscl =1
 Ymin =-10
 Ymax=150
 Yscl =10
```

APPLY *continued*

All three patterns of motion are straight down, with motion getting faster as the object approaches the surface. Jupiter's object moves fastest (think of one dot being made every 0.25 seconds), Earth's is second fastest, and the Moon's is slowest.

c. Students may use algebraic reasoning, graphs, or tables to find these times.
$t \approx 4.52$ seconds for Earth
$t \approx 10.98$ seconds for the Moon
$t \approx 2.96$ seconds for Jupiter

d.

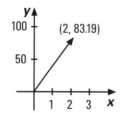

The vector starts at the origin in this coordinate system and ends at (2, 83.19). The y-component is $-0.83(4.5)^2 + 100 \approx 83.19$ m. This represents the height above the ground at time $t = 4.5$.

ASSIGNMENT *pp. 127–133*

Students can now begin Organizing Task 1 or 4 or Reflecting Task 3 from the MORE assignment following Investigation 4.

EXPLORE small-group investigation

INVESTIGATION 2 Parametric Models for Nonlinear Motion

If you did a general launch for Investigation 1, reminding students of their previous work with projectiles, then you will need only a brief connecting introduction here. You might just ask why a thrown football does not continue on the path on which it starts out. Gravity is a force continually acting on the football, unlike the force of the throw, which acts only until the ball leaves the thrower's hand. Sketch a vector diagram to show the directions of the motions of the ball for small increments of time. (See the following diagrams.) Are these motions constant over time? (The motion caused by the throwing force is constant, but that caused by gravity gradually changes because the downward speed increases.) Where is the resultant vector in each part of the diagram? Will the resultant vector be a constant length? (No; students should know this from completing Activity 9 and the "On Your Own" in Investigation 1.)

The diagrams below show that gravity is becoming the dominant force as time increases.

| Second 0.1 sec interval | Third 0.1 sec interval | Fourth 0.1 sec interval | Fifth 0.1 sec interval |

EXPLORE *continued*

Could you redraw this diagram with only horizontal and vertical vectors? (The motion due to the throwing force could be redrawn as a vertical and horizontal component. Then you would have a total horizontal component originating in the throwing force, and a total vertical component, which is a combination of the original upward thrust of the throwing force and the continual force of gravity.)

The first three activities in this investigation deal with slow-pitch softball. Check to see if students have played softball and get someone to describe the slow-pitch version of the game. You may wish to have someone illustrate pitching a softball with a paper ball.

In assigning Activities 4–6 to various groups in your class, make sure that at least one group works on each activity. It would be even better if two groups worked on each activity so that the groups can compare notes and answers. When the work is done, the groups working on each activity could prepare a class presentation using the clearest thinking of all the groups.

As students work on this investigation, ask them what the equations for *x* and *y* represent (horizontal and vertical motion). Why is the equation for *y* not linear? (Because the vertical motion is a sum of two motions, one of which shows acceleration) Does the graph of $y = 12t \sin 55° − 4.9t^2$ on (*t, y*)-axes, represent the path of the ball? Note: This graph can be created in parametric mode by letting $X = T$ and $Y = 12T \sin 55° − 4.9T^2$. (See Activity 2. This equation gives the height of the ball, not the path of the ball.) Why are both the *x*- and *y*-components needed to see the path of the ball? Try to keep students focused on the idea that these equations together track the location of the ball, that is, model the path. This investigation should not become focused on getting answers from the convenient technology, but rather should maintain focus on the idea of modeling motion. Students need to keep thinking about the three variables involved (*t, x, y*) and what the graph and table represent.

1. **a.** The drawing should show a vector with direction 55° and magnitude 12 m. The origin represents the point where the pitcher is standing.

    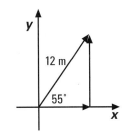

    b. The parametric equations are $X_T = 12T \cos 55°$ and $Y_T = 12T \sin 55°$, where T is measured in seconds.

    c.

    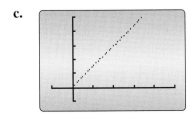
    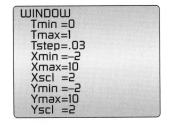

EXPLORE *continued*

d. The model shows the ball continuing to go up at the 55° angle, but you know that it will curve and fall to Earth. This graph of the motion shows what would happen if no additional forces acted on the ball.

2. a. $X_T = 12T \cos 55°$

$Y_T = 12T \sin 55° + 4.9T^2 \sin(-90°) = 12T \sin 55° - 4.9T^2$

b.

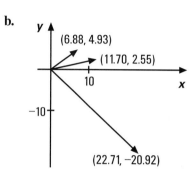

- After 1 second, the ball is located at (6.88, 4.93).

- After 1.7 seconds, the ball is located at (11.70, 2.55).

- After 3.3 seconds, according to the model, the ball is located at (22.71, −20.92). Actually, the location of the ball after 3.3 seconds cannot be determined since it hit the ground before 3.3 seconds.

c. For the path of the ball, see the screen shown below.

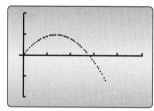

```
WINDOW
 Tmin =0
 Tmax=2.5
 Tstep=.05
 Xmin =-1
 Xmax=25
 Xscl =5
 Ymin =-10
 Ymax=10
 Yscl =5
```

- The ball is in the air for about 2 seconds.

- The maximum height is about 4.93 m after about 1 second.

d. Yes, the ball will make it to the plate. It goes about 13.8 m horizontally before hitting the ground.

e. This model does not account for the fact that the ball is released above ground level and in front of the pitching rubber. It also does not take into account the effect of wind.

3. a. Responses may vary. A reasonable estimate is about 1 m. The new equation would be $X_{1T} = 12T \cos 55°$ and $Y_{1T} = 12T \sin 55° - 4.9T^2 + 1$.

b. Responses may vary. A reasonable estimate is about 1.5 meters. The new equation would be $X_T = 12T \cos 55° + 1.5$ and $Y_T = 12T \sin 55° - 4.9T^2 + 1$.

EXPLORE *continued*

c. Responses will depend on the constants chosen in Parts a and b. Using the equations in Part b, the ball is about 3.0 m high (well above any batter's head) when it crosses the plate. This is not a strike.

d. With an initial velocity of 11.3 m/s, the ball is about 1 m high as it crosses the plate. Students will probably need to change the initial velocity and then look at the table or graph until they get an initial velocity that will satisfy the conditions.

e. An angle of 67° gets the ball over the plate at about 1.5 m. (T = 2.4, X ≈ 13.7, Y ≈ 1.5) A release angle of 67.5° also works. If you want to throw it without so much height, an angle of 22° will also work. (However, pitches at this angle are usually easier to hit.)

f. Small changes in either the angle or the initial velocity cause substantial change in the height of the ball when it crosses the plate.

4. a. $X_T = 45T \cos 14° + 2$
        $Y_T = 45T \sin 14° - 16T^2 + 3$

    b. The horseshoe is in the air for about 0.89 second. This can be determined by solving $Y_T = 0$ (using the quadratic formula) or tracing the graph or looking at a table of values to find the T-value when $Y_T = 0$.

c. The horseshoe hits the ground at about 40.9 ft if the stake is not in the way. (At 40 ft it is about 4 in. above the ground.)

d. If he changes to 13°, his pitch is short by nearly a foot. Changing to 15° makes the horseshoe hit the ground at about 42 ft if the stake is not in the way. The height of the horseshoe when it reaches the stake is about 0.94 ft, so the horseshoe might catch the stake.

5. a. The parametric equations that model this situation are $X_T = 40T \cos 29°$ and $Y_T = 40T \sin 29° - 4.9T^2 + 1$. Yes, it will be a home run. It is over 7 m high when it has traveled 125 m horizontally.

    b. The ball is in the air about 4 seconds.

    c. The ball travels approximately 140 m horizontally.

    d. The maximum height of the ball is approximately 20.2 m.

    e. The ball would travel approximately 146 m horizontally.

6. a. $X_T = 150T \cos 30°$
        $Y_T = 150T \sin 30° - 16T^2$

    b. The ball is in the air about 4.7 seconds. Students may use the graph, the table, or algebraic reasoning to find this value.

    c. The ball travels approximately 610 ft horizontally (approximately 203 yd). Adding the 30 to 50 yd run, the total drive length is approximately 233 to 253 yd.

EXPLORE *continued*

d. A 5° improvement in angle drives the ball about 660 ft horizontally. A 5 ft/sec increase in velocity yields 650 ft drives. Thus, either would be useful, but changing the angle is slightly better than changing the speed. However, it is probably easier to swing a little faster than to change the angle of attack using a driver.

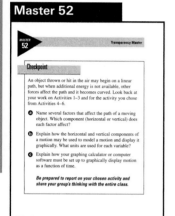

Master 52

CONSTRUCTING A MATH TOOLKIT: Students should provide for themselves one example of parametric equations which model projectile motion.

SHARE AND SUMMARIZE **full-class discussion**

Checkpoint

See Teaching Master 52.

ⓐ Gravity, initial velocity, angle of release, and initial release location all affect the path of a moving object.

initial velocity: both

angle of initial vector: both

gravity: vertical component

initial horizontal distance: horizontal component

initial height: vertical component

ⓑ The components give the parametric equations that model the motion and permit the motion to be displayed graphically using a third variable t to compute x and y independently. The variable t is a measure of time, and x and y are horizontal and vertical measures of distance such as meters, miles, or inches.

ⓒ You must use parametric mode and enter equations for both X_T and Y_T as functions of T.

APPLY **individual task**

▶**On Your Own**

a. $X_T = 2.3T \cos 85°$
$Y_T = 2.3T \sin 85° - 4.9T^2 + 10$

b. Louisa is in the air about 1.68 seconds. This can be determined by solving $2.3T \sin (85°) - 4.9T^2 + 10 = 0$ for T, from the graph, or from the table of values.

c. The maximum height is about 10.27 m after 0.23 second, so she starts moving back toward the water when her feet are about 0.27 m above the platform.

Unit 2

APPLY *continued*

d. She moves about 0.34 m horizontally before hitting the water. This can be found by sub-stituting 1.68, the amount of time Louisa is in the air, for T in X_T.

e. When Louisa is level with the platform (when $Y_T = 10$), she is about 0.094 m or about 9.4 cm from the end of the platform. This value can be found by solving $Y_T = 10$ for T ($T = 0.4676$) and substituting that T value into X_T. It can also be found by looking at a table of values or by tracing the graph.

f. If the push-off angle is changed to 80°, the diver will pass the platform about 0.18 m or 18 cm from the end of it. Students need to find the value of X_T when $Y_T = 10$, $X_T = 2.3T \cos 80°$, and $Y_T = 2.3T \sin 80° - 4.9T^2 + 10$. Using symbolic reasoning, they can solve $Y_T = 10$ for T and then substitute that value of T, 0.4622, into X_T, to get approximately 0.18 m. They could also find this distance by looking at a table of values or by tracing the graph.

MORE

ASSIGNMENT *pp. 127–133*

Students can now begin Modeling Task 1, 2, 3, or 4; or Reflecting Task 2 from the MORE assignment following Investigation 4.

EXPLORE small-group investigation

INVESTIGATION 3 Representing Circles and Arcs Parametrically

This investigation introduces circular motion. Students can use their knowledge of vector components to give the coordinates of any point on the circular path, but they have to realize that the length of the vector is constant, while the direction is variable. Thus, the equations they have been using, $x = At \cos θ$ and $y = At \sin θ$, where $θ$ is constant and At varies with time, are no longer appropriate. Activity 1 introduces this idea. Let your students struggle with this shift in thinking about what the variables are when they are asked to enter their parametric equations for circular motion on a calculator (Activity 1 Part e). Once this big idea has been under-stood, Activities 2–4 deal with the technicalities of how to choose window settings to make variations on the circular path. Teaching Master 53 and 54 can be dupli-cated for student use in completing Activity 3.

1. a. $\overrightarrow{OP}$ is 6 cm long.

   b. The direction of $\overrightarrow{OP}$ is $θ$.

   c. The horizontal component of $\overrightarrow{OP}$ is $6 \cos θ$. The vertical component of $\overrightarrow{OP}$ is $6 \sin θ$.

   d. $x = 6 \cos θ$, $y = 6 \sin θ$
   In parametric mode, these will be displayed on a calculator with T in place of $θ$. By the time students complete Activity 2, where they need to set the T values for various portions of a circle, they should be comfortable with moving between $θ$ and T for parametric circular motion.

EXPLORE *continued*

e. The appearance of the students' graphs depends on the window used. If students say that "nothing happened" or "I didn't get a complete circle," they should check their mode and be sure that Tmax and Tstep are set appropriately. The mode should be degrees and Tmax should be at least 360. A Tstep = 5 works well.

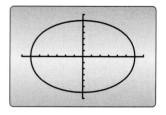

The graph may look oval rather than circular. Students should recognize that on a TI calculator, selecting ZSquare from the (ZOOM) menu will make the displayed graph look circular.

f. The variable T is the measure of $\angle AOP$ or the direction of $\overrightarrow{OP}$. The smallest Tmax needed to produce a complete circle is 360 since there are 360° in one revolution of a circle. If the student is using radians, the smallest Tmax is 2π.

2. In all the following graphs, a square viewing window has been used to ensure that the circle part is "circular." The calculator is set in degree and connected mode. The only window values displayed below are for T.

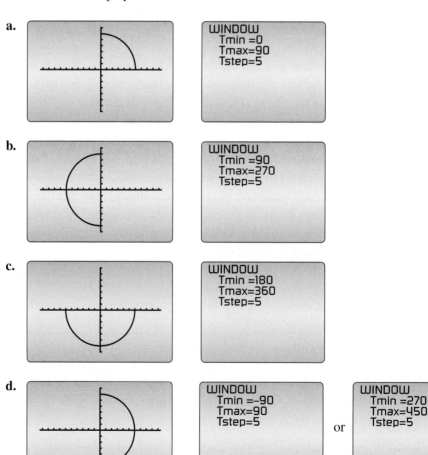

a.
```
WINDOW
 Tmin =0
 Tmax=90
 Tstep=5
```

b.
```
WINDOW
 Tmin =90
 Tmax=270
 Tstep=5
```

c.
```
WINDOW
 Tmin =180
 Tmax=360
 Tstep=5
```

d.
```
WINDOW
 Tmin =-90
 Tmax=90
 Tstep=5
```
or
```
WINDOW
 Tmin =270
 Tmax=450
 Tstep=5
```

EXPLORE *continued*

e.

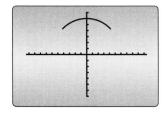

```
WINDOW
 Tmin =45
 Tmax=135
 Tstep=5
```

f. Responses will vary.

See Teaching Masters 53 and 54.

3. **You may wish to supply Master 54 to allow students to check their work.**

a.

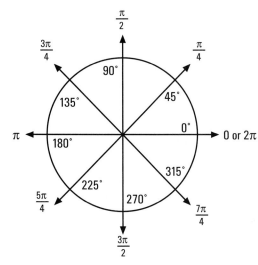

b.

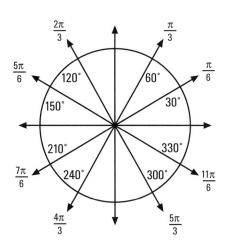

Master 53

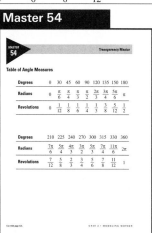

c.

Degrees	0	30	45	60	90	120	135	150	180	210	225	240	270	300	315	330	360
Radians	0	$\frac{\pi}{6}$	$\frac{\pi}{4}$	$\frac{\pi}{3}$	$\frac{\pi}{2}$	$\frac{2\pi}{3}$	$\frac{3\pi}{4}$	$\frac{5\pi}{6}$	π	$\frac{7\pi}{6}$	$\frac{5\pi}{4}$	$\frac{4\pi}{3}$	$\frac{3\pi}{2}$	$\frac{5\pi}{3}$	$\frac{7\pi}{4}$	$\frac{11\pi}{6}$	2π
Revolutions	0	$\frac{1}{12}$	$\frac{1}{8}$	$\frac{1}{6}$	$\frac{1}{4}$	$\frac{1}{3}$	$\frac{3}{8}$	$\frac{5}{12}$	$\frac{1}{2}$	$\frac{7}{12}$	$\frac{5}{8}$	$\frac{2}{3}$	$\frac{3}{4}$	$\frac{5}{6}$	$\frac{7}{8}$	$\frac{11}{12}$	1

4. Student graphs will not be smooth. Choosing a smaller increment for t (**Tstep**) may help them to look smoother.

a. The equations should be $x = 6 \cos \theta$ and $y = 6 \sin \theta$, which should be entered as $X_T = 6 \cos T$ and $Y_T = 6 \sin T$. These are the same equations as those in Activity 1, although t values need to be set differently. Use a square viewing window.

Master 54

EXPLORE *continued*

b.

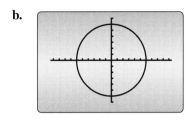

WINDOW
  Tmin =0
  Tmax=2π
  Tstep=.05

c.

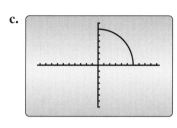

WINDOW
  Tmin =0
  Tmax=π/2
  Tstep=.05

d.

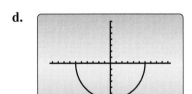

WINDOW
  Tmin =π
  Tmax=2π
  Tstep=.05

e.

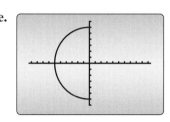

WINDOW
  Tmin =π/2
  Tmax=3π/2
  Tstep=.05

f.

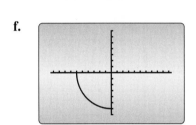

WINDOW
  Tmin =π
  Tmax=3π/2
  Tstep=.05

g.

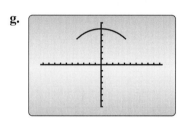

WINDOW
  Tmin =π/4
  Tmax=3π/4
  Tstep=.05

h. **Using the** Tmin **and** Tmax **as indicated in Parts c–g, all of the graphs were drawn in a counterclockwise direction. Students may come up with a variety of ways to draw these graphs in a clockwise direction. Discussion at the Checkpoint on page 126 should focus on changing the equation by using the opposite direction for the angle. Other methods need only arise if students initiate the method.**

Two ways to draw the graphs clockwise would be to use the equations $X_T = 6 \cos T$ and $Y_T = -6 \sin T$ or $X_T = 6 \cos (-T)$ and $Y_T = 6 \sin (-T)$ and adjust the T values as needed to obtain sections of the circle for Parts c–g. For Part c, $\frac{3\pi}{2} \leq t \leq 2\pi$; for Part d, $0 \leq t \leq \pi$; Part e, $\frac{\pi}{2} \leq t \leq \frac{3\pi}{2}$; for Part f, $\frac{\pi}{2} \leq t \leq \pi$; for Part g, $\frac{5\pi}{4} \leq t \leq \frac{7\pi}{4}$. Other representations are possible. For example, Part d could be represented in $X_T = -6 \cos T$ and $Y_T = 6 \sin T$ using the same window as before.

A third way that students familiar with computer programming might mention is to interchange the Tmin and Tmax values and the opposite of the Tstep.

SHARE AND SUMMARIZE full-class discussion

Checkpoint

Master 55

See Teaching Master 55.

Before going on to investigate the situation where rate of change of the angle is also modeled, students need to be comfortable with the idea that the angle is now a variable and that you have been calling this *t* in our parametric equations.

ⓐ The first pair of equations gives a line, the second a circle. The variable, *t*, is acted upon by the trigonometric functions in the equations for the circle. This is not the case for the line.

ⓑ For the line, "3" represents the velocity of the moving object. For the circle, "3" represents the radius of the circle.

ⓒ For the line, "*t*" represents a unit of time. For the circle, "*t*" represents an angle measure.

APPLY individual task

▶On Your Own

Turning the axes off allows for a better view of the dots. The windows below are set to eliminate the repetition of the last point which would occur if the Tmax were 360° or 2π.

$X_T = 8 \cos T$
$Y_T = 8 \sin T$

a. Tstep $= \frac{360}{42} \approx 8.571428...$

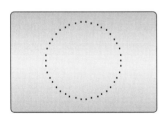

```
WINDOW
 Tmin =0
 Tmax=355
 Tstep=8.571428...
 Xmin =-13
 Xmax=13
 Xscl =1
 Ymin =-8.574468...
 Ymax=8.574468...
 Yscl =1
```

b. Tstep $= \frac{2\pi}{25} \approx 0.251327...$

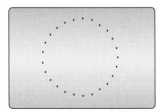

```
WINDOW
 Tmin =0
 Tmax=6.2
 Tstep=.251327...
 Xmin =-13
 Xmax=13
 Xscl =1
 Ymin =-8.574468...
 Ymax=8.574468...
 Yscl =1
```

MORE
ASSIGNMENT *pp. 127–133*

Students can now begin Organizing Task 5 or Reflecting Task 5 from the MORE assignment following Investigation 4.

Unit 2

INVESTIGATION 4 Simulating Orbits

Activity 1 will probably be challenging for students. In Investigation 3, students have become comfortable thinking of *t* as the angle size in *x* = *a* cos *t* and *y* = *a* sin *t*, but now they are about to be asked to shift back to thinking about *t* as time. Consider doing Activity 1 as a large group, and collecting the answers for Part b in a table.

θ is a constant multiple of *t*, so the equations for *x* = *a* cos θ and *y* = *a* sin θ, where θ is a variable and *a* is fixed, can be rewritten to show the angle in terms of the angular velocity. Once students are comfortable with this switch in representation, Activities 2–4 should be accessible to students working in groups. Activity 3 adjusts the starting position on the circle. As students are working on this, you can remind them that they have seen this transformation many times: the graph of *y* = *f*(*x* + *a*) is the same graph as *y* = *f*(*x*) but translated horizontally. The situation is more complicated this time since *t* is not the horizontal axis, but the idea is the same. Activity 4 revisits the effect of a vertical translation: *y* = *f*(*x*) + *b*.

1. **a.** Eight revolutions translates into 8 · 360° = 2,880 degrees per second and 8 · 2π = 16π radians per second.

    b.

Time (seconds)	Angle (degrees)	Angle (radians)
$\frac{1}{100}$	28.8	0.16π
$\frac{1}{50}$	57.6	0.32π
$\frac{1}{10}$	288	1.6π

c. The location of *P* when the angle is in degrees is given by *x* = 2.25 cos 2,880*t* and *y* = 2.25 sin 2,880*t*. The location of *P* when the angle is in radians is given by *x* = 2.25 cos 16π*t* and *y* = 2.25 sin 16π*t*.

d. The variable *t* represents time in seconds. Angular velocity multiplied by time gives the measure of an angle. This measure describes the number of degrees or radians through which a point on the circle has rotated in the elapsed time (0 to *t*).

e. The point rotates around the circle eight times. This makes sense because the *t* values are set for 1 second and the angular velocity is 8 revolutions per second.

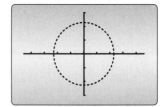

f. Exactly one revolution occurs when the angle, 16πT, goes from 0 to 2π. Thus, T will need to be limited to the interval from 0 to $\frac{1}{8}$ since 16π · $\frac{1}{8}$ = 2π. To make two revolutions, let T range from 0 to $\frac{1}{4}$, and to make it go around three times, 0 ≤ T ≤ $\frac{3}{8}$.

If students use the connected mode, they may need to lower the **Tstep** or increase the **Tmax** slightly to get a complete circle because the last dot must be exactly at an angle of 2π or beyond 2π.

TECHNOLOGY NOTE: It is sometimes helpful to graph parametric equations using the path (-0) style, found to the left of the equations in the **Y=** menu. With this graph style, a circular cursor traces the leading edge of the graph as it is being drawn.

Unit 2

EXPLORE *continued*

g. It looks like the graph is a ring being filled out as the point goes around.

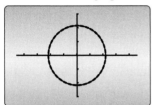

2. Be sure to allow students time to explore different **Tsteps**. Turning the axes off and using the TRACE feature should assist their investigations.

a. Equilateral Triangle

b. Hexagon

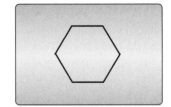

c. Eight-pointed star

d. Twelve-pointed star

e. Graphs will vary. You may wish to have some discussion of the patterns produced. The choice of **Tstep** forces the calculator to graph only a fixed number of points and the connected mode draws the lines between them, as they are plotted.

3. **a.** At $t = 0$, the components are $x = 7 \cos \frac{2\pi}{3} = -3.5$ and $y = 7 \sin \frac{2\pi}{3} \approx 6.06$. The direction is $\frac{2\pi}{3}$; the length is 7 units. This can be determined by interpreting the equations for x and y when $t = 0$.

b. For $t = 0.1$, $x = 7 \cos \left(0.5\pi + \frac{2\pi}{3} \right) \approx -6.06$ and $y = 7 \sin \left(0.5\pi + \frac{2\pi}{3} \right) = -3.5$.

For $t = 0.2$, $x = 7 \cos \left(1.0\pi + \frac{2\pi}{3} \right) = 3.5$ and $y = 7 \sin \left(1.0\pi + \frac{2\pi}{3} \right) \approx -6.06$.

For $t = 0.3$, $x = 7 \cos \left(1.5\pi + \frac{2\pi}{3} \right) \approx 6.06$ and $y = 7 \sin \left(1.5\pi + \frac{2\pi}{3} \right) = 3.5$.

For $t = 0.4$, $x = 7 \cos \left(2.0\pi + \frac{2\pi}{3} \right) = -3.5$ and $y = 7 \sin \left(2.0\pi + \frac{2\pi}{3} \right) \approx 6.06$.

t	x	y
0.1	−6.06	−3.5
0.2	3.5	−6.06
0.3	6.06	3.5
0.4	−3.5	6.06

c. Students should see point P moving around a circle with radius 7.

Unit 2

EXPLORE *continued*

d. Since you want $5\pi \cdot$ Tmax $= 2\pi$, setting Tmax $= \frac{2}{5}$ will graph one revolution.

e. The angular velocities and radii of the circles are different, but the form of the equation is the major difference. These parametric equations have a constant added to the angle on which the trigonometric function operates. This means that the starting and ending point for one revolution is approximately (−3.5, 6.06), rather than a point on the positive *x*-axis.

4. a. For these equations, the center of the circle will be at (0, 24) and the radius will be 20 ft. These correspond to the center and radius of the Ferris wheel. Also, when *t* = 1 minute, the point will have made exactly one revolution.

b. The window is shown at the right. **Tmax** was chosen to be 1 so that one revolution (2π) would be shown. **Tstep** was chosen small enough for the circle to be fairly well-defined. **Xmin** = −25 and **Xmax** = 25 were chosen to be able to accommodate the 20 ft radius of the Ferris wheel. **Ymax** = 50 was chosen because the highest point of the wheel will be 44 ft above the ground.

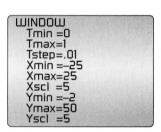

After plotting the graph, **ZSquare** was used to make the graph look circular. That graph and the resulting window settings are shown below.

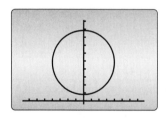 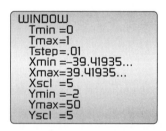

c. When *t* = 0, the point is located at 3 o'clock, or even with the center of the wheel and on the right-hand side. The coordinates of the point are (20, 24).

d. After 0.1 minute, the 3 o'clock seat is approximately 35.8 ft above the ground. After 0.5 minute, the seat is 24 ft above the ground. After 0.75 minute, the seat is 4 ft above the ground. These heights can be found by evaluating *y* for the appropriate *t* values.

e. They are similar to those in Activity 1, but have a constant term, 24, added to the *y*-component. They are similar to those for Activity 3, but have no constant angle added and do have a constant added to the *y*-component.

5. a. The coefficient on the *x*-component should be larger than the coefficient on the *y*-component. One example is $x = 12 \cos 2\pi t$ and $y = 8 \sin 2\pi t$.

b. Responses may vary. One pair of equations is $x = 8 \cos 2\pi t$ and $y = 12 \sin 2\pi t$.

c. $x = 10 \cos 2\pi t$ and $y = 5 \sin 2\pi t$

EXPLORE *continued*

    d. $x = 10 \cos (2\pi t \pm \pi)$
           $y = 5 \sin (2\pi t \pm \pi)$

6. **a.** The path is circular with a radius of 4 units. It will make 1 revolution for 2π units of time, and the revolution will start at the point (4, 0).

    b. $x = 4 \cos t + 2$
         $y = 4 \sin t + 1$

    c. $x = 4 \cos (-t)$ or $x = 4 \cos t$
         $y = 4 \sin (-t)$ $y = -4 \sin t$

    d. $x = 4 \cos \left(t + \frac{\pi}{2}\right)$
         $y = 4 \sin \left(t + \frac{\pi}{2}\right)$

    e. $x = 8 \cos t$
         $y = 2 \sin t$

    f. $x = 8 \cos (-t \pm \pi)$
         $y = 2 \sin (-t \pm \pi)$

SHARE AND SUMMARIZE   full-class discussion

Checkpoint

See Teaching Master 56.

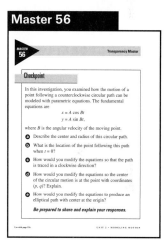

Master 56

  ⓐ The center is at the origin and the radius is A units.

  ⓑ When $t = 0$, the moving point is at $(A, 0)$.

  ⓒ Equations modeling clockwise circular motion are

      $x = A \cos (-Bt)$
      $y = A \sin (-Bt)$

  ⓓ The parametric equations would be

      $x = A \cos Bt + p$
      $y = A \sin Bt + q$.

    Since this is a shift, p units in the x direction and q units in the y direction, of the center of the circle, p is added to the x-component, and q is added to the y-component. Another way to say this is that the moving point is located by the sum of two vectors, one with components p and q and the other with components $A \cos Bt$ and $A \sin Bt$.

  ⓔ Equations modeling elliptical paths would be of the form:

      $x = A \cos Bt$
      $y = C \sin Bt$, where $A \neq C$.

CONSTRUCTING A MATH TOOLKIT: Students should provide an example of parametric equations that model circular and elliptical motion. Then, they should compare these equations to those previously provided for linear and projectile motion and explain what the constants and variable t mean for each pair of equations.

APPLY individual task

▶**On Your Own**

a.

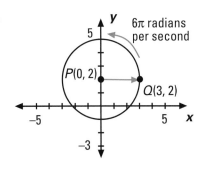

b. $x = 3 \cos 6\pi t$ and $y = 3 \sin 6\pi t + 2$

When $t = 0.1$, the coordinates of Q are approximately $(-0.93, 4.85)$.

When $t = 0.5$, the coordinates of Q are $(-3, 2)$.

c. To make one revolution, $6\pi t$ must have a maximum value of 2π, so $6\pi \cdot$ **Tmax** $= 2\pi$. Thus, **Tmax** $= \frac{2\pi}{6\pi} = \frac{1}{3}$.

d. Responses will vary. One possible window setting is given here.

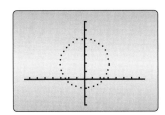

```
WINDOW
  Tmin =0
  Tmax=.333333...
  Tstep=.01
  Xmin =-7.580645...
  Xmax=7.580645...
  Xscl =1
  Ymin =-3
  Ymax=7
  Yscl =1
```

MORE
ASSIGNMENT *pp. 127–133*

Modeling: Choose two from
1–4, and 5*
Organizing: 1, 4, and 5
Reflecting: 2, 3, and 5
Extending: 3 or 4, and 5*

*When choice is indicated, it is impor-
tant to leave the choice to the student.
NOTE: It is best if Organizing tasks are
discussed as a whole class after they
have been assigned as homework.*

MORE independent assignment

Modeling

1. a. The arrow should be shot at an angle of elevation of about 4.1°. However, this part of the task asks students to estimate based on experience or common sense, so responses will vary. The estimate is revised in Part d.

b. The angle measure used in the equation should match the estimate from Part a. The x- and y-components for an angle of 4.1° are $x = 150t \cos 4.1°$ and $y = 150t \sin 4.1° - 16t^2$.

MORE *continued*

c. Responses will vary and depend on the estimate in Part a. Using 4.1°, the arrow will hit the target near the bull's eye after about $\frac{2}{3}$ second. If the student's angle is greater than 4.1°, the arrow will be too high, and if the angle is less than 4.1°, the arrow will fall short.

d. The angle should be close to 4.1°. (A more precise value is 4.088°.)

2. a. A dart thrown with an initial velocity of 20 ft/sec will hit the bull's eye. To get this result, students will need to consider parametric equations of the form $x = At \cos 20°$ and $y = At \sin 20° - 16t^2$. If $A = 20$, then when $x = 8$, $y \approx 0$. Thus, parametric equations modeling this situation are

$$x = 20t \cos 20°$$
$$y = 20t \sin 20° - 16t^2$$

b. This dart is in the air for about 0.43 second. Solving $20t \sin 20° - 16t^2 = 0$ gives $t \approx 0.43$. Students may also use tables to obtain their answers.

c. If she throws the dart at an angle of about 8.25°, she will hit the bull's eye. Students will likely adjust the angle and check the tables until they obtain $x \approx 8$ and $y \approx 0$. Answers should be close to 8.25°.

d. Using an angle of 8.25°, the equations are $x = 30t \cos 8.25°$ and $y = 30t \sin 8.25° - 16t^2$. Using these equations, her dart is in the air for about 0.27 second.

3. a. See student sketches. The release point is most likely about 5 ft above the field. Pitchers are still on the mound but release somewhere around waist high.

b. Students first need to change 100 mph into feet per second.

$$\frac{100 \text{ mi}}{1 \text{ hour}} \cdot \frac{5,280 \text{ ft}}{1 \text{ mi}} \cdot \frac{1 \text{ hour}}{3,600 \text{ sec}} \approx 146.7 \text{ ft/sec}$$

Parametric equations that model this situation are $x = 146.7t \cos \theta + 4$ and $y = 146.7t \sin \theta - 16t^2 + 5$, with θ measured in degrees. If the ball is pitched at an angle of $-0.8°$, it will be approximately 2 ft high when it has traveled the remaining 55 ft to the plate. That is, if $\theta = -0.8$, then when $x \approx 59$, $y \approx 2$.

c. $x = 146.7t \cos (-3.2°) + 4$ and $y = 146.7t \sin (-3.2°) + 5$

■ Wood releases the ball on a path 3.2° below horizontal ($-3.2°$).
■ It takes about 0.375 second for the ball to get to the plate.

4. a. Parametric equations for this situation are $x = 650t \cos 0°$ and $y = 650t \sin 0° - 16t^2 + 5$. Under these conditions, the dart does not hit the gorilla since it hits the ground after approximately 0.56 second have passed and it has traveled approximately 364 ft.

b. Responses may vary. One possible set of parametric equations is $x = 650t \cos 0.8°$ and $y = 650t \sin 0.8° - 16t^2 + 5$. With this angle the dart will be about 4.5 ft above the ground when it gets to the gorilla.

MORE *continued*

c. She has about a 0.4°-range, from 0.86° to 0.45°, in choosing her angle at which to shoot.

5. a. Two revolutions per second for a 5-cm radius pulley rotates a 2-cm pulley at $\left(\frac{5}{2} \cdot 2\right) = 5$ revolutions per second. (This is equal to 10π radians per second.)

b. The position of *A* is (x, y), where $x = 5 \cos 4\pi t$ and $y = 5 \sin 4\pi t$.

c. The position of *C* is (x, y), where $x = 2 \cos 10\pi t + 10$ and $y = 2 \sin 10\pi t$.

d.

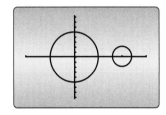

```
WINDOW
 Tmin =0
 Tmax=.5
 Tstep=.002
 Xmin =−10
 Xmax=15
 Xscl =5
 Ymin =−8.244680...
 Ymax=8.244680...
 Yscl =1
```

e. In order for circle *O* to be traced only once, set **Tmax = 0.5**. Each revolution of circle *B* takes $\frac{1}{5}$ of a second, and $\frac{0.5}{0.2} = 2.5$, so the circle at *B* is traced $2\frac{1}{2}$ times.

f. Circle *B* will complete 1 revolution in $\frac{1}{5} = 0.2$ second, so set **Tmax = 0.2**. Only $\frac{0.2}{0.5} = \frac{2}{5}$ of circle *O* is traced.

Organizing

1. a. $y = 3t + 2$

b. Yes, the graph is a line.

c. Depending on the values set for **Tmin**, **Tmax**, and **Tstep**, the parametric display may look like a line segment. Setting **Tmin = −5**, **Tmax = 5**, and **Tstep = 0.1**, will make the two representations look the same in the given viewing window.

Some students may argue that it is impossible to make the graphs look the same. This happens because the calculator actually evaluates the functions differently. In the function mode, you do not get to choose the *x* values that are used to graph the line, but in parametric mode you do get to choose the T values. One way to see that they are the same is to look at the tables using identical setups. On some TI calculators, ZDecimal in Function mode lets each pixel on the screen have *x* values that differ by 0.1. Looking at a table in this setting should give the same values as looking at a table of the parametric equations in Part a using Tstep = 0.1. This will show that the points are the same on the two lines.

MORE *continued*

Also, you may wish to discuss the fact that two graphs that do not look the same may be the same graph and two graphs that do look the same may not be the same. This can be demonstrated by graphing the same function in different windows.

2. **a.** If t is allowed to vary over all values, the graph of each pair of equations is a line with slope 2 and y-intercept -3. The graph of each is the same line, but they may "start" at different places, depending on Tmin value.

   b. When $t = 1$, the x and y values for the two sets of equations are $(1, -1)$ and $(4, 5)$ respectively. The points are different, but they are on the same line and occur at the same time, $t = 1$.

   c. In the first set of equations, if $t = 0$, then $x = 0$ and $y = -3$. By substituting 0 for x in $x = 2t + 2$, you get $0 = 2t + 2$ or $t = -1$. Substituting $t = -1$ in $y = 4t + 1$ will give $y = -3$ in the second set of equations. Thus, $t = -1$ gives the point $(0, -3)$ in both sets of equations.

3. **a.** They are the same line.

   b. For the first, x changes at the same rate as t does, while y changes at twice that rate. For the second, x changes at 3 times the rate of t, while y changes at 6 times the rate of t.

   c. For the first pair of equations, t changes at the same rate that x does and at half the rate that y does. For the second pair of equations, t changes at $\frac{1}{3}$ the rate that x does and at $\frac{1}{6}$ the rate that y does.

   d. In each case, take the rate of change of y with respect to t and divide by the rate of change of x with respect to t. This tells us that y changes at twice the rate of x. (You may want to have students graph both sets of equations and trace back and forth between them for several values of t. They can compare the changes in x, y, and t.)

   e. The points in the second graph move at three times the rate of the points of the first graph. This can also be observed by tracing.

4. **a.** To find the slope of the line, divide the rate of the change of y with respect to t by the rate of the change of x with respect to t.

   i. The slope is $\frac{3}{2}$.

   ii. The slope is $-\frac{2}{3}$.

   iii. The slope is $-\frac{1}{2}$.

   iv. The slope is $\frac{b}{a}$.

   b. To get a single equation that expresses y as a function of x, solve for t in the equation that includes x and substitute the expression for t into the equation for y.

   i. $y = \frac{3}{2}x$

MORE *continued*

    ii. $y = -\frac{2}{3}x$

    iii. $y = -\left(\frac{x-1}{2}\right) - 2$ or $y = -\frac{1}{2}x - \frac{3}{2}$

    iv. $y = \frac{b}{a}x$

5. **a.** 1 radian

    b. Arc *AB* to arc *CD*, magnitude = 2

    Arc *AB* to arc *EF*, magnitude = 3.5

    Arc *AB* to arc *GH*, magnitude = 5

    c. Arc *CD* has length 2 units.

    Arc *EF* has length 3.5 units.

    Arc *GH* has length 5 units.

    d. Responses will vary. Since the angle at *O* is fixed, the arcs are multiples of the length of arc *AB*. Each arc is the same length as the radius of its circle.

Reflecting

1. The ball would go farther on the Moon because the effect of gravity is less on the Moon. On the other hand, it may be a bit more cumbersome because of the spacesuit you would need to wear to stay alive.

2. **a.** The graph is more helpful when visualizing the path of the object.

    b. Both the graph and the table are helpful in finding the maximum height. Individuals may prefer one over the other.

    c. Both the graph and the table are helpful in finding the horizontal distance. Individuals may prefer one over the other.

    d. The graph is more helpful when looking for vertical velocity that is equal to 0. It occurs at the same time that the maximum height is reached. Students who are thinking of vertical velocity as a change in height might look at the table to see if there is ever a time when height is not changing. It may help to note that in order to go from positive to negative velocity, the velocity had to be 0.

3. **a.** The variable *A* is the velocity of the object. The variable θ is the direction of the motion.

    b. Change the equation for the *x*-component to $x = At \cos \theta + 4$.

    c. Change the equation for the *y*-component to $y = At \sin \theta - 3$.

Unit 2

MORE *continued*

4. They define approximately the same motion because $3 \cos 42° \approx 2.2294$ and $3 \sin 42° \approx 2.0074$.

5. The radian is larger than the degree, and thus the numbers you work with are smaller. For example, 90° is about 1.57 radians. That may have been more important at the time of the quotation (before the invention of scientific calculators in the early 1970s) than it is in our technological age.

   Another consideration might be that if circular motion is being compared with the circumference of the circle, the irrational number π could be used directly in both contexts, introducing less error. Thus, if radians are used, the linear velocity of a point on the edge of a rotating circle is the radius of the circle multiplied by the angular velocity of the rotation. If degrees are used, the relationship would involve π and 360°.

Extending

1. **a.** Line: $y = x + 1$

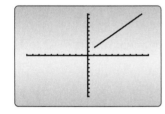

```
WINDOW
 Tmin =0
 Tmax=10
 Tstep=.1
 Xmin =–10
 Xmax=10
 Xscl =1
 Ymin =–0
 Ymax=10
 Yscl =1
```

   b. Line: $y = -\frac{1}{3}x + \frac{17}{3}$

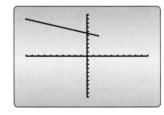

```
WINDOW
 Tmin =0
 Tmax=10
 Tstep=.1
 Xmin =–10
 Xmax=10
 Xscl =1
 Ymin =–10
 Ymax=10
 Yscl =1
```

   c. Inverse power model: $y = \frac{3}{x}$. Note: This window is set from **Tmin = –10** to **Tmax = 10** to display both branches of the function.

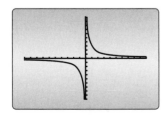

```
WINDOW
 Tmin =–10
 Tmax=10
 Tstep=.1
 Xmin =–10
 Xmax=10
 Xscl =1
 Ymin =–10
 Ymax=10
 Yscl =1
```

Unit 2

MORE *continued*

d. Circle: $x^2 + y^2 = 16$

The method used for combining equations used in Organizing Task 4 and the other parts of this task won't work here. Students should recall the equation of a circle with radius 4. Another method, using symbolic reasoning follows:

$$\begin{aligned} x^2 + y^2 &= (4 \cos t)^2 + (4 \sin t)^2 \\ &= 16 \cos^2 t + 16 \sin^2 t \\ &= 16(\cos^2 t + \sin^2 t) \\ &= 16 \cdot 1 \\ x^2 + y^2 &= 16 \end{aligned}$$

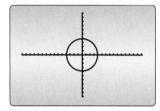 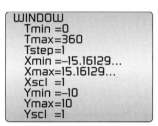

```
WINDOW
  Tmin =0
  Tmax=360
  Tstep=1
  Xmin =-15.16129...
  Xmax=15.16129...
  Xscl =1
  Ymin =-10
  Ymax=10
  Yscl =1
```

e. Parabola: $y = \frac{x^2}{2} + 2x + 2$. Note: Setting the window from **Tmin = -2** to **Tmax = 2** will display both sides of the parabola.

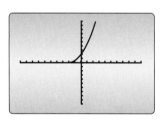 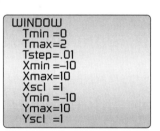

```
WINDOW
  Tmin =0
  Tmax=2
  Tstep=.01
  Xmin =-10
  Xmax=10
  Xscl =1
  Ymin =-10
  Ymax=10
  Yscl =1
```

2. a. Students need to realize that the ball hits the ground 235 yd or 705 ft from the tee. Using the equations $x = At \cos 27°$ and $y = At \sin 27° - 16t^2$ and substituting values for A, they can determine that the speed must be approximately 167 ft/sec. Students may choose to reason algebraically as follows.

   The ball hits the ground when $x = 705$, so $At = \frac{705}{\cos 27°} \approx 791.24$. When the ball hits the ground, $y = 0$, so

   $$0 \approx 791.24 \sin 27° - 16t^2$$
   $$16t^2 \approx 359.22$$
   $$t^2 \approx 22.45$$
   $$t \approx 4.74 \text{ seconds,}$$

   and $A = \frac{791}{4.74} \approx 167$ ft/sec.

   b. The ball reaches its maximum height halfway through its flight (at the vertex of the parabola) or after about 2.37 seconds. When $t = 2.37$, y is approximately 89.8 ft, so the maximum height of the ball is approximately 89.8 ft.

   c. The ball is in the air for about 4.74 seconds.

MORE *continued*

3. This solution positions Memphis at the origin.

a. A 307° heading is the same as a 143° direction, and a 260° heading is the same as a 190° direction. A northwest wind has direction −45°.

Memphis to Seattle: $x = 600t \cos 143° + 70t \cos (−45°)$
$y = 600t \sin 143° + 70t \sin (−45°)$

Detroit to L.A.: $x = 600t \cos 190° + 70t \cos (−45°) + 400$
$y = 600t \sin 190° + 70t \sin (−45°) + 500$

b. Let $t = 1$. Memphis: $x = 600 \cos 143° − 70 \cos (−45°) = −528.7$
$y = 600 \sin 143° − 70 \sin (−45°) = 410.6$
$\tan \theta = \frac{410.6}{528.7}$
$\theta = 37.8°$

The direction is $180° − 37.8° = 142.2°$; the heading is $270° + 37.8° = 307.8°$.

Let $t = 1$. Detroit: $x = 600 \cos 190° − 70 \cos (−45°) = −640.4$
$y = 600 \sin 190° − 70 \sin (−45°) = −54.7$
$\tan \theta = \frac{−54.7}{−640.4}$
$\theta = 4.9°$

The direction is $180° + 4.9° = 184.9°$; the heading is $270° − 4.9° = 265.1°$.

c. Memphis: The direction is 142.2° and the plane is flying at 600 mph in still air. Therefore, in t hours the path of the airplane is described by the vector

$x = 600t \cos 142.2° + 70t \cos (−45°) = −424.6t$ and
$y = 600t \sin 142.2° + 70t \sin (−45°) = 318.2t$.

The length of the vector then determines the effective speed of the plane. This is $\sqrt{424.6^2 + 318.2^2} \approx 530.6$ mph.

Detroit: The direction is 184.9° so the vector is

$x = 600t \cos 184.9° + 70t \cos (−45°) = −548.3t$
$y = 600t \sin 184.9° + 70t \sin (−45°) = −100.7t$.

Letting $t = 1$, the effective speed is $\sqrt{548.3^2 + 100.7^2} \approx 557.5$ mph.

d. The paths do intersect. By tracing the functions

$X_{1T} = −424.6T$ and $X_{2T} = −548.3T + 400$
$Y_{1T} = 318.2T$ and $Y_{2T} = −100.7T + 500$

you will find that the common point has coordinates of about (−455, 340). The airplanes will not collide however, because they are at the point at different times. The Memphis airplane is at (−455, 340) at $t \approx 1.07$ hours and the Detroit airplane is at (−455, 340) at $t \approx 1.56$ hours.

Unit 2

MORE *continued*

e. The plane traveling from Memphis to Seattle has an effective speed of 530.6 mph so it will take $\frac{1,800}{530.6} \approx 3.39$ hours. The plane traveling from Detroit to Los Angeles has an effective speed of 557.5 mph, so it will take $\frac{2,000}{557.5} \approx 3.59$ hours.

4. a. Parametric equations for the locations of the two ships are

Mystic Star: $x = 8t \sin 280° + 20$ and $y = 8t \cos 280°$

Queensland: $x = 10t \sin 70° - 15$ and $y = 10t \cos 70° - 4$

b.

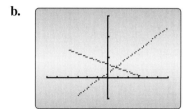
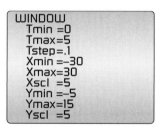

```
WINDOW
 Tmin =0
 Tmax=5
 Tstep=.1
 Xmin =-30
 Xmax=30
 Xscl =5
 Ymin =-5
 Ymax=15
 Yscl =5
```

c. The paths cross, but this does not necessarily indicate that the freighters collide, since they could reach the location where the paths cross at different times.

d. At $t = 2.05$, the *Mystic Star* crosses the path of the *Queensland*. At that time, the *Mystic Star* is at (3.85, 2.85). The *Queensland* has already passed this point and is at (4.26, 3.01). Students may argue that if the length of either freighter is greater than $3.01 - 2.85 = 0.16$ unit, there could be a collision.

At $t = 2.00$, the *Queensland* crosses the path of the *Mystic Star*. At that time, the *Queensland* is at (3.79, 2.84), while the *Mystic Star* is at (4.24, 2.78). The *Mystic Star* has not yet crossed the path of the *Queensland*.

Depending on the scales they select for their graphs, students may need to discuss just how far apart the ships actually are in nautical miles.

Tracing in the window at the right shows that the ships are actually closest together at $t = 2.02$, when the x values are 4.08 and 3.98. Look at the units of $8t$ and $10t$ to decide if this is a problem.

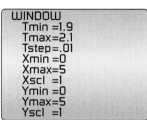

```
WINDOW
 Tmin =1.9
 Tmax=2.1
 Tstep=.01
 Xmin =0
 Xmax=5
 Xscl =1
 Ymin =0
 Ymax=5
 Yscl =1
```

5. a. Earth: $x = 4,000 \cos t$
$y = 4,000 \sin t$

Space Station: The distance between the x-intercepts of the ellipse is 400 mi + 4,000 mi + 4,000 mi + 200 mi = 8,600 mi, so the distance from the center of the ellipse to each x-intercept is 4,300 mi. The center of the circle (Earth) is 100 mi to the right of the center of the ellipse. Therefore, the parametric equations are: $x = 4,300 \cos t - 100$ and $y = 4,298.8 \sin t$

MORE *continued*

b. The graph of the two sets of equations is shown at the right. This is an opportunity for students to verify that their equations are correct.

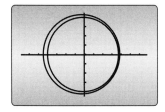

```
WINDOW
 Tmin =0
 Tmax=6.283185...
 Tstep=.1
 Xmin =-6670.967...
 Xmax=6670.9677...
 Xscl =1000
 Ymin =-4400
 Ymax=4400
 Yscl =1000
```

See Assessment Resources pages 50–55.

REVIEW AND PRACTICE individual task

▶**PUMP**

Answers

1. **(d)**   6. **(e)**

2. **(a)**   7. **(c)**

3. **(e)**   8. **(b)**

4. **(d)**   9. **(a)**

5. **(b)**   10. **(a)**

Assessments 50–52

Assessments 53–55

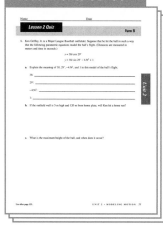

Lesson 3 *Looking Back*

SYNTHESIZE UNIT IDEAS small-group activity

1. **a.** See sketch for Part c.

    b. See sketch for Part c.

    c.

    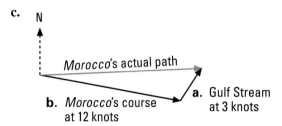

    d. Current:

    east: $3 \cos 55° = 3 \sin 35°$
    north: $3 \sin 55° = 3 \cos 35°$

    Desired course:

    east: $12 \cos 10° = 12 \sin 80°$
    north: $-12 \sin 10° = 12 \cos 80°$

    Amended course:

    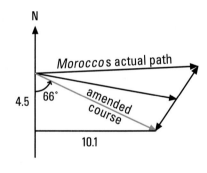

    east: $12 \cos 10° - 3 \cos 55° \approx 10.1$
    north: $-12 \sin 10° - 3 \sin 55° \approx -4.5$
    $\tan^{-1}\left(\frac{10.1}{4.5}\right) \approx 66°$

    The course should be set at a heading of $180° - 66° = 114°$.

    e. The rate the boat must use in order to follow the amended course is $\sqrt{10.1^2 + 4.5^2} \approx$ 11.1 knots. Then, the combination of the amended course and the current allows the boat to travel at 12 knots. Assuming that the Gulf Stream is 50 nm wide in the direction of the course, it will take $\frac{50}{12} = 4\frac{1}{6}$ hours to cross.

2. **a.** The equations are

$$X_{1T} = 20T \quad \text{and} \quad X_{2T} = 30(T - 0.5)$$
$$Y_{1T} = 1 \qquad\qquad Y_{2T} = 2$$

SYNTHESIZE *continued*

   b. The second robocarrier reaches the end of the test track first at $T = \frac{10}{3}$ or $3\frac{1}{3}$ minutes. At that time, the first robocarrier is $18\frac{1}{3}$ m from the end of the track.

   c. Yes, the second robocarrier overtakes the first. This happens when $30(T - 0.5) = 20T$ or $T = 1.5$ minutes after the first robocarrier started.

   d. Responses will vary. Students could choose to adjust the speed of one or of both robocarriers. One possible solution occurs when the speed of the first robocarrier is increased to 25.5 m/min. This can be found by solving for a speed for X_{1T} that results in the first robocarrier reaching 85 m when $T = \frac{10}{3}$ minutes, the time that the second robocarrier reaches the end of the track.

3. **a.** See student sketches.

   b. $x = At \cos 25°$ and $y = At \sin 25° - 16t^2$, where A is the initial velocity of the ball.

   c. It is necessary to find A such that the x-component is 600 ft (200 yards) at the same time that the y-component is 0 ft. Students may do this algebraically or by guessing an initial value for A and then using the graph or table of values and revising their guess until the requirements are satisfied. She will need to hit the ball so that the initial velocity is about 158.3 ft/sec.

   d. The ball will be in the air for about 4.18 seconds.

   e. A 5 mph wind is 7.3 ft/sec, so the wind will add $7.3t$ to the x-component. If she hits the ball at 158.3 ft/sec, it will travel a distance of $158.3(4.18) \cos 25° + 7.3(4.18) \approx 630.2$ ft ≈ 210 yd. The total distance including the roll will be 240 yd.

   f. The y-component will now be $y = 158.3t \sin 25° - 16t^2 + 30$. Using symbolic reasoning, the graph, or a table of values, it can be determined that the ball will be in the air for about 4.59 seconds. In this amount of time, the ball will travel about 658 ft or 219.3 yd. Adding the 30 yd roll gives a total distance of 249.3 yd.

4. **a.** $\frac{54,000}{30} = 1,800$ seconds of film will fit on a side of a CAV.

     $\frac{1,800}{60} = 30$ minutes of film on a side

     One hour, 59 minutes (119 minutes) would take both sides of two 12-inch laserdiscs (4 sides).

     An alternate solution:

         $7,140 \times 30 = 214,200$ frames are needed for the picture.

         $\frac{214,200}{54,000} \approx 3.97$ sides, or approximately two laserdiscs are needed.

   b. 1,800 rpm = 30 revolutions per second = 60π radians per second or $30 \times 360° = 10,800$ degrees per second

   c. $x = 4.5 \cos 60\pi t$ and $y = 4.5 \sin 60\pi t$ in radian mode.
      $x = 4.5 \cos 10,800t$ and $y = 4.5 \sin 10,800t$ in degree mode.

Unit 2

SYNTHESIZE *continued*

5. Students may choose a constant velocity or represent the velocity with a parameter.

    a. $x = 5$
            $y = -2At$

    b. There are many possibilities. Three are given here.

    $x = t$ $x = 4t - 2$ $x = At \cos{(-56.3°)} + 2$
    $y = -\frac{3}{2}t + 7$ $y = -6t + 10$ $y = At \sin{(-56.3°)} + 4$

    c. $x = -5 \sin t$ or $x = 5 \cos{(t + 90°)}$
            $y = 5 \cos t$ $y = 5 \sin{(t + 90°)}$

    d. $x = 8 \cos At$
            $y = 12 \sin At$, and $A > 0$

    e. To trace clockwise, use $x = -5 \sin{(-t)}$ and $y = 5 \cos{(-t)}$, or $x = 5 \cos{(-t + 90°)}$ and $y = 5 \sin{(-t + 90°)}$. Let $A < 0$ for the ellipse.

6. The first choice that needs to be made in this problem is how to set up the coordinate system that will be used to help model these motions. Using this coordinate system, the center of the wheel is located at (20, 20); when $T = 0$, point A is at (40, 20); the ball is thrown from (95, 0).

    Equations that model the two motions are

    Friend: $X_F = 20 \cos 30T + 20$
              $Y_F = 20 \sin 30T + 20$

    Ball: $X_B = 60T \cos 120° + 95$
              $Y_B = 60T \sin 120° - 16T^2$

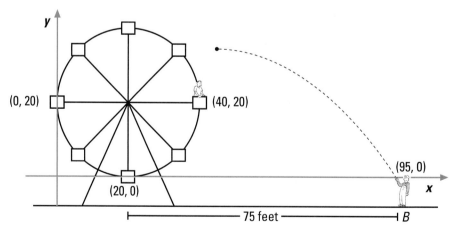

Students may trace the graphs and observe that the ball and the friend are very close at around $T = 2.2$. Symbolically, the distance formula can be used to write a rule giving distance as a function of time. This rule is $d = \sqrt{(x_B - x_F)^2 + (y_B - y_F)^2} =$
$\sqrt{((60T \cos 120° + 95) - (20 \cos 30T + 20))^2 + ((60T \sin 120° - 16T^2) - (20 \sin 30T + 20))^2}$.

SYNTHESIZE *continued*

Entering this equation in the ⎡Y=⎤ menu and graphing the function will give the following graph.

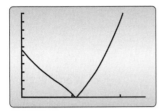
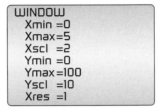

```
WINDOW
 Xmin =0
 Xmax=5
 Xscl =2
 Ymin =0
 Ymax=100
 Yscl =10
 Xres =1
```

The minimum point on this graph is (2.185, 1.5789), so the closest the ball gets to the person is approximately 1.579 ft approximately 2.185 seconds after it is thrown.

SHARE AND SUMMARIZE   full-class discussion

Checkpoint

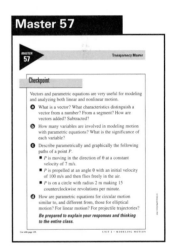

Master 57

See Teaching Master 57.

ⓐ A vector is a mathematical representation of a direction and a magnitude (length). A number has no direction. A segment has a position defined by its endpoints, while a vector of a given length and direction may be represented in multiple locations.

    Vectors are added by drawing the second vector from the terminal point of the first one. The sum is the vector that begins at the initial point of the first and ends at the terminal point of the second. Another way to add two vectors is to add their components. $\vec{v}$ is subtracted from $\vec{u}$ by adding the vector with the same magnitude but opposite direction of $\vec{v}$ to $\vec{u}$: $\vec{u} - \vec{v} = \vec{u} + (-\vec{v})$.

ⓑ Three variables are needed to model motion using parametric equations. Two give the horizontal and vertical locations of a point and the third, t, is the independent variable, usually representing time or angle measure.

ⓒ ■ $x = 7t \cos \theta$ and $y = 7t \sin \theta$
    The path is linear and makes an angle of θ with the positive x-axis.

   ■ $x = 100t \cos \theta$ and $y = 100t \sin \theta - 4.9t^2$
    The path is parabolic.

   ■ $x = 2 \cos 30\pi t$ and $y = 2 \sin 30\pi t$
    The path is circular with radius 2, beginning at (2, 0) when $t = 0$.

SYNTHESIZE *continued*

d Parametric equations for circular motion have the same constant coefficient for both *x*- and *y*-equations. For elliptical motion, these constants are different.

Parametric equations for circular motion differ from linear motion by having a variable angle rather than a constant angle.

Parametric equations for circular motion are not affected by gravity as projectile motion is. Thus, parametric equations for projectile motion must have the vertical component adjusted by $-4.9t^2$ or $-16t^2$. In addition, parametric equations for projectile motion have a constant angle, whereas parametric equations for circular motion have a variable angle.

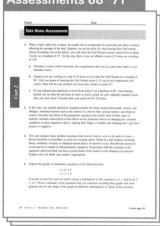

APPLY individual task

On Your Own

See Teaching Masters 58a–58c.

Responses will vary. Above all, this should be something that is useful to the individual student. You may wish to have students use the Teaching Masters 58a–58c, the "Modeling Motion" Unit Summary, to help them organize the information.

See Assessment Resources pages 56–71.

Unit 2

Looking Back, Looking Ahead

This unit introduced a new way to think about points in the plane—as position vectors with the tail at the origin and the head at the point. This way of thinking is especially powerful since it permits modeling situations in which both direction and magnitude are important. Thus, this work relates to physics as well as to the pure mathematical topic of vectors and operations on vectors.

Vectors are useful in representing both linear motion and nonlinear motion. The importance of the Pythagorean Theorem and trigonometric functions are clearly evident as one analyzes the motion created by throwing a dart, shooting an arrow, or hitting a golf ball. The same tools are also useful in the representation of circular motion and elliptical motion.

Looking ahead to more advanced mathematics courses, vectors, studied here in two dimensions, are also useful in three or more dimensions. At the college level, students who take courses in linear algebra study "vector spaces," which include as elementary examples two- and three-dimensional vectors. The trigonometric functions used in "Modeling Motion" are studied more fully in Unit 7, "Functions and Symbolic Reasoning." In that unit, students will model periodic behavior with trigonometric functions, solve trigonometric equations, and study the relationships among the various trigonometric functions. Trigonometric functions are a major tool in modeling complex periodic motion when they are used in conjunction with elementary operations to form Fourier series representations.

Unit 2 Assessment

Logarithmic Functions and Data Models

UNIT OVERVIEW The main goal of this unit is to introduce students to the common logarithmic function and its applications, including logarithmic scales and linearizing data. Logarithmic functions are introduced as inverses of exponential functions first studied in Course 1. In order for this introduction to be meaningful, the concepts and skills associated with function inverse are developed first.

The idea of an inverse of a function f is introduced in Lesson 1 as a "reversing" function that maps the range elements of f to the corresponding domain elements of f. Conditions for a function to have an inverse are examined. Graphical representation is highlighted to establish the geometric relationship between the graph of a function and that of its inverse (if it exists) and, in particular, the role of reflection across the line $y = x$ in graphing inverses of functions. Applying the transformation $(x, y) \rightarrow (y, x)$ provides an algebraic method for determining the equation of an inverse function.

In Lesson 2, logarithmic functions are introduced as the inverses of exponential functions. Logarithmic notation is introduced and used; graphs are studied; conversions between exponential and logarithmic representations are investigated; rules for computing logarithms of products, quotients, and powers are developed; and logarithms are used to solve exponential equations. Logarithmic scales are introduced to illustrate that multiplicative scales can sometimes be more useful than linear scales.

Since it is easier to identify a linear pattern than a nonlinear pattern in a set of data, methods for linearizing data are introduced in Lesson 3. Both semi-log transformations $(x, log\ y)$ and log-log transformations $(log\ x, log\ y)$ of data are studied.

Only the common logarithm is studied in detail in this unit. In Unit 7, "Functions and Symbolic Reasoning," logarithms are revisited and the natural logarithm is introduced.

Unit 3 Objectives

- To explore, understand, and represent inverse relationships in algebraic and numerical settings
- To understand when a function has an inverse
- To produce and use inverses for $y = ax + b$ and $y = a(b^x)$
- To understand the inverse relationship between logarithms and exponents, and to use this relationship to simplify complex computations and solve exponential equations
- To linearize bivariate (x, y) data by transforming one or both variables
- To use linearizing as a tool in finding an appropriate model for bivariate data

Unit 3

Unit 3 Planning Guide

Lesson Objectives	Assignments	Suggested Pacing	Materials
Lesson 1 *Inverses of Functions* • To be able to examine the graph, equation, or table for a function and to determine whether or not the function has an inverse • To know how to find the inverse of a linear function, and to describe relationships between the representations (equations, tables, and graphs) of the original function and its inverse • To be able to graph the composite of a function and its inverse and explain the nature of that graph	**MORE** **after page 147** Students can begin Organizing Task 1 or 5 or Reflecting Task 1 or 2 from p. 150. **page 150** **Modeling:** 1 or 2, and 3 or 4* **Organizing:** 1, 2, and 5 **Reflecting:** 1, 2, and 3 **Extending:** 3 or 4, and 5* **PUMP** pages 156–157	**Path A:** 5 days **Path B:** 6 days	• Graph paper • Teaching Resources 59–63 • Assessment Resources 77–82
Lesson 2 *Logarithmic Functions* • To know and be able to use the definition of a logarithm • To know and be able to use properties of logarithms • To be able to solve exponential equations using logarithms • To be able to set up and use logarithmic scales • To understand why logarithmic scales are useful and how they compare to linear scales	**MORE** **after page 164** Students can begin Organizing Task 1 or 5, Reflecting Task 1, or Extending Task 4 from p. 173. **after page 168** Students can begin Modeling Task 1 or 2, Organizing Task 2 or 3, Reflecting Task 2, or Extending Task 2 from page 173. **page 173** **Modeling:** 1 or 2, and 3 or 4* **Organizing:** 1, 2, 3, and 5 **Reflecting:** 1, 2, and 3 **Extending:** 2, 4, and choice of one* **PUMP** pages 178–179	**Path A:** 9 days **Path B:** 11 days	• Graph paper • Semi-log graph paper • Teaching Resources 64–69 • Assessment Resources 83–90
Lesson 3 *Linearizing Data* • To understand the importance of linearization and how to transform data in order to linearize it • To understand and apply the procedure for fitting non-linear functions to data • To review least squares linear regression	**MORE** **after page 185** Students can begin Modeling Task 3 or 4, Organizing Task 1, Reflecting Task 1 or 4, or Extending Task 2 or 3 from page 190. **page 190** **Modeling:** 2 and choice of one* **Organizing:** 1, 3 or 4, and 5* **Reflecting:** 1, 2, and 3 **Extending:** 2, and 3 or 4* **PUMP** pages 196–197 **MORE** **page 203** **Modeling:** Choose two* **Organizing:** 1, 2, and 4 **Reflecting:** 4 and choice of one* **Extending:** 1 and choice of one* **PUMP** pages 208–209	**Path A:** 7 days **Path B:** 9 days	• Teaching Resources 70–74 • Assessment Resources 91–96
Lesson 4 *Looking Back* • To review and test the major objectives of the unit		**Path A:** 3 days **Path B:** 3 days	• Teaching Resources 75–77 • Assessment Resources 97–113

* *When choice is indicated, it is important to leave the choice to the student.*
Note: *It is best if Organizing tasks are discussed as a whole class after they have been assigned as homework.*

Lesson **1** *Inverses of Functions*

LESSON OVERVIEW The two investigations in this lesson are designed to develop the concept of an inverse of a function. Investigation 1 introduces the concept of inverse functions by first examining tables of function values. Then the conditions defining an inverse function are made explicit. Students investigate the characteristics of graphs and tables of functions that ensure a function has an inverse. Investigation 2 explores the relationship between the graph of a function and that of its inverse and introduces a method for finding an equation of the inverse by using a geometric transformation. This method is applied to linear functions, but is equally applicable for other functions that have inverses, such as $y = x^3$. In Lesson 2, the logarithmic function will be introduced as the inverse of the exponential function.

Lesson Objectives

- To be able to examine the graph, equation, or table for a function and to determine whether or not the function has an inverse
- To know how to find the inverse of a linear function, and to describe relationships between the representations (equations, tables, and graphs) of the original function and its inverse
- To be able to graph the composite of a function and its inverse and explain the nature of that graph

Unit 3

Master 59

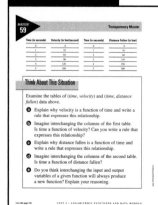

LAUNCH full-class discussion

Think About This Situation

See Teaching Master 59.

a *Velocity* is a function of *time* because at each time, the drop bag can have only one velocity. The rule for the relationship is $v = f(t) = 32t$.

b From the table, it appears that *time* is a function of *velocity*. This makes sense because the velocity will continue to increase, so there won't be any velocity that occurs at more than one time. The rule for this relationship is $t = \frac{v}{32}$ or $t = \frac{1}{32}v$.

c *Distance fallen* is a function of *time* because for each time, there is only one distance. The equation is $d = 16t^2$.

LAUNCH *continued*

d Yes, *time* is a function of *distance fallen*. The distance fallen is increasing and so for each distance, there is only one time. Students may volunteer that the equation is $t = \frac{1}{4}\sqrt{d}$.

e No. For example, consider these points on the graph of $y = x^2$: $(-2, 4)$, $(-1, 1)$, $(0, 0)$, $(1, 1)$, and $(2, 4)$. Interchanging x and y does not yield a function, as $f(4) = -2$ and $f(4) = 2$. If students do not recognize this at this time, it will become apparant as they work through Investigation 1.

EXPLORE small-group investigation

INVESTIGATION 1 When Does a Function Have an Inverse?

This investigation is designed to get students to explore when a function has an inverse and to evaluate $f^{-1}(x)$ for specific values of x, from graphs, tables, and equations. Functions represented as graphs, tables, and equations are examined to determine when the function has an inverse. Students should be able to do the investigation with little assistance. The Checkpoint discussion for this investigation is very important.

1. **a.** $f(3) = 96$. This means that after 3 seconds, the drop bag has velocity 96 ft/sec.

   b. $f^{-1}(160) = 5$. So, at 5 seconds, the drop bag has velocity of 160 ft/sec.

   c. $g(4) = 256$. So, after 4 seconds, the drop bag has fallen a total distance of 256 ft.

   d. $g^{-1}(64) = 2$. So, the time at which the total distance fallen is 64 feet is 2 seconds.

2. If g^{-1} is an inverse of a function g, then (i) the domain of g^{-1} is the range of g, (ii) the range of g^{-1} is the domain of g, and (iii) $g^{-1}(r) = q$ if and only if $g(q) = r$.

   Condition ii implies that the domain of g is the range of g^{-1}. Condition i implies that the range of g is the domain of g^{-1}. From Condition iii, it follows that $g(q) = r$ if and only if $g^{-1}(r) = q$. Hence, the function g satisfies the three conditions to be an inverse of g^{-1}.

3. **a.** The range (as well as the domain) of f is all real numbers. Since each element p in the domain of f is mapped to exactly one element in the range of f, $32p$, an inverse for f exists that maps $32p$ back to p, by the rule $f^{-1}(x) = \frac{x}{32}$. This rule defines a function whose domain and range are all real numbers.

   b. The range of $g(x)$ is all nonnegative real numbers. The function $g(x) = x^2$ does not have an inverse function since reversing the correspondence $x \xrightarrow{\;g\;} x^2$ would map range elements back to more than one element in the domain. For example, since $g(1) = 16$ and $g(-1) = 16$, $g^{-1}(16)$ would have to have two values, 1 and -1, but then it wouldn't be a function.

Unit 3

EXPLORE *continued*

4. The functions whose graphs are shown in Parts a, e, and h have inverses since each element in the domain is mapped to a different range value. In each case, the correspondence $x \xrightarrow{f} y$ can be reversed to form an inverse function, where the domain of the inverse is the range of the graphed function and the range of the inverse is the domain of the graphed function.

   The functions whose graphs are shown in Parts b, c, d, f, and g do not have inverses because some domain values are mapped to the same range values. The relation formed by reversing the correspondence $x \xrightarrow{f} y$ will not be a function.

NOTE: As you monitor student's work, be sure they are using all real numbers as the domain for $y = |x|$.

---

5. A function f has an inverse if for each y value, there is exactly one x value such that $f(x) = y$. This means that you will not see any y value used more than one time. This condition is not satisfied for functions that do not have inverses. The function $y = |x|$ does not have an inverse. For example, $y = 2$ occurs on the graph of $y = |x|$ in two places, at $(-2, 2)$ and at $(2, 2)$. (See Organizing Task 1 on page 152 for horizontal line test.)

6. If a function f is one-to-one, then for each r in the range there is a unique q in the domain of the function, such that $f(q) = r$. Thus, the inverse will be the function f^{-1}, where the domain of f^{-1} is the range of f and the range of f^{-1} is the domain of f, such that $f^{-1}(r) = q$.

   If an inverse exists for a function f, f must be a one-to-one function, otherwise you would not be able to determine how to map r in the range of f to q in the domain of f. There would be values in the range of f that would be paired with more than one value from the domain of f, thus reversing the correspondence would not yield a function.

7. **a.** From the equation, students might reason as follows: The range of $T(x)$ is $0 < T(x) \leq 5.625$. For any r in this range, $r = \frac{450}{x}$ has solution $x = \frac{450}{r}$. So, there will exist exactly one x value such that $T(x) = r$. Thus, $T(x)$ has an inverse.

   From the graph, students will see that there is exactly one x value such that $T(x) = r$.

   b. ■ $T^{-1}(7.5) = 60$. This means that a trip that takes 7.5 hours will have an average speed of 60 mph.

   ■ $T(50) = 9$. This means that at an average speed of 50 mph, the trip will take 9 hours.

   ■ $T^{-1}(9.375) = 48$. This means that a trip that takes 9.375 hours will have an average speed of 48 mph.

   ■ $T^{-1}(7.03125) = 64$. This means that a trip that takes 7.03125 hours will have an average speed of 64 mph.

8. **a.** Since the function g is a one-to-one function (for each value of $g(x)$, there is exactly one corresponding value of x in the table), g has an inverse.

   b. ■ $g^{-1}(-3) = 0$ ■ $g^{-1}(5) = 4$ ■ $g^{-1}(-9) = -3$ ■ $g^{-1}(1) = 2$

   c. Student tables should have a duplicate number in the $g(x)$ row.

EXPLORE *continued*

9. **a.** $g^{-1}(g(0)) = g^{-1}(-3) = 0$ and $g(g^{-1}(1)) = g(2) = 1$

   b. ■ $g^{-1}(g(3)) = g^{-1}(3) = 3$ ■ $g^{-1}(g(-4)) = g^{-1}(-11) = -4$

   ■ $g(g^{-1}(-5)) = g(-1) = -5$ ■ $g(g^{-1}(5)) = g(4) = 5$

NOTE: The typical definition of an inverse function is the statement in the student text following Activity 9. You may wish to have students extend the diagram to include $f^{-1}(f(x))$.

10. **a.** The domain of f^{-1} is the same as the range of f. The range of f^{-1} is the same as the domain of f.

   b. If (p, q) is on the graph, then $f(p) = q$. Thus, $f^{-1}(q) = p$. But, this means that (q, p) is on the graph of f^{-1}.

   c. For any (p, q) on the graph of $f(x)$, $q = 2p + 6$. Solving for p, $q - 6 = 2p$ and $\frac{1}{2}q - 3 = p$. Thus, $(q, \frac{1}{2}q - 3)$ must be on the graph of the inverse. But this means that $f^{-1}(x) = \frac{1}{2}x - 3$. (Some students may directly show that $f^{-1}(f(x)) = x$ and $f(f^{-1}(x)) = x$ using $f(x) = 2x + 6$ and $f^{-1}(x) = \frac{1}{2}x - 3$. This method is fully developed in Investigation 2.)

SHARE AND SUMMARIZE   full-class discussion

Checkpoint

Master 60

See Teaching Master 60.

ⓐ The graph must be that of a one-to-one function: for each value of y there is a unique value of x. This means that you would not see any y value more than once on the graph. (This can be determined from a graph of the function by using the horizontal line test described in Organizing Task 1 on page 152. If the function is continuous, it has an inverse if and only if it is always increasing or always decreasing.)

ⓑ For every value of y, there is only one value of x such that $f(x) = y$. There will be no duplicate y values in the table. (You may wish to assign Extending Task 4 on page 155 to have students think about the inverses of the sine and cosine functions.)

ⓒ Non-constant linear and exponential functions are the only families of functions listed for which each member of the family has a unique range value for each domain value. Power, quadratic polynomial, and trigonometric functions are not one-to-one functions.

ⓓ $h^{-1}(8) = -2$
$h^{-1}(0) = 0$
$h^{-1}(h(8)) = 8$

ⓔ A function can have only one inverse function. Assume that there are two inverses for a function f. Call them g and h. Since both g and h are inverses of f, they must have the same domain and range (corresponding to the range and domain of f, respectively). Since for each x in the common domain of g and h, $g(x) = y$ if and only if $f(y) = x$ if and only if $h(x) = y$, it follows that g and h are identical functions.

NOTE: "Always increasing" is not the same as "nondecreasing" or just "increasing." Other ways to express "always increasing" are "strictly increasing" or "monotone increasing."

CONSTRUCTING A MATH TOOLKIT: Students should record how they can determine, from a graph or table of a function, whether or not the function has an inverse.

Unit 3

APPLY individual task

▶ On Your Own

a. Yes, the function has an inverse since each y value is unique, that is, the function is one-to-one; $f^{-1}(2) = 1$.

b. No, the function does not have an inverse because it is not one-to-one. There are many y values for which there are two different x values such that $f(x) = y$. For example, $f(1) = f(-1) = 6.25$.

MORE

ASSIGNMENT *pp. 150–155*

Students can now begin Organizing Task 1 or 5 or Reflecting Task 1 or 2 from the MORE assignment following Investigation 2.

c. Yes, the function has an inverse since it is one-to-one; $f^{-1}(2) = 2$.

d. No, the function does not have an inverse because it is not one-to-one; for example, $f(-1) = f(1) = 1$.

EXPLORE small-group investigation

INVESTIGATION 2 Function Inverses and Their Graphs

This investigation uses linear equations to introduce students to finding the graph of the inverse of a function. Students should learn that corresponding points on the graphs of a function and its inverse are reflections across the line $y = x$. Students also learn how to find the rule for the inverse of a linear function by interchanging x and y and then solving for y.

Most of the activities in this investigation can be completed by students working in small groups. However, you may find it helpful to draw the whole class together after Activity 2 to be sure that everyone has found out that the inverse of a linear function is another linear function, and that the graphs of the two functions are reflections of each other across the line $y = x$. Since the method of finding an inverse function is laid out in the example before Activity 3, you may choose to discuss this example as a class before groups begin Activity 3.

EXPLORE *continued*

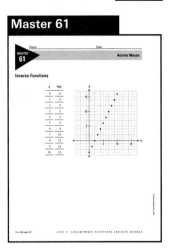

1. **See Teaching Master 61.**

    If your students have a good understanding of reflection across the line $y = x$ and its connection to inverses from previous units and Activity 10 on page 146, you may be able to quickly discuss Activity 1 as a class and have groups begin with Activity 2.

    a. Students should create the graph by plotting the points $(f(x), x)$.

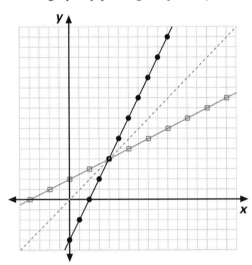

b. $f^{-1}(x) = \frac{1}{2}x + 2$

    Some students will read the slope and y-intercept from the graph. Others may use two points to find the equation of the line.

c. See the graph in Part a.

d. The graph of $y = f^{-1}(x)$ is a reflection of the graph of $y = f(x)$ across the line $y = x$. To provide evidence, students should note that a reflection across $y = x$ uses the rule $(a, b) \rightarrow (b, a)$.

e. Students should choose their own linear equation, find the inverse equation, and verify that the graphs are reflections of each other across the line $y = x$.

f. Sketch the graph of $f(x) = 3x + 1$ and the line $y = x$. Then, reflect the graph of $y = f(x)$ across the line $y = x$. The coordinates of the reflection of the point (x, y) across the line $y = x$ are (y, x). This corresponds to the fact that if the point (x, y) is on a graph of a function, then the point (y, x) is on the graph of its inverse.

Unit 3

EXPLORE *continued*

2. **a.** **i.** 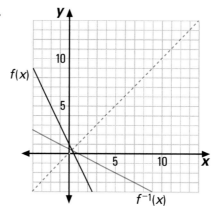 **ii.**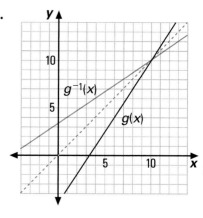

iii.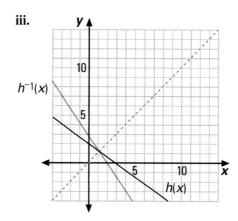

b. To find the rule for the inverse, students will probably need to find two points on the graph of the inverse and use them to write an equation of the line containing those points.

  i. $f^{-1}(x) = -\frac{1}{2}x + \frac{1}{2}$

  ii. $g^{-1}(x) = \frac{2}{3}x + \frac{10}{3}$

  iii. $h^{-1}(x) = -\frac{10}{7}x + \frac{20}{7}$

c. The reflection of a line across the line $y = x$ is always a line.

3. **a.** $f^{-1}(x) = x + 7$

  $f^{-1}(f(x)) = (x - 7) + 7 = x$ and $f(f^{-1}(x)) = (x + 7) - 7 = x$.

  So $f^{-1}(x) = x + 7$ is the inverse of $f(x) = x - 7$.

EXPLORE *continued*

b. $g^{-1}(x) = \frac{x-1}{-2} = -\frac{1}{2}x + \frac{1}{2}$

$g^{-1}(g(x)) = -\frac{1}{2}(-2x + 1) + \frac{1}{2} = x - \frac{1}{2} + \frac{1}{2} = x$ and $g(g^{-1}(x)) = -2\left(-\frac{1}{2}x + \frac{1}{2}\right) + 1 = x$.

So $g^{-1}(x) = -\frac{1}{2}x + \frac{1}{2}$ is the inverse of $g(x) = -2x + 1$.

c. $h^{-1}(x) = 2x + 4$

$h^{-1}(h(x)) = 2\left(\frac{1}{2}x - 2\right) + 4 = x$ and $h(h^{-1}(x)) = \frac{1}{2}(2x + 4) - 2 = x$.

So $h^{-1}(x) = 2x + 4$ is the inverse of $h(x) = \frac{1}{2}x - 2$.

4. a. The input value x is first multiplied by 3 and then 9 is subtracted.

b. To undo these operations, you would add 9 and then divide by 3. The example shows $f^{-1}(x)$ as multiplying by $\frac{1}{3}$ and adding 3. (Students will need to recognize that $\frac{1}{3}x + 3 = \frac{x+9}{3}$.)

c. $f^{-1}(x) = 2(x + 2) = 2x + 4$

$g^{-1}(x) = \frac{x-1}{-2} = -\frac{1}{2}x + \frac{1}{2}$

$h^{-1}(x) = x + 7$

These are the same inverse functions that were found in Activity 3.

5. a. Since $f(x) = x^3$ is one-to-one, the function will have an inverse. Students might also indicate that for every real number r, there is only one value of x such that $x^3 = r$.

b.

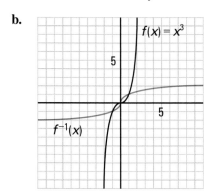

c. $f^{-1}(x) = x^{\frac{1}{3}}$

$f^{-1}(125) = 5$

$f^{-1}(-64) = -4$

d. A power function of the form $g(x) = x^n$, n a positive integer, will have an inverse as long as n is odd. The inverse will be the function $g^{-1}(x) = x^{\frac{1}{n}}$. This function also belongs to the family of power functions. (Students are not as familiar with these power functions as they are with those where the power is a positive integer. However, they did consider these functions in Course 2, Unit 4, "Power Models.")

Unit 3

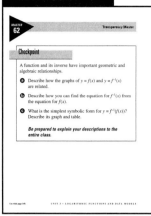

SHARE AND SUMMARIZE full-class discussion

Checkpoint

See Teaching Master 62.

ⓐ The graphs of $y = f(x)$ and $y = f^{-1}(x)$ are reflections of each other across the line $y = x$. If the point (a, b) is on the graph of $y = f(x)$, then the point (b, a) will be on the graph of $y = f^{-1}(x)$.

ⓑ To find an equation for $f^{-1}(x)$, interchange x and y in the equation for $y = f(x)$, then solve for y.

ⓒ $y = x$

The graph of $y = f^{-1}(f(x))$ is the line $y = x$ which contains the points (x, x). In the table, the x and y values are identical.

CONSTRUCTING A MATH TOOLKIT: Students should include a description of how an inverse function "undoes" or "reverses" the effect of the original function. Students should note that geometrically the graph of a function and its inverse are reflections of each other across the line $y = x$. In addition, students should describe how to find the equation of an inverse function and the fact that $f^{-1}(f(x)) = x$.

APPLY individual task

On Your Own

NOTE: More current exchange rates are available at www.xe.net/ucc.

a. If 1 peso = 0.1051 U.S. dollar, then 100 pesos = 100(0.1051) U.S. dollar = 10.51 U.S. dollars.

b. $f(x) = 0.1051x$, where x is the number of pesos and $f(x)$ is the number of U.S. dollars.

c. $f^{-1}(x) = \frac{x}{0.1051} = 9.515x$, where x is the number of U.S. dollars.

d. The inverse tells you that for each U.S. dollar you exchange, you will get 9.515 Mexican pesos. More generally, it tells you how many pesos you will receive for x U.S. dollars.

ASSIGNMENT pp. 150–155

Modeling: 1 or 2, and 3 or 4*
Organizing: 1, 2, and 5
Reflecting: 1, 2, and 3
Extending: 3 or 4, and 5*

*When choice is indicated, it is important to leave the choice to the student.
NOTE: It is best if Organizing tasks are discussed as a whole class after they have been assigned as homework.

MORE independent assignment

Modeling

1. a. $f(32) = -0.8$. This means that if the actual temperature is 32°F and there is a 40 mph wind, it will feel as cold as if the temperature were −0.8°F with no wind.

MORE *continued*

b. Yes, the function $f(T)$ has an inverse. The most straightforward justification is that $f(T)$ is a one-to-one function because of the positive slope, thus it will have an inverse.

c. $f^{-1}(20) = 45$ means that if the wind is blowing at 40 mph and the wind chill temperature is 20°F, then the actual temperature is 45°F.

$f^{-1}(-12) = 25$ means that if the wind is blowing at 40 mph and the wind chill temperature is –12°F, then the actual temperature is 25°F.

Students can determine these values by solving the equations $20 = -52 + 16T$ and $-12 = -52 + 1.6T$.

d. $f^{-1}(T) = \frac{T+52}{1.6} = \frac{T}{1.6} + 32.5$ or $0.625T + 32.5$

e. $f^{-1}(20) = 0.625(20) + 32.5 = 45$

$f^{-1}(-12) = 0.625(-12) + 32.5 = 25$

The answers here should match those in Part c.

2. **a.** $P(625) = 2,812.5$. This means that the theater will make a profit of \$2,812.50 if 625 tickets are sold.

b. The profit function is linear and has a positive slope. Thus, it is a one-to-one function and has an inverse.

c. $P^{-1}(900) = 400$

d. Students can verify this without finding an equation for the inverse: $P(820) = 8.5(820) - 2,500 = 4,470$. This means that if the theater has a daily operating profit of \$4,470, then 820 tickets were sold.

e. $P^{-1}(x) = \frac{x + 2,500}{8.5}$

$P^{-1}(P(450)) = P^{-1}(8.5(450) - 2,500)$

$= P^{-1}(1,325)$

$= \frac{3,825}{8.5} = 450$

3. **a.** $f(x) = \pi x^2$. The domain of this function is all positive real numbers. The graph is shown at the right.

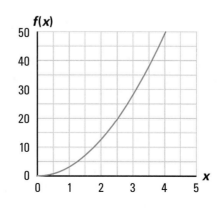

Unit 3

MORE *continued*

b. Yes, the function has an inverse because the domain is restricted to $x \geq 0$, and on this domain the function is one-to-one. The inverse rule is $f^{-1}(x) = \sqrt{\frac{x}{\pi}}$. This rule gives the radius $f^{-1}(x)$ of the circle as a function of the area of the circle, x.

c. The radius of a circle is a function of its area because for each area, there is only one possible radius. As the area increases, the radius must also increase. The rule giving the radius as a function of the area would be helpful if you wanted to know how big a circle to make in order to enclose a given amount of area. Specific contexts suggested by students may vary.

d. If x can be any real number, then $f(x) = \pi x^2$ does not have an inverse since it is not a one-to-one function.

e. $g(x) = \frac{4}{3}\pi x^3$. The domain of this function, for this volume of a sphere context, is all positive real numbers. (If students don't know this formula, encourage them to look in a reference book.) The graph is shown at the right.

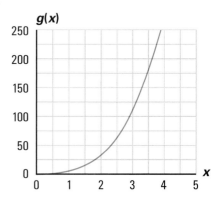

f. Yes, this function has an inverse. The inverse is $g^{-1}(x) = \sqrt[3]{\frac{3x}{4\pi}}$, $x > 0$. This rule gives the radius $g^{-1}(x)$ of the sphere as a function of the volume of the sphere, x.

g. It makes sense that the radius of a sphere is a function of its volume because the greater the volume, the bigger the radius must be. Contexts in which this function would be useful are ones in which you need to know the radius or diameter for a specific volume.

h. Yes, the function $g(x) = \frac{4}{3}\pi x^3$, where x is any real number, has an inverse because it is one-to-one. The only difference between the inverses is that the domain and range are restricted in the volume of a sphere context to all positive real numbers rather than all real numbers.

4. a. The function $B(n) = 2^n$ is one-to-one, so it has an inverse.

b. $B(16) = 2^{16} = 65,536$ represents the number of new branches at Stage 16 of the fractal. $B^{-1}(16)$ represents the stage number for which there are 16 new branches.

c. $B^{-1}(512) = 9$

d. $B^{-1}(128) = 7$

$B^{-1}(32,768) = 15$

MORE *continued*

e.

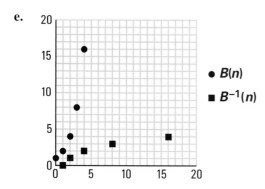

f. The function $y = B^{-1}(n)$ does not belong to one of the basic function families that students have studied. (Students may try an exponential or power regression for these points, but should recognize that they are getting equations that do not contain the exact points and thus are not inverses that map $B(n)$ to n. They will learn that $y = B^{-1}(n)$ belongs to the logarithmic function family in Lesson 2.)

Organizing

1. **a.** In order to have an inverse, g must be a one-to-one function. The two points of intersection indicate that two different input values will give the y value of 9. Therefore, g is not one-to-one, so it does not have an inverse.

b. Only functions i and iii have inverses.

c. If any vertical line crosses a graph in more than one point, then the graph is not the graph of a function because there would be two different y values for a given x value.

2. **a.** $f^{-1}(x) = \frac{1}{3}x + \frac{2}{3}$

$f^{-1}(f(x)) = \frac{1}{3}(3x - 2) + \frac{2}{3} = x$

$f(f^{-1}(x)) = 3\left(\frac{1}{3}x + \frac{2}{3}\right) - 2 = x$

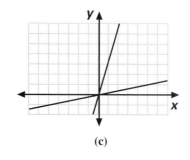

(a)

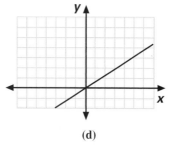

(b)

b. $f^{-1}(x) = -\frac{1}{2}x + \frac{3}{2}$

$f^{-1}(f(x)) = -\frac{1}{2}(-2x + 3) + \frac{3}{2} = x$

$f(f^{-1}(x)) = -2\left(-\frac{1}{2}x + \frac{3}{2}\right) + 3 = x$

c. $f^{-1}(x) = \frac{1}{4}x$

$f^{-1}(f(x)) = \frac{1}{4}(4x) = x$

$f(f^{-1}(x)) = 4\left(\frac{1}{4}x\right) = x$

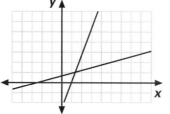

(c)

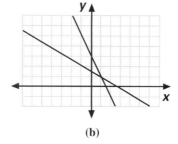

(d)

d. $f^{-1}(x) = x$

$f^{-1}(f(x)) = x$

$f(f^{-1}(x)) = x$

Unit 3

MORE *continued*

3. **a.** The graph of $f(x) = ax$, $a \neq 0$ is a line through the origin that is neither horizontal nor vertical.

   b. The graph of $y = f^{-1}(x)$ is the reflection across the line $y = x$ of the graph of $y = f(x)$. Since $(0, 0)$ is a point on $y = f(x)$, the reflection of $(0, 0)$ across the line $y = x$ is $(0, 0)$. Thus, $y = f^{-1}(x)$ will also contain the origin. Another way to explain this is if $(x, y) = (0, 0)$ is on $f(x)$, then $(y, x) = (0, 0)$ is on $f^{-1}(x)$.

   c. $f^{-1}(x) = \frac{1}{a}x$

   To find the equation for the inverse, some students may use the general procedure described in Investigation 2.

   $f(x) = y = ax$

   $\quad\quad x = ay$ \quad\quad\quad\quad Reflect over the line $y = x$.

   $\quad\quad \frac{1}{a}x = y$ \quad\quad\quad\quad Solve for y.

   Therefore, $f^{-1}(x) = \frac{1}{a}x$.

   Other students may note that to undo multiplying a number x by a, you need to divide by a, so the inverse equation would be $y = \frac{1}{a}x$ or $f^{-1}(x) = \frac{1}{a}x$.

4. **a.** The graph of $f(x) = ax + b$ $(a \neq 0, b \neq 0)$ is a line with y-intercept at $(0, b)$ and slope of a. This is a line that is neither horizontal nor vertical and does not go through the origin.

   b. $f^{-1}(x) = \frac{x - b}{a}$

   To prove that $y = \frac{x - b}{a}$ is the inverse of f, consider $f^{-1}(f(x)) = \frac{(ax + b) - b}{a} = \frac{ax}{a} = x$ and $f(f^{-1}(x)) = a\left(\frac{x - b}{a}\right) + b = x$. Thus, since $f^{-1}(f(x)) = x$ and $f(f^{-1}(x)) = x$, $f^{-1}(x) = \frac{x - b}{a}$.

   c. The two graphs will have a single point in common as long as the lines are not parallel or coincident. They will be parallel or coincident only if the slopes are the same, so the lines will have a single point in common as long as $a \neq \frac{1}{a}$. Since $a = \frac{1}{a}$ if and only if $a = \pm 1$, the graphs will have a single point in common whenever $a \neq \pm 1$.

   d. To find the x-coordinate of the point of intersection, solve the equation $ax + b = \frac{x - b}{a}$ for x. Then substitute to get the y-coordinate. The coordinates are $\left(\frac{b}{1 - a}, \frac{b}{1 - a}\right)$. (If students realize that the common point must lie on the line $y = x$, they can write the coordinates after solving for x and won't need to substitute to find the y-coordinate.)

5. **a.** **i.**

x	–3	–2	–1	0	1	2	3
$f(g(x))$	–8	–4	–3	–7	10	7	8

   ii.

x	–3	–2	–1	0	1	2	3
$g(g(x))$	–2	–3	2	–1	3	0	1

MORE *continued*

   iii. The composite function $g(f(x))$ cannot be found because there are values in the range of $f(x)$ that are not in the domain of $g(x)$. For example, $f(-3) = 10$ and $g(10)$ is not defined by the table, so no value can be determined for $g(f(-3)) = g(10)$.

b.   **i.** $g(-1) = 3(-1) + 4 = 1$, so $f(g(-1)) = f(1) = -1^2 + 7 = 6$

      $f(g(2)) = f(10) = -93$

      $f(g(0.5)) = f(5.5) = -23.25$

      $f(g(8)) = f(28) = -777$

   ii. $f(-1) = -(-1)^2 + 7 = 6$, so $g(f(-1)) = g(6) = 3(6) + 4 = 22$

      $g(f(2)) = g(3) = 13$

      $g(f(0.5)) = g(6.75) = 24.25$

      $g(f(8)) = g(-57) = -167$

c. In order for $f(g(x))$ to make sense, the range of g must be contained in the domain of f. In order for $g(f(x))$ to make sense, the range of f must be contained in the domain of g.

Reflecting

1. **a.** These are inverse actions. The price will return to exactly the same place where it began. Suppose x is the original price of gasoline in cents. The price after the holiday will be $(x + 6) - 6 = x$, the original price.

   b. No, they are not inverse actions because the 6% pre- and post-Memorial Day adjustments were not calculated on the same price per gallon. The pre-Memorial Day increase was smaller than the post-Memorial Day decrease. The customers came out slightly ahead. If x is the original price, then the price after the holiday will be $(0.94x)(1.06) = 0.9964x$.

2. **a.** Inverse: Clockwise rotation of 60° about the origin

     This is the inverse because a clockwise rotation undoes a counterclockwise rotation of the same angle.

   b. Inverse: Translation with horizontal and vertical components −3 and 4 respectively

     To demonstrate that this is the inverse, first apply the given translation to a point (x, y). This gives the point $(x + 3, y - 4)$. Now apply the translation with components −3 and 4 to that point. This gives the point $(x + 3 - 3, y - 4 + 4) = (x, y)$, which is the original point.

MORE *continued*

   c. Inverse: Size transformation with magnitude $\frac{1}{4}$ and center at the origin

      The original size transformation maps the point (x, y) to the point $(4x, 4y)$. A size transformation with magnitude $\frac{1}{4}$ and center at the origin will map this point to $\left(\frac{1}{4}(4x), \frac{1}{4}(4y)\right) = (x, y)$, which is the original point.

   d. Inverse: A size transformation of magnitude 2, followed by a clockwise rotation of $80°$

      This is the inverse because, as described above, these actions will undo the given transformations. It is important to first undo the size change and then undo the rotation.

   e. Inverse: Reflection across the line $y = 5$

      This is the inverse because applying the same reflection twice (to a point and its image) will always produce the original point.

3. If g is always increasing, then g has a unique y value for each x value. This follows from the definition of an increasing function. Symbolically, if $x_1 < x_2$, then $g(x_1) < g(x_2)$. Thus, g is a one-to-one function and has an inverse. Further, g^{-1} is an always increasing function as well. (Some students might be challenged to prove that if $x_1 < x_2$, then $g^{-1}(x_1) < g^{-1}(x_2)$. One possible approach would be to note that either $g^{-1}(x_1) < g^{-1}(x_2)$, $g^{-1}(x_1) = g^{-1}(x_2)$, or $g^{-1}(x_1) > g^{-1}(x_2)$. If $g^{-1}(x_1) = g^{-1}(x_2)$, then $g(g^{-1}(x_1)) = g(g^{-1}(x_2))$, so $x_1 = x_2$. But that is a contradiction of the assumption $x_1 < x_2$. Similarly, since g is increasing, $g^{-1}(x_1) > g^{-1}(x_2)$ leads to $g(g^{-1}(x_1)) > g(g^{-1}(x_2))$. But this implies $x_1 > x_2$, which is also a contradiction of the assumption $x_1 < x_2$. Therefore, $g^{-1}(x_1) < g^{-1}(x_2)$, which means that g^{-1} is an increasing function.)

4. **a.** Yes, the composite of two functions will always be a function. If $f(x)$ and $g(x)$ are two functions, then you need to show that $f(g(a))$ is unique for each value of a. Because $g(x)$ is a function, $g(a)$ is unique. Because $f(x)$ is a function, $f(g(a))$ is unique. Thus, $f(g(x))$ is a function.

   b. ■ $f(g(x)) = -(3x + 4)^2 + 7 = -9x^2 - 24x - 9$

      ■ $g(f(x)) = 3(-x^2 + 7) + 4 = -3x^2 + 25$

   c. For these functions, $g(f(x)) \neq f(g(x))$.

Extending

1. Student tasks and responses should be analogous to Reflecting Task 3 and its answer.

2. **a.** Solve $x = t - 1$ for t to get $t = x + 1$. If $y = 2t + 3$ and $t = x + 1$, then
$y = 2(x + 1) + 3 = 2x + 2 + 3 = 2x + 5$.

Unit 3

MORE *continued*

b.

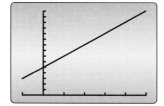

c.

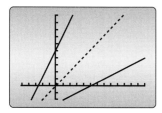

d. The graphs are reflections over the line $y = x$ as shown on the following calculator screen.

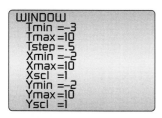

This graph was made by using the window

```
WINDOW
  Tmin =-3
  Tmax =10
  Tstep =.5
  Xmin =-2
  Xmax=10
  Xscl  =1
  Ymin =-2
  Ymax=10
  Yscl  =1
```

and then squaring that window (using **Zsquare** on a TI calculator) to obtain the following window.

```
WINDOW
  Tmin =-3
  Tmax =10
  Tstep =.5
  Xmin =-5.096774...
  Xmax=13.096774...
  Xscl  =1
  Ymin =-2
  Ymax=10
  Yscl  =1
```

The functions are inverses of each other.

e. By looking at the equations, you see that the first graph is of points with coordinates $(t - 1, 2t + 3)$ and the second graph is of points with coordinates $(2t + 3, t - 1)$. The functions are inverses of each other since the domain of the second function is the range of the first function, the range of the second function is the domain of the first function, and the first-function mapping of $t - 1 \rightarrow 2t + 3$ is reversed to the second-function mapping of $2t + 3 \rightarrow t - 1$.

MORE *continued*

3. The algebraic representation of the inverse will be a piecewise-defined function where each piece is the inverse of the original function and the domain is restricted according to the range of $g(x)$.

$$g^{-1}(x) = \begin{cases} x + 2 \text{ if } x \leq 0 \\ \frac{1}{2}x + 2 \text{ if } x \geq 0 \end{cases}$$

The graph of $y = g^{-1}(x)$ is shown below.

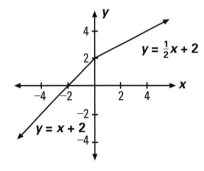

4. **a.** The instantaneous rate of change of $f(x) = ax + b$ at $x = x_0$ is a. Students might use the difference quotient or they may remember that the rate of change of a linear function is always equal to the slope.

   b. $f^{-1}(x) = \frac{x - b}{a} = \frac{1}{a}x - \frac{b}{a}$

   c. The instantaneous rate of change of $f^{-1}(x)$ at $x = x_0$ is $\frac{1}{a}$.

   d. At $x = x_0$, the instantaneous rate of change of $f^{-1}(x)$ is the multiplicative inverse (or reciprocal) of the instantaneous rate of change of $f(x)$.

5. **a.**

   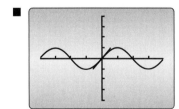

   - Yes, this is a graph of a function. For each x value, there is only one y value.

   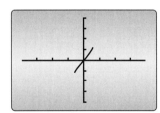

   - The domain of $y = \sin x$ is restricted to $-\frac{\pi}{2} \leq x \leq \frac{\pi}{2}$ so that the function is one-to-one.

   - There are many different ways in which the domain of $y = \sin x$ could be restricted in order that an inverse function exists. Any domain of the form $-\frac{\pi}{2} + n\pi \leq x \leq \frac{\pi}{2} + n\pi$, for n, an integer, will work.

MORE *continued*

b.

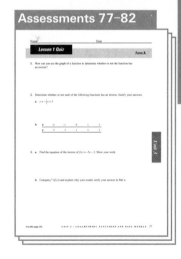

Masters 63a–63e

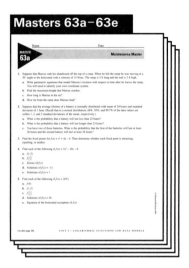

■ The domain of $y = \cos x$ is restricted to $0 \le x \le \pi$ so that the function is one-to-one.

■ Yes, because $y = \cos x$ is a periodic function, there are an infinite number of ways to restrict the domain so that an inverse function exists. One other way is to use $\pi \le x \le 2\pi$. Any domain of the form $n\pi \le x \le \pi + n\pi$, for n an integer will work.

See Teaching Masters 63a–63e for Maintenance tasks that students can work on after Lesson 1.

See Assessment Resources pages 77–82.

Unit 3

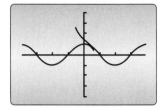

REVIEW AND PRACTICE individual task

▶**PUMP**

Assessments 77–82

Answers

1. (c)	6. (d)
2. (b)	7. (d)
3. (d)	8. (c)
4. (c)	9. (b)
5. (e)	10. (a)

Lesson **2** *Logarithmic Functions*

LESSON OVERVIEW In Lesson 1, inverse functions were introduced, along with ways to determine whether a function has an inverse and if so, how to find the inverse. The fundamental idea of the inverse as an "undoing" operation or function should, at this point, be relatively familiar to students. Also, they should realize that the graph of the inverse of a function can be sketched by reflecting the graph of the original function over the line $y = x$ using the transformation $(x, y) \rightarrow (y, x)$. The equation for the inverse function can be found by interchanging the symbols x and y and then solving for y. The three investigations in this lesson build on these ideas.

The first investigation introduces the inverse of the exponential function. Since the exponential function defined by $y = a^x$, $a > 0$, $a \neq 1$, is always increasing ($a > 1$) or always decreasing ($0 < a < 1$) and so one-to-one, it has an inverse. This inverse is called the logarithmic function. The equation that results from interchanging the variables x and y is $x = a^y$. The logarithm is, by definition, the solution, $y = \log_a x$.

Students are given many opportunities to develop their understanding of logarithm, but you should expect misconceptions. Students often believe things like $\log(a + b) = \log a + \log b$. Such common errors are confronted in Reflecting Task 2 on page 176.

The second investigation of this lesson extends the development of logarithms. Functional characteristics are emphasized, but computational, equation solving, and scaling applications are also covered. Logarithmic scales are explored in Investigation 3 in preparation for the process of linearizing data in Lesson 3.

In this lesson, students will concentrate on common (base 10) logarithms. The natural logarithm (base e) will be studied in Unit 7 "Functions and Symbolic Reasoning."

Lesson Objectives

- To know and be able to use the definition of a logarithm
- To know and be able to use properties of logarithms
- To be able to solve exponential equations using logarithms
- To be able to set up and use logarithmic scales
- To understand why logarithmic scales are useful and how they compare to linear scales

Unit 3

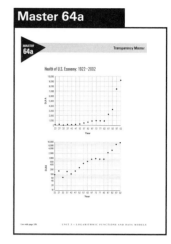
LAUNCH full-class discussion

Think About This Situation

See Teaching Master 64.

The "Think About This Situation" for this lesson considers data on the Dow Jones Industrial Average and graphs of that data. You can launch the lesson by discussing the DJIA and how it is used to help determine the overall trend of the stock market. The data are the averages of the DJIA for each year shown. Ask the students how they might represent the data table graphically. Ask if their graphs would resemble those in the student text. Then, look at the given graphs and discuss the four questions in the "Think About This Situation."

ⓐ Linear; exponential

ⓑ 101.8; 1,379.6

The top plot shows that the difference from 1982 to 1987 was much larger than from 1932 to 1937.

ⓒ The ratio from 1937 to 1932 is approximately 2.6 which is the same as the ratio from 1987 to 1982. The bottom plot shows equal jumps for these two pairs, indicating equal ratios (or equal factor increases), and therefore is better for comparing ratios.

ⓓ Equal vertical distances represent equal ratios of values:

$$\frac{\text{DJIA (1987)}}{\text{DJIA (1982)}} = \frac{\text{DJIA (1937)}}{\text{DJIA (1932)}}$$

EXPLORE small-group investigation

INVESTIGATION 1 Common Logarithms

This investigation is the first of three about logarithms and their properties. Throughout this lesson, common logarithms are emphasized. The first two activities review exponential functions and ask students to consider what might be the inverse for such a function. As you know, the inverse is the logarithm function. After student groups have completed Activity 2, you can carry out a class discussion of the idea of a logarithm of a number as the exponent in an exponential equation. One way to emphasize the relationship is to read "$\log_2 x$" as "the base 2 log of x" and "2^x" as "the xth power of the base 2." This language helps to keep the base prominently displayed. Another way to emphasize the meaning of logarithm is to ask students how they would express the relationship $2^y = x$ as "$y = \ldots$." (See Activity 1 Part e.) Without any new notation, they can only say that $y =$ "the exponent to which you raise the base 2 to get x." They will need time and practice to be

Unit 3

EXPLORE *continued*

comfortable understanding that "base 2 logarithm" has the same meaning as "exponent to which you raise the base 2." After Activity 4, you might want to assign some practice, but be aware that manipulating the symbols does not always mean that students have understood the meaning of "logarithm." The other confusion for students is that $y = 2^x$ and $x = 2^y$ are inverses, but $x = 2^y$ is expressed as $y = \log_2 x$.

Activity 6 asks students to examine the characteristics of the graph of $y = \log x$. Encourage them to use calculators, different windows, and their understanding of inverse functions to determine these characteristics.

It is important with logarithms, as it was with other inverses, to keep the connections between a function and its inverse in the forefront. This is the purpose of Activity 7, which groups ought to be able to do because it is so similar to activities done with the other inverses. Activities 8 and 9 require students to evaluate logarithmic expressions and solve logarithmic equations.

1. **a.** $y = 2^7 = 128$ sheets thick

    b. In order to have 500 pages in the book, there must be 250 sheets of thickness. Since 2^8 is 256, 8 folds are needed to get the number of sheets in a 500-page book.

    c. Yes, $y = 2^x$ has an inverse because the function is one-to-one; that is, no horizontal line will intersect the graph of $y = 2^x$ at more than one point. (See the graph at the right.)

    d. When the domain of $y = 2^x$ is all real numbers, the range is all positive numbers. The domain of the inverse is all positive numbers. The range of the inverse is all real numbers.

    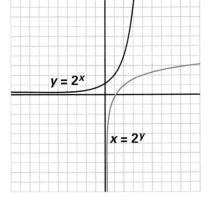

    e. The equation of the inverse is $x = 2^y$ because the inverse is found by interchanging the x and y variables. At this point, the students do not have any way to rewrite the equation $x = 2^y$ with y expressed as a function of x.

2. **a.** $\log_2 32 = 5$

    b. $\log_2 1{,}024 = 10$

    c. $\log_2 8 = 3$ because $2^3 = 8$.

    d. $\log_2 1 = 0$ because $2^0 = 1$.

EXPLORE *continued*

In the paragraph following Activity 2, the text states that any positive number not equal to 1 can be the base of a logarithm. You may wish to ask students to explain why 1 cannot be the base of a logarithm. Here is a possible response:

If there were a logarithmic function $g(x) = \log_1 x$, it would have to be the inverse of $f(x) = 1^x$. However, $f(x) = 1^x = 1$ for all values of x, so f is not one-to-one and therefore cannot have an inverse. (Notice that $f(x) = 1^x$ is a constant linear function, not an exponential function.)

3. **a.** $\log 1 = 0$ **b.** $\log_2 16 = 4$ **c.** $\log 1{,}000 = 3$

     d. $\log 100{,}000 = 5$ **e.** $\log \frac{1}{10} = -1$ **f.** $\log_2 \frac{1}{64} = -6$

4. **a.** $2^1 = 2$ **b.** $10^2 = 100$ **c.** $2^7 = 128$

     d. $10^{-2} = 0.01$ **e.** $10^{-3} = 0.001$ **f.** $2^{-2} = 0.25$

5. **a.** The rate of change of $y = \log x$ decreases as x increases. The slope of the graph of the function near $x = 0$ is very large. This is shown on the plot as a nearly vertical graph and in the table as large changes in y values for small changes in x values. For large x values, the slope of the graph is approaching zero and the graph appears nearly horizontal. This is apparent in the table as almost no change in the y values for large x values.

 b. The domain of $y = \log x$ is $x > 0$. The range is all real numbers. There is no logarithm of either a negative number or 0 because the value of 10^x is always greater than 0. Since the range of $f(x) = 10^x$ is all positive real numbers, the domain of $f^{-1}(x) = \log x$ is also $x > 0$.

 While students may use their graphs from Part a to guide them in this part of the activity, it is important for them to think more generally and reason from the fact that $y = \log x$ is the inverse of $y = 10^x$.

 c. $y = \log x$ crosses the x-axis at $x = 1$ because $\log 1 = 0$. It doesn't cross the y-axis because an x value of 0 would mean that 10 can be raised to some power y such that $10^y = 0$. But 10^y is always a positive number, so the graph of $y = \log x$ is not defined for $x \le 0$.

 d. $\log x$ is positive for $x > 1$. $\log x$ is negative for $0 < x < 1$. (Students could read these values off the graph or reason from the symbols.)

 e. When $x = 10$, $\log x = 1$, since $10^1 = 10$.

 f. $\log 0.5 \approx -0.301$ and $\log 20 \approx 1.301$.

 g. To solve $1.6 = \log x$, first rewrite it as $10^{1.6} = x$. Thus, $x \approx 39.811$. (Some students might approximate the solution by using the graph or a table of values. Encourage all students to know more than one way to solve this equation. They should keep in mind though, that one of the objectives of this unit is to be able to solve logarithmic and exponential equations by reasoning with the symbols.)

NOTE: On the TI-83, students must be careful to close parentheses when evaluating logarithms. For example, $\log$ (41/$\log$ (7 is not the same as $\log$ (41)/$\log$ (7).

Unit 3

EXPLORE *continued*

6. a. Since log 461 is the number you raise 10 to in order to get 461, and $10^2 = 100$ and $10^3 = 1,000$, log 461 must be between 2 and 3.

b.

Estimate	Calculation
$1 < \log 16 < 2$	1.20412
$0 < \log 1.6 < 1$	0.20412
$3 < \log 1,600 < 4$	3.20412
$0 < \log 3 < 1$	0.47712
$-1 < \log 0.3 < 0$	-0.52288
$1 < \log 30 < 2$	1.47712

c. $\log (a \cdot 10^n) = n + \log a$. Since $\log (a \cdot 10^n)$ is the power that 10 is raised to in order to get $a \cdot 10^n$, the power will be n more than log a.

7. a. $f^{-1}(x) = \log x$; $g^{-1}(x) = \log_2 x$

b.

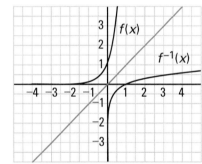

The graph of $y = f(f^{-1}(x)) = 10^{\log x}$ is the part of the line $y = x$ in the first quadrant. Since $f^{-1}(x) = \log x$ is defined only for $x > 0$, the composite function $f(f^{-1}(x))$ is defined only for $x > 0$. Thus, since the graph of $y = f(f^{-1}(x))$, in general, is always $y = x$ or part of it, the graph here is the line $y = x$ when $x > 0$.

The graph of $y = f^{-1}(f(x)) = \log 10^x$ is the line $y = x$. Since $f(x) = 10^x$ is defined for all x and is positive, $f^{-1}(f(x))$ is defined for all x, and the graph of $y = f^{-1}(f(x))$ is the entire line $y = x$.

c. The graph of $y = g(g^{-1}(x))$ is $y = x$, $x > 0$. The graph of $g(g^{-1}(x))$ is only the positive part of the line $y = x$ because $g^{-1}(x) = \log_2 x$ has a domain of $x > 0$, and thus $g(g^{-1}(x))$ also has a restricted domain of $x > 0$.

The graph of $y = g^{-1}(g(x))$ is the line $y = x$ because $g(x) = 2^x$ has a domain of all real numbers and a range of all positive numbers. This allows the graph of $g^{-1}(g(x))$ to be the whole line $y = x$.

d. $f(f^{-1}(x)) = 10^{\log x}$; $f(f^{-1}(x)) = x$, $x > 0$

$f^{-1}(f(x)) = \log 10^x$; $f^{-1}(f(x)) = x$

EXPLORE *continued*

$g(g^{-1}(x)) = 2^{\log_2 x}; \; g(g^{-1}(x)) = x, \; x > 0$

$g^{-1}(g(x)) = \log_2 2^x; \; g^{-1}(g(x)) = x$

e. When $x = 5$, each of these expressions has a value of 5. Compare the expressions here to the functions in Part d.

8. a. $\log_2 1 = 0$ since $2^0 = 1$.

b. $\log_2 256 = 8$ since $2^8 = 256$.

c. $2^{\log_2 15} = 15$ since if $f(x) = 2^x$ and $f^{-1}(x) = \log_2 x$, then $f(f^{-1}(x)) = x$. Students may also recognize that the inverse functions are being applied to 15, so the result $f(f^{-1}(15)) = 15$.

d. $\log_b b^9 = 9$ since writing in exponential form, $b^9 = b^9$.

e. $\log_{10} 10{,}000 = 4$ since $10^4 = 10{,}000$.

f. $\log 0.01 = -2$ since $10^{-2} = 0.01$.

g. $\log \sqrt{10} = \frac{1}{2}$ since $10^{\frac{1}{2}} = \sqrt{10}$

h. $\log 10^a = a$ since $10^a = 10^a$.

i. $3^x = 81$
$3^x = 3^4$
$x = 4$

j. $\log_2 x = -4$
$2^{-4} = x$
$x = \frac{1}{16}$

k. $\log_x \frac{1}{16} = \frac{1}{2}$
$x^{\frac{1}{2}} = \frac{1}{16}$
$x = \frac{1}{256}$

l. $\log_7 7 = x$
$7^x = 7$
$x = 1$

m. $\log_{10} x = 6$
$10^6 = x$
$x = 1{,}000{,}000$

n. $\log_x 0.0001 = -4$
$x^{-4} = 0.0001$
$x = 10$

o. $\log x = -3$
$10^{-3} = x$
$x = 0.001$

p. $\log 1 = x$
$10^x = 1$
$x = 0$

q. $\log x = \log 100$
$x = 100$

r. $\log x = \log (2x - 3)$
$x = 2x - 3$
$x = 3$

9. The distances between 60 and 80, 600 and 800, and 6,000 and 8,000 are all equal. The differences between the logs of these pairs of numbers are all equal; that is $\log 80 - \log 60 = \log 800 - \log 600 = \log 8{,}000 - \log 6{,}000 \approx 0.12494$. This follows from a rule of logs that students have yet to learn:

$$\log 80 - \log 60 = \log \tfrac{80}{60} = \log \tfrac{4}{3},$$

$$\log 800 - \log 600 = \log \tfrac{800}{600} = \log \tfrac{4}{3},$$

$$\log 8{,}000 - \log 6{,}000 = \log \tfrac{8{,}000}{6{,}000} = \log \tfrac{4}{3}.$$

In other words, whenever pairs of numbers have the same ratio, their logs will have the same difference.

Unit 3

Masters 65a–65b

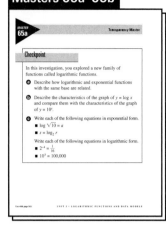

CONSTRUCTING A MATH TOOLKIT: Ask students to record definitions of log x and $\log_2 x$ and to illustrate the relationship between $\log_a b = c$ and $a^c = b$. Ask them to include a discussion of why $10^{\log x} = x$ and $\log_2 2^x = x$. Have them include a sketch of $f(x) = \log x$ with key points $(1, 0)$ and $(10, 1)$ labeled. You may wish to have students add logarithmic functions to their list of families of functions. (See Teaching Masters 159a–c for Course 3.)

SHARE AND SUMMARIZE full-class discussion

Checkpoint

See Teaching Masters 65a and 65b.

a The functions $f(x) = a^x$ and $g(x) = \log_a x$ are inverses of each other.

b The domain of $y = \log x$ is all positive real numbers, and the range is all real numbers. The graph crosses the x-axis at $x = 1$ and does not cross the y-axis. The function is always increasing, but more and more slowly as x increases. The domain of $y = 10^x$ is all real numbers, and the range is all positive real numbers. The graph crosses the y-axis at 1 and does not cross the x-axis. The function is always increasing and increases more and more rapidly as x gets large. The two graphs are reflections of each other across the line $y = x$.

c ■ $10^a = \sqrt{10}$ or $10^a = 10^{\frac{1}{2}}$

■ $2^s = r$

■ $\log_2 \frac{1}{16} = -4$

■ $\log 100,000 = 5$

d ■ True, because $10^3 = 10^3$.

■ False, because $10^4 = 10,000$, not 40.

■ True, because $x^1 = x$.

■ True. Students may reason either of the following two ways:

(1) $\log_5 3$ is the exponent to apply to 5 to get 3.

(2) If $f(x) = 5^x$, then $f^{-1}(x) = \log_5 x$ and $5^{\log_5 3} = f(f^{-1}(3))$. But $f(f^{-1}(x)) = x$, for $x > 0$, so $5^{\log_5 3} = 3$.

APPLY individual task

▶On Your Own

a.   **i.** $\log_2 64 = 6$ since $2^6 = 64$.

     ii. $\log_2 2 = 1$ since $2^1 = 2$.

     iii. $\log 1 = 0$ since $10^0 = 1$.

     iv. $\log 0.001 = -3$ since $10^{-3} = 0.001$.

b.   **i.** $\log_3 x = 4$

$$x = 3^4$$
$$x = 81$$

     ii. $\log_x 64 = 3$

$$x^3 = 64$$
$$x = 4$$

APPLY *continued*

    iii. Since $10^{\log x} = x$, $10^{\log 6} = 6$.

    iv. $\log (10^3)^2 = x$

$$10^x = (10^3)^2$$
$$10^x = 10^6$$
$$x = 6$$

c.   ■ $2 < \log 275 < 3$

    ■ $0 < \log 3 < 1$

    ■ $-1 < \log 0.5 < 0$

EXPLORE   **small-group investigation**

INVESTIGATION 2 Re-expression and Equation Solving with Logarithms

Logarithms were introduced in Investigation 1. In this investigation, key properties are developed and their use in solving exponential equations is illustrated. The manipulations of logarithmic expressions will be especially useful in Lesson 3 when techniques to linearize data are discussed.

In many classes, it may be appropriate to do Activities 1 and 2 Parts a–e as a whole class discussion. Questions like the following can help students to recall the general rules:

■ Does $3^4 \cdot 3^5$ equal 3^{20}, 9^{20}, 6^{20}, 6^9, 9^{20}, or 3^9? Explain your choice.

■ Does $3^5 \div 3^4$ equal $3^{\frac{5}{4}}$, $1^{\frac{5}{4}}$, 1^1, or 3^1? Explain your choice.

  A few questions such as these should be enough to remind your students of the properties they will need to call on in this investigation. If you choose to do Activity 2 as a large group, you can ask similar questions:

■ Does log 36 equal log 30 + log 6, log 18 + log 18, log 6 × log 6, log 4 × log 9, log 6 + log 6, log 3 + log 12, or log 18 + log 2? Make a conjecture.

You will definitely want to bring the whole class together to be sure that they have correctly identified the properties of logarithms, before going on to Activity 3.

  Activities 3–5 should be done in small groups. You may wish to hold a mini-Checkpoint discussion following Activity 5 to discuss methods for solving exponential equations. When students are relatively secure in the methods, have the groups work on Activities 6 and 7.

MORE
ASSIGNMENT *pp. 173–177*

Students can now begin Organizing Task 1 or 5, Reflecting Task 1, or Extending Task 4 from the MORE assignment following Investigation 3.

Unit 3

EXPLORE *continued*

1. Numerical examples will vary. Note that the expressions below aren't defined for all real numbers. The properties hold, however, whenever all expressions are defined.

   a. $b^r \cdot b^s = b^{r+s}$

   b. $\frac{t^r}{t^s} = t^{r-s}$

   c. $(a \cdot b)^r = a^r \cdot b^r$

   d. $(m^r)^s = m^{rs}$

   e. $d^{-s} = \frac{1}{d^s}$

2. **a.** $\log 36 \approx 1.5563$
   $\log 30 \approx 1.4771$
   $\log 6 \approx 0.7782$
   $\log 4 \approx 0.6021$
   $\log 9 \approx 0.9542$
   $\log 3 \approx 0.4771$
   $\log 12 \approx 1.0792$
   $\log 6 \approx 0.7782$

   The sum of the logs of 4 and 9 is equal to the log of 36.

   The sum of the logs of 3 and 12 is equal to the log of 36.

   The sum of the logs of 6 and 6 is equal to the log of 36.

   Conjecture: The sum of the logs of the factors of a number is equal to the log of the number. However, the sum of the logs of x and y isn't equal to the log of $(x + y)$: $\log x + \log y$.

   b. Students will find that $\log (xy) = \log x + \log y$, but $\log (x + y) \neq \log x + \log y$.

   c. *Step 1* Definition of logarithm

   Step 2 Multiplication Property of Equality and Substitution

   Step 3 Product of Powers property

   Step 4 Definition of logarithm (or $\log 10^p = p$) and Substitution

   d. Examples will vary.

   $\log 16 = \log 2 + \log 8$ is one example.

   e. The log of a product is the sum of the logs of the factors.

   f. In order to show this is a property of logarithms with base 2, replace the logarithms with base 10 with base 2 logarithms:

EXPLORE *continued*

If $r = \log_2 x$ and $s = \log_2 y$, then by definition of logarithms $x = 2^r$ and $y = 2^s$. But then $x \cdot y = 2^r \cdot 2^s = 2^{r+s}$. By definition of logarithm, $\log_2 (xy) = r + s = \log_2 x + \log_2 y$.

g. Predictions may vary. The correct relationship is $\log \left(\frac{x}{y}\right) = \log x - \log y$.

h. Let $r = \log x$ and $s = \log y$, then $x = 10^r$ and $y = 10^s$.

$$\frac{x}{y} = \frac{10^r}{10^s}$$
$$\frac{x}{y} = 10^{r-s}$$
$$\log \left(\frac{x}{y}\right) = r - s$$
$$\log \left(\frac{x}{y}\right) = \log x - \log y$$

i. The log of a quotient is the log of the numerator minus the log of the denominator.

j. Let $r = \log_2 x$ and $s = \log_2 y$. Then $x = 2^r$ and $y = 2^s$, so $\frac{x}{y} = \frac{2^r}{2^s} = 2^{r-s}$. Therefore, $\log_2 \left(\frac{x}{y}\right) = r - s = \log_2 x - \log_2 y$.

3. a. ■ $\log 25 + \log 40 = \log (25 \cdot 40)$

$$= \log 1{,}000$$
$$= 3$$

■ $\log 700 - \log 7 = \log \left(\frac{700}{7}\right)$

$$= \log 100$$
$$= 2$$

b. The key here is to express each of the numbers 1 through 10 as a product or quotient of the numbers 2, 3, 7, and 10. Then, the properties of logarithms can be used to find each logarithm.

$\log 1 = 0$

$\log 2 \approx 0.3010$

$\log 3 \approx 0.4771$

$\log 4 = \log 2 + \log 2 \approx 0.3010 + 0.3010 = 0.6020$

$\log 5 = \log \left(\frac{10}{2}\right) = \log 10 - \log 2 \approx 1 - 0.3010 = 0.6990$

$\log 6 = \log (3 \cdot 2) = \log 3 + \log 2 \approx 0.7781$

$\log 7 \approx 0.8451$

$\log 8 = \log (4 \cdot 2) = \log 4 + \log 2 \approx 0.6020 + 0.3010 = 0.9030$

$\log 9 = \log (3 \cdot 3) = \log 3 + \log 3 \approx 0.4771 + 0.4771 = 0.9542$

$\log 10 = 1$

4. a. Use the properties already established:

$\log x^2 = \log (x \cdot x) = \log x + \log x = 2 \log x$

$\log x^3 = \log (x^2 \cdot x) = \log x^2 + \log x = 2 \log x + \log x = 3 \log x$

$\log x^5 = \log (x^3 \cdot x^2) = \log x^3 + \log x^2 = 3 \log x + 2 \log x = 5 \log x$

Unit 3

EXPLORE *continued*

b. The log of a power is the exponent times the log of the base. Symbolically, this is written $\log x^m = m \log x$.

c. *Step 1* Definition of logarithm

Step 2 Raise both sides of the equation to the same exponent.

Step 3 Power of a Power property

Step 4 Definition of logarithm (or since the logarithm is a function, you can take the log of both sides of the equation and use the property $\log 10^{ym} = ym$).

Step 5 Substitution ($y = \log x$)

d. $\log 5^3 \approx 3(0.69897) = 2.09691$

$\log 5^{1.3} \approx 1.3(0.69897) = 0.908661$

$\log 5^{10,000} \approx 10,000(0.69897) = 6,989.7$

e. Yes, all reasons in the proof are applicable with a base 2 logarithm.

f. The log of a power is the exponent times the log of the base.

5. a. The 10 indicates that 10 units of insulin were in the bloodstream at time 0. The 0.95 indicates that 95% of the insulin remains from one minute to the next.

b. *Step 1* You want to know when half of the insulin (5 units) is left, so the equation you need to solve is $5 = 10(0.95^x)$.

Step 2 Division Property of Equality: divide both sides of the equation by 10.

Step 3 Since the logarithm is a function, you can take the log of both sides of the equation.

Step 4 Power Property of logarithms

Step 5 Division Property of Equality: divide both sides of the equation by $\log 0.95$.

c. Students should get approximately the same solution using graphical and numerical methods.

d. If the log of both sides was taken before dividing both sides by 10, the solution could still be obtained, but there are a few more steps:

$$5 = 10(0.95^x)$$

$$\log 5 = \log (10(0.95^x))$$

$$\log 5 = \log 10 + \log (0.95^x)$$

$$\log 5 - \log 10 = x \log (0.95)$$

$$\frac{\log 5 - \log 10}{\log 0.95} = x$$

$$x \approx 13.51$$

EXPLORE *continued*

6. a. $2^x = 250$

$x \log 2 = \log 250$

$x = \frac{\log 250}{\log 2}$

$x \approx 7.97$

To get a thickness of at least 250 sheets, 8 folds are needed. (This is the same as the number of folds needed to produce a 500-page book, since each sheet holds two pages of text.)

b. The equation for the population of China, P (in billions), x years after 2001 is $P = 1.273(1.0088)^x$. To determine when the population will reach 2 billion, solve the equation $2 = 1.273(1.0088)^x$.

$$2 = 1.273(1.0088)^x$$

$$\frac{2}{1.273} = 1.0088^x$$

$$\log\left(\frac{2}{1.273}\right) = x \log 1.0088$$

$$\frac{\log\left(\frac{2}{1.273}\right)}{\log 1.0088} = x$$

$$x \approx 51.56$$

Assuming growth at 0.88%, the population of China will reach 2 billion approximately 51.56 years after 2001, during the year 2053.

7. a. i. $\frac{5}{2} = 1.3^x$

$\log 2.5 = x \log 1.3$ (Power Property)

$\frac{\log 2.5}{\log 1.3} = x$

$x \approx 3.49$

ii. $0.75 = 2^x$

$\log 0.75 = x \log 2$ (Power Property)

$\frac{\log 0.75}{\log 2} = x$

$x \approx -0.415$

iii. $\frac{40}{5} = \left(1 + \frac{0.03}{12}\right)^x$

$\log 8 = x \log\left(1 + \frac{0.03}{12}\right)$ (Power Property)

$\frac{\log 8}{\log 1.0025} = x$

$x \approx 832.82$

iv. $5^{2x} = \frac{8}{3}$

$2x \log 5 = \log\left(\frac{8}{3}\right)$ (Power Property)

$x = \frac{\log\left(\frac{8}{3}\right)}{2 \log 5}$

$x \approx 0.305$

b. i. $3 \cdot 10^x = 1.7$

$\log 10^x = \log 0.567$

$x \log 10 = \log 0.567$ (Power Property)

$x = \frac{\log 0.567}{\log 10}$

$x \approx -0.246$

Alternatively, using the definition of a logarithm, you can rewrite $3 \cdot 10^x = 1.7$ as $x = \log 0.567$, so $x \approx -0.246$. This is the same solution that was obtained by taking the log of both sides of the original equation.

Unit 3

EXPLORE *continued*

ii. $2.3 = 10^{x+1}$

$\log 2.3 = \log 10^{x+1}$

$\log 2.3 = (x+1) \log 10$

$\frac{\log 2.3}{\log 10} - 1 = x$

$-0.6383 \approx x$

Using the definition of a logarithm, you can rewrite $\log 2.3 = x + 1$. Then $x = \log(2.3) - 1 \approx -0.6383$. Note that this is the same solution.

c. First, rewrite the equation so that the exponential expression is by itself on one side of the equals sign. Then take the log of both sides. To finish, use the properties of logarithms and algebraic properties to simplify and solve for the variable.

8. a. $2 \log(5 \cdot 2) = 2$ 　　　　　　　　b. $\log\left(\frac{2^4}{4}\right) = \log 4$

c. $3(\log 8 + \log 5) = 3 \log 40 = 3 + 3 \log 4$ 　　　　d. $\log x^2 = 2 \log x$

Unit 3

Master 66

MASTER
66   Transparency Master

Checkpoint

In this investigation, you have discovered and verified three useful properties of logarithms.

ⓐ Summarize in symbols and in words each property of logarithms:
 ■ Product Property
 ■ Quotient Property
 ■ Power Property

ⓑ For what kinds of equations are logarithms useful in the solution process? Explain the general solution procedure.

Be prepared to share your summary of properties of logarithms and their use in equation solving with the entire class.

Use with page 168.　　UNIT 3 • LOGARITHMIC FUNCTIONS AND DATA MODELS

CONSTRUCTING A MATH TOOLKIT: Ask students to summarize the properties for applying logarithms to products, quotients and powers. Ask them also to summarize how logarithms can be used to solve exponential equations.

SHARE AND SUMMARIZE full-class discussion

Checkpoint

See Teaching Master 66.

ⓐ ■ Taking the logarithm of the product of two numbers is the same as adding the logarithms of the factors.
$$\log(xy) = \log x + \log y$$

■ Taking the logarithm of the quotient of two numbers is the same as subtracting the logarithm of the denominator from the logarithm of the numerator.
$$\log\left(\frac{x}{y}\right) = \log x - \log y$$

■ Taking the logarithm of a power is the same as multiplying the exponent by the logarithm of the base to which the exponent was applied.
$$\log m^x = x \log m$$

ⓑ Logarithms are useful in solving exponential equations of the form $A = B \cdot C^x$. The general procedure is

$$A = B \cdot C^x$$
$$\frac{A}{B} = C^x$$
$$\log\left(\frac{A}{B}\right) = \log C^x$$
$$\log\left(\frac{A}{B}\right) = x \log C$$
$$\frac{\log\left(\frac{A}{B}\right)}{\log C} = x$$

APPLY individual task

▶On Your Own

a. $A = 500\left(1 + \frac{0.0275}{12}\right)^{60}$

$A \approx \$573.61$

b. $1{,}000 = 500\left(1 + \frac{0.0275}{12}\right)^{x}$

$2 = \left(1 + \frac{0.0275}{12}\right)^{x}$

$\log 2 = x \log\left(1 + \frac{0.0275}{12}\right)$

$x \approx 302.81$ months or 25.23 years

It would take 25 years and 3 months for your balance to double.

c. $1{,}000 = 500\left(1 + \frac{0.055}{12}\right)^{x}$

$2 = \left(1 + \frac{0.055}{12}\right)^{x}$

$\log 2 = x \log\left(1 + \frac{0.055}{12}\right)$

$x \approx 151.58$ months or 12.63 years

It would take 12 years and 8 months for your balance to double.

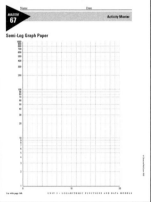

Master 67

MORE
ASSIGNMENT *pp. 173–177*

Students can now begin Modeling Task 1 or 2, Organizing Task 2 or 3, Reflecting Task 2, or Extending Task 2 from the MORE assignment following Investigation 3.

EXPLORE small-group investigation

INVESTIGATION ▶3▶ Logarithmic Scales

One of the characteristics of the logarithmic function is that it increases at a decreasing rate. Thus, logarithms are often used to scale phenomena where there are many small values of interest and increasingly sparse larger values, as with exponential growth.

In this investigation, students first explore logarithmic scales in the contexts of sound intensity (decibels) and the acidity of substances (pH). The Richter scale for measuring earthquake intensity is explored in Activity 3. In Activity 4, students experiment with the graphs of various functions when the *y*-axis is a log scale. Students should see that the different scale changes the way the graph looks. In particular, $y = a^x$ becomes a line!

If students construct the semi-log paper, they will develop a better understanding of logarithmic scales. If you think they will benefit from the process of constructing it, some class discussion of the construction of the log scale may be needed. You may choose to instead provide the semi-log graph paper (See Teaching Master 67). The key idea is to find the location of log *x* (for example, log 2 = 0.3010) and label it with *x*. The locating is done on an arithmetic scale and the labeling changes it to a logarithmic scale.

Unit 3

Master 68

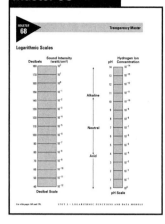

NOTE: A logarithmic scale is helpful for measuring intensity of sounds because our ears seem to operate on a ratio scale. We can discern the differences in sounds of low intensity better than equal differences in sounds of high intensity.

EXPLORE *continued*

1. **See Teaching Master 68.**

   a. The decibel rating for a whisper is

   $D = 10 \log (10^{16} \cdot 10^{-13}) = 10(3) = 30$ decibels.

   The decibel rating for the roar of a jet is

   $D = 10 \log (10^{16} \cdot 0.1) = 10(15) = 150$ decibels.

   The ratings agree with the chart. According to the chart, the decibel rating for ordinary conversation is 60, so it seems reasonable that the decibel rating for a whisper is 30. The chart indicates that the decibel rating for a jet plane at 100 ft is 140. It makes sense that the rating next to the engine (closer than 100 feet away) would be higher, so the rating of 150 seems reasonable.

   b. $D = 10 \log (10^{16} \cdot I)$

   $D = 10(\log 10^{16} + \log I)$

   $D = 10(16 \log 10 + \log I)$

   $D = 160 + 10 \log I$

   c.
$50 = 10 \log I + 160$	$70 = 10 \log I + 160$
$-110 = 10 \log I$	$-90 = 10 \log I$
$-11 = \log I$	$-9 = \log I$
$I = 10^{-11}$ watt/cm^2	$I = 10^{-9}$ watt/cm^2

   The ratio of $\frac{I_{70}}{I_{50}}$ is $\frac{10^{-9}}{10^{-11}} = 100$. Thus, $I_{70} = 100 I_{50}$, so the increase from 50 to 70 decibels corresponds to a hundred-fold increase in sound intensity.

   d. $D_1 - D_2 = (10 \log I_1 + 160) - (10 \log I_2 + 160)$

   $= 10 \log I_1 - 10 \log I_2$

   $= 10(\log I_1 - \log I_2)$

   $= 10 \log \left(\frac{I_1}{I_2}\right)$

   e. If $D_1 - D_2 = 30$,

   $30 = 10(\log I_1 - \log I_2)$

   $3 = \log I_1 - \log I_2$

   $3 = \log \left(\frac{I_1}{I_2}\right)$

   $10^3 = \frac{I_1}{I_2}$

Unit 3

EXPLORE *continued*

$$1,000 = \frac{I_1}{I_2}$$
$$I_1 = 1,000 I_2.$$

Thus, if D_1 is 30 decibels greater than D_2, I_1 will be 1,000 times I_2.

2. **a.** pH $= -\log([H^+])$

   b.

Substance	[H⁺]	pH
lemon juice	0.00501	2.3
apple juice	0.000794	3.1
milk	0.000000355	6.4

   c. Lemon juice is more acidic. The pH of milk is approximately 2.8 times the pH of lemon juice.

3. **a.** $R = \log(10^7 \cdot D)$ or $R = 7 + \log D$, where R is the Richter scale rating and D is the displacement on the seismogram in meters.

   b.
   $$8.6 = \log(10^7 \cdot D) \quad \text{or} \quad 8.6 = 7 + \log D$$

$10^{8.6} = 10^7 \cdot D$	$1.6 = \log D$
$\frac{10^{8.6}}{10^7} = D$	$D = 10^{1.6}$
$10^{1.6} = D$	$D \approx 39.8$
$39.8 \approx D$	

   The displacement would have been about 39.8 m.

   c. The amount of displacement for a quake with Richter scale rating 6.7 will be $\frac{10^{6.7}}{10^{4.2}} = 10^{6.7 - 4.2} = 10^{2.5} \approx 316.23$ times greater than the displacement for a quake with Richter scale rating 4.2.

   d. $R = \log(10^7 \cdot 0.007)$ or $R = 7 + \log(0.007)$
   $$R \approx 4.845$$

   The Richter scale rating for this quake would be 4.8.

Unit 3

EXPLORE *continued*

NOTE: Students are sharing the work for these graphs. All graphs are not displayed here but the pattern is clear.

4. **a.** See the sketch of the graphs below. The graphs look like the beginning of a logarithmic curve. The larger the value of *a*, the more steeply the graph rises.

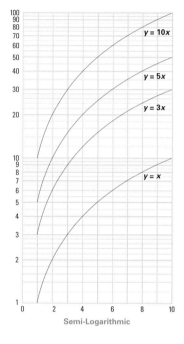

b. The graph of $y = ax^2$ will be a curve. The larger the value of *a*, the more steeply the graph rises.

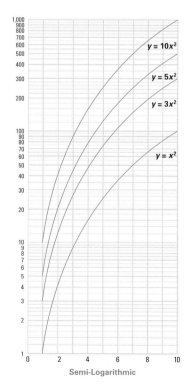

EXPLORE *continued*

c. As the exponent *m* increases, the graph of $y = x^m$ rises more rapidly.

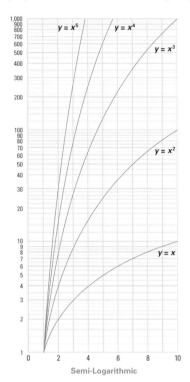

Semi-Logarithmic

d. The graph of $y = b^x$ is a straight line. As *b* increases, the line gets steeper.

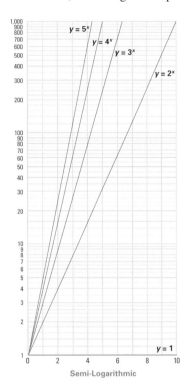

Semi-Logarithmic

Master 69

SHARE AND SUMMARIZE   full-class discussion

Checkpoint

See Teaching Master 69.

a On a linear scale, if $a - b = c - d$, then the points representing *a* and *b* are as far apart as those representing *c* and *d*. On a logarithmic scale, if $\frac{a}{b} = \frac{c}{d}$, then the points representing *a* and *b* are as far apart as those representing *c* and *d*.

b An increase of one unit on a logarithmic scale (base 10) corresponds to a tenfold increase in the original values.

Unit 3

SHARE AND SUMMARIZE *continued*

C ■ The pattern is similar to the log function

Graphing $y = ax$ on semi-log graph paper is equivalent to graphing $y = \log (ax)$ on rectangular graph paper. Since $y = \log (ax) = \log a + \log x$, you would expect a logarithmic-appearing graph.

■ The pattern is similar to the log function.

Graphing $y = ax^2$ on semi-log paper is equivalent to graphing $y = \log (ax^2)$ on rectangular paper. Since $y = \log (ax^2) = \log a + 2 \log x$, you would expect a logarithmic-appearing graph.

■ The pattern is similar to the log function.

Graphing $y = x^m$ on semi-log paper is equivalent to graphing $y = \log x^m$ on rectangular paper. Since $y = \log x^m = m \log x$, you would expect a logarithmic-appearing graph.

■ The pattern is similar to a linear function.

Graphing $y = b^x$ on semi-log paper is equivalent to graphing $y = \log b^x$ on rectangular paper. Here $y = \log b^x = x \log b$. This is a linear function in x with the slope being the constant $\log b$.

APPLY individual task

On Your Own

a. pH = 5.8; $[H^+] = 10^{-5.8}$

pH = 7.8; $[H^+] = 10^{-7.8}$

pH = 8.2; $[H^+] = 10^{-8.2}$

b. $\frac{10^{-5.8}}{10^{-8.2}} = \frac{10^{8.2}}{10^{5.8}} = 10^{2.4} \approx 251.2$

Thus, the hydrogen ion concentration of a substance with a pH of 5.8 is about 251.2 times the hydrogen ion concentration of a substance with a pH of 8.2.

MORE independent assignment

Modeling

1. **a.** The area of the carpet at stage $n = 0$ is 3 square meters. The area at each stage is 75% of the area at the previous stage.

b. To find the stage where there is more hole than carpet remaining, solve the equation $1.5 = 3(0.75^n)$.

MORE *continued*

MORE
ASSIGNMENT *pp. 173–177*

Modeling: 1 or 2, and 3 or 4*
Organizing: 1, 2, 3, and 5
Reflecting: 1, 2, and 3
Extending: 2, 4, and choice
of one*

*When choice is indicated, it is impor-
tant to leave the choice to the student.
NOTE: It is best if Organizing tasks are
discussed as a whole class after they
have been assigned as homework.

- To use symbolic reasoning:

$$0.5 = 0.75^n$$

$$\log 0.5 = n \log 0.75$$

$$\frac{\log 0.5}{\log 0.75} = n$$

$$2.41 \approx n$$

Rounding up to the next integer, there is more hole than carpet at stage 3.

- To use graphical reasoning, draw the graphs of $y = 1.5$ and $y = 3(0.75^x)$. The point of intersection, approximately (2.41, 1.5), has x and y values that are impossible in this context because n (represented by x on the graph) must be a whole number. However, you can infer that $n = 3$ represents the first stage where there is more hole than carpet.

- To use numerical reasoning look at a table of values for $y = 3(0.75^n)$ and find the first integer n such that y is less than or equal to 1.5. From the table, it can be seen that at stage 3 there is more hole than carpet.

c. $\quad 0.1 = 3(0.75^n)$

$$\log\left(\frac{0.1}{3}\right) = \log 0.75^n$$

$$\log\left(\frac{0.1}{3}\right) = n \log 0.75$$

$$\frac{\log\left(\frac{0.1}{3}\right)}{\log 0.75} = n$$

$$11.8 \approx n$$

At stage 12, there will be less than 0.1 m^2 of carpet remaining.

2. a. $14.7 = a \cdot b^0$ since $x = 0$ at sea level, so $a = 14.7$.

b. $P = 14.7 \cdot b^x$

Since $P = 7.53$ psi when $x = 3$, $7.53 = 14.7b^3$, so $b^3 = \frac{7.53}{14.7}$ and $b \approx 0.8$.

c. $P = 14.7(0.8^x)$ with x in miles.

$$P = 14.7(0.8)^{\frac{10,000}{5,280}}$$

$$P \approx 9.63 \text{ psi}$$

d. $\quad P = a \cdot b^x$

$$\log\left(\frac{P}{a}\right) = \log b^x$$

$$\log\left(\frac{P}{a}\right) = x \log b$$

$$x = \frac{\log\left(\frac{P}{a}\right)}{\log b} \text{ or } x = \frac{\log P - \log a}{\log b}, \text{ where } 0 < P \leq 14.7$$

Unit 3

MORE *continued*

e. $x = \dfrac{\log\left(\frac{4.55}{14.7}\right)}{\log 0.8} \approx 5.26$ mi

$x = \dfrac{\log\left(\frac{10}{14.7}\right)}{\log 0.8} \approx 1.73$ mi

f. Graph $y = \dfrac{\log\left(\frac{x}{14.7}\right)}{\log 0.8}$ for $0 < P \le 14.7$. The y-axis is a vertical asymptote and the x-intercept is 14.7.

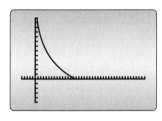

3. a. Stomach gastric juices and soft drinks are acidic. Sea water is alkaline.

b. Since the pH scale is logarithmic, a change of 1 unit indicates a tenfold change in the concentration of hydrogen ions.

Gastric juices have $\dfrac{10^{-1.7}}{10^{-8.5}} = 10^{-1.7\,+\,8.5} = 10^{6.8}$ times as many hydrogen ions as sea water. Soft drinks have $\dfrac{10^{-3.1}}{10^{-8.5}} = 10^{-3.1\,+\,8.5} = 10^{5.4}$ times as many hydrogen ions as sea water.

c. $\dfrac{10^{-1.7}}{10^{-3.1}} = 10^{-1.7\,+\,3.1} \approx 25.12$. Thus, the concentration of hydrogen ions in gastric juices is about 25 times that of soft drinks.

d. The ion concentration in the new soft drink is $\frac{1}{5} \cdot 10^{-3.1}$.

So pH $= -\log[H^+]$
$= -\log\left[\frac{1}{5} \cdot 10^{-3.1}\right]$
≈ 3.799

The pH is about 3.8.

4. a. Exponential function; radioactive material usually decays by a constant percentage for uniform time periods.

b. The exponential regression equation for these data is approximately $y = 10{,}224(0.76)^x$.

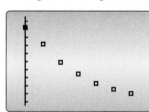

c. $f(30) = 10{,}224(0.76)^{30} \approx 2.72$ counts per minute

MORE *continued*

d. To determine the half-life solve:

$$5{,}112 = 10{,}224(0.76)^x$$
$$0.5 = (0.76)^x$$
$$\log 0.5 = x \log 0.76$$
$$x = \frac{\log 0.5}{\log 0.76}$$
$$x \approx 2.5 \text{ minutes}$$

Organizing

1. **a.** **i.**

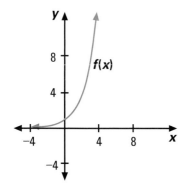

ii.

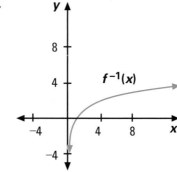

iii. $f^{-1}(x) = \log_2 x$

iv. $f^{-1}(f(x)) = \log_2 (2^x) = x \log_2 2 = x$

b. **i.**

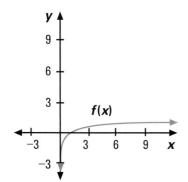

ii.

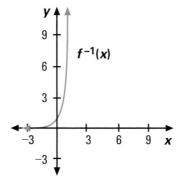

MORE *continued*

      iii. $f^{-1}(x) = 10^x$

      iv. $f^{-1}(f(x)) = 10^{\log x} = x$

c. **i.**

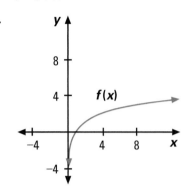

ii.

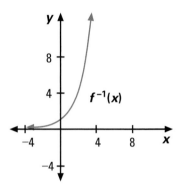

      iii. $f^{-1}(x) = 2^x$

      iv. $f^{-1}(f(x)) = 2^{\log_2 x} = x$

2. The solutions obtained using the different methods should be approximately the same.

    a. ■ $100 = 4.5x - 885$

      $985 = 4.5x$

        $x = \frac{985}{4.5} = \frac{1{,}970}{9}$ or $218\frac{8}{9}$

    ■ The intersection of the graphs of $y = 100$ and $y = 4.5x - 885$ is at $x = 218.\overline{8}$.

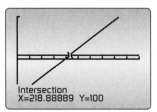

MORE *continued*

■ Students should use a table of values for $y = 4.5x - 885$ to find the x value that gives a y value of 100.

b. ■ $3x^2 + x + 12 = 14$

$3x^2 + x - 2 = 0$

Use factoring or the quadratic formula to get the solutions $x = -1$ and $x = \frac{2}{3}$.

■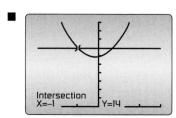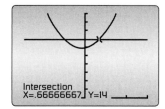

■ Students should use the table of values for $y = 3x^2 + x + 12$ to find the x values that give y values of 14. They need to remember to find both solutions.

c. ■ $3(1.2^t) = 14$

$1.2^t = \frac{14}{3}$

$t \log 1.2 = \log \left(\frac{14}{3} \right)$

$t = \dfrac{\log \left(\frac{14}{3} \right)}{\log 1.2}$

$t \approx 8.45$

■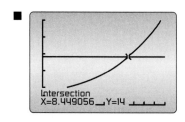

■ Students should enter $y = 3(1.2^x)$ in the Y= menu and then use a table of values to find the x value that gives a y value of 14.

3. **a.** $\log x = -2$

$10^{-2} = x$

$x = \frac{1}{100}$

b. $\log 10^x = 4$

$x = 4$

MORE *continued*

c. $15 = 3.21^x$

$\log 15 = x \log 3.21$

$x = \frac{\log 15}{\log 3.21} \approx 2.32$

d. $\log x = 2 \log 3 + 3 \log 2$

$= \log 3^2 + \log 2^3$

$= \log 3^2 \cdot 2^3$

$= \log 72$

$x = 72$

e. $\log x = \frac{1}{2} \log 36 - \log 2$

$= \log 36^{\frac{1}{2}} - \log 2$

$= \log 6 - \log 2$

$= \log \left(\frac{6}{2} \right)$

$= \log 3$

$x = 3$

f. $\log x = 4 \log 2 + \log 3 - 3 \log 5$

$= \log 2^4 + \log 3 - \log 5^3$

$= \log (16 \cdot 3) - \log 125$

$= \log \left(\frac{48}{125} \right)$

$x = \frac{48}{125}$ or 0.384

g. $2^{2x + 2} = 8^{x + 2}$

$2^{2x + 2} = (2^3)^{x + 2}$

$2^{2x + 2} = 2^{3x + 6}$

$2x + 2 = 3x + 6$

$x = -4$

4. Students should use a difference quotient such as $\frac{f(x + 0.01) - f(x)}{0.01} = \frac{\log (x + 0.01) - \log x}{0.01}$ to estimate the derivative.

a. The derivative of $f(x) = \log x$

at $x = 0.25$ is approximately 1.70333;
at $x = 0.5$ is approximately 0.86002;
at $x = 1$ is approximately 0.43214;
at $x = 10$ is approximately 0.04341;
at $x = 20$ is approximately 0.02171;
at $x = 40$ is approximately 0.01086;
at $x = 60$ is approximately 0.00724.

b. The rate of change of $f(x)$ is decreasing as x increases. Specifically, the derivative is proportional to $\frac{1}{x}$.

NOTE: The derivative of
$f(x) = \log x$ is $f'(x) = \frac{1}{x \ln 10}$.

c. Since $f(x) = \log x$ is always increasing, the derivative is positive so the graph of $y = f'(x)$ is always in the first quadrant. The graph of $y = f'(x)$ is decreasing since $f(x) = \log x$

MORE *continued*

grows more and more slowly as x increases. The x-axis is a horizontal asymptote for the derivative since the slope of the graph of $f(x)$ approaches zero as x increases. The y-axis is a vertical asymptote since the slope of $y = \log x$ approaches zero near the y-axis.

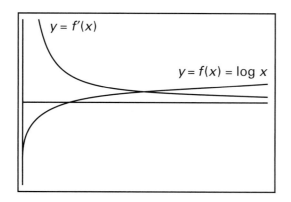

5. **a.** Yes, the graphs seem reasonable. (Students should know the graph of $y = 2^x$. They should also know that $y = \log_2 x$ is the inverse of $y = 2^x$ and thus, that its graph is the reflection of the graph of $y = 2^x$ across the line $y = x$.)

   b. ■ $2^y = 7$

   $$\log 2^y = \log 7$$
   $$y \log 2 = \log 7$$
   $$y = \frac{\log 7}{\log 2}$$

   ■ Graph the function $y = \frac{\log x}{\log 2}$.

   c. Students should match their calculator display with that in the text.

Reflecting

1. $\log a = b$ means that $10^b = a$.

   a. $\log 1 = 0$ since $10^0 = 1$.

   b. $\log 10 = 1$ since $10^1 = 10$.

   c. $\log 10^x = x$ since $10^x = 10^x$.

   d. $10^{\log x} = x$ since $\log x$ is the power to which 10 can be raised to get x.

2. To convince someone the expressions are not equivalent, students may suggest substituting values for a and b and seeing that the resulting values are not equal. Examples follow.

   a. $\log (2 + 8) = \log 10 = 1$

   $\log 2 + \log 8 \approx 0.301 + 0.903 \approx 1.204$

   Thus, $\log (a + b) \neq \log a + \log b$.

Unit 3

MORE *continued*

b. $\log(12-2) = \log 10 = 1$

$\log 12 - \log 2 \approx 0.778$

Thus, $\log(a-b) \neq \log a - \log b$.

c. $\log(2 \cdot 5) = \log 10 = 1$

$(\log 2)(\log 5) \approx 0.210$

Thus, $\log ab \neq (\log a)(\log b)$.

d. $\log\left(\frac{20}{2}\right) = \log 10 = 1$

$\frac{\log 20}{\log 2} \approx 4.322$

Thus, $\log\left(\frac{a}{b}\right) \neq \frac{\log a}{\log b}$.

e. Let $a = 4$ and $x = 5$.

$\log(4 \cdot 5^2) = \log 100 = 2$

$2 \log(4 \cdot 5) = 2 \log 20 \approx 2.602$

Thus, $\log ax^2 \neq 2 \log ax$.

3. Logarithmic scales allow you to compare the ratios of pairs of numbers easily. If two pairs of values have the same ratio, they will be equal distances apart on a log scale.

4. Linear scales are like arithmetic sequences because to move to the next "mark" on the scale, you add a constant value. Logarithmic scales are like geometric sequences because to move to the next tick mark on the scale, you multiply by a constant value.

5. Responses will vary. (You may wish to let students know that they will study logarithms again in Unit 7, "Functions and Symbolic Reasoning.")

Extending

1. The Prime Number Theorem says that the number of primes not exceeding the positive integer n is asymptotic to $\frac{n}{\ln n} = \frac{n}{\frac{\log n}{\log e}} = \frac{n \log e}{\log n}$. Since $\log e \approx 0.4343$, the form given in the text,

$\frac{0.4343n}{\log n}$, is the common log equivalent to $\frac{n}{\ln n}$.

a.

n	10	25	40	55	70	85	100	115	130	145
Number of Primes $\leq n$	4	9	12	16	19	23	25	30	31	34

b. The actual counts tend to lie above the graph over this domain. For example, the actual number of primes less than or equal to 115 is 30, but the formula gives an estimate of 24.24. This is an error of about 20%.

c. $P(1,000) = \frac{0.4343 \cdot 1,000}{\log 1,000} = 145$ primes (the actual count is 168)

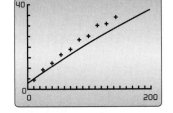

$P(100,000) = \frac{0.4343 \cdot 100,000}{\log 100,000} = 8,686$ primes (the actual count is 9,592)

MORE *continued*

$$P(1,000,000) = \frac{0.4343 \cdot 1,000,000}{\log 1,000,000} = 72,383 \text{ primes (the actual count is 78,498)}$$

$$P(10^{18}) = \frac{0.4343 \cdot 10^{18}}{\log 10^{18}} = 2.41 \times 10^{16} \text{ primes}$$

d. $\frac{P(10^6)}{10^6} = \frac{72,383}{10^6} \approx 0.072$

Approximately 7.2% of the numbers up to 10^6 are prime.

$\frac{P(10^{18})}{10^{18}} \approx 0.024$

Approximately 2.4% of the numbers up to 10^{18} are prime.

2. The function that models the amount of carbon-14 remaining is $y = a(1 - 0.000121)^t = a(0.999879^t)$, where y is the amount of carbon-14 remaining after t years and a is the original amount. To find the half-life, solve the equation:

$$0.5a = a(0.999879^t).$$

$$0.5 = 0.999879^t$$

$$\log 0.5 = t \log 0.999879$$

$$\frac{\log 0.5}{\log 0.999879} = t$$

$$5,728.1 \approx t$$

The half-life of carbon-14 is approximately 5,728 years.

3. Students will first need to change all weights into common units; this solution uses pounds.

Animal	Weight (in pounds)	Log (Weight)
Hummingbird	0.0044	−2.357
Shrew	0.1875	−0.727
Gerbil	0.2756	−0.5597
Rat	1.003	0.0013
Guinea pig	1.54	0.1875
Ringtail monkey	6	0.7782
Otter	13	1.114
Raccoon	21	1.322
Porpoise	103	2.013
Alligator	150	2.176
Llama	375	2.574
Moose	800	2.903
Cow	1,800	3.255
African elephant	14,000	4.146
Blue whale	307,000	5.487

Unit 3

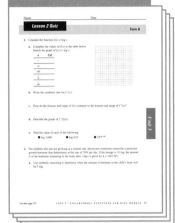

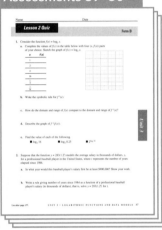

MORE *continued*

In order to graph these data on log paper, you would need to insert a cycle for between 0.1 and 1 to plot 0.1875 and 0.2756, and then add cycles for 10^{-2} and 10^{-3} to plot 0.0044. In all, nine cycles would be needed to plot these data.

4. **a.** If $0 < \log n < 1$, then $1 < n < 10$

   b. If $5 < \log n < 6$, then $10^5 < n < 10^6$ or $100{,}000 < n < 1{,}000{,}000$.

   c. If $p < \log n < p + 1$, then $10^p < n < 10^{p+1}$

5. **a.**
$$P = P_0 a^t$$
$$\frac{P}{P_0} = a^t$$
$$\log\left(\frac{P}{P_0}\right) = t \log a$$
$$t = \frac{\log\left(\frac{P}{P_0}\right)}{\log a}$$

   b.
$$A = P(1 + r)^{nt}$$
$$\frac{A}{P} = (1 + r)^{nt}$$
$$\log\left(\frac{A}{P}\right) = nt \log(1 + r)$$
$$t = \frac{\log\left(\frac{A}{P}\right)}{n \log(1 + r)}$$

   c.
$$A = P(1 + r)^{nt}$$
$$\frac{A}{P} = (1 + r)^{nt}$$
$$\left(\frac{A}{P}\right)^{\frac{1}{nt}} = ((1 + r)^{nt})^{\frac{1}{nt}}$$
$$r = \left(\frac{A}{P}\right)^{\frac{1}{nt}} - 1$$

See Assessment Resources pages 83–90.

REVIEW AND PRACTICE   individual task

▶PUMP

Answers

1. (b)
2. (c)
3. (b)
4. (a)
5. (b)

6. (b)
7. (e)
8. (d)
9. (c)
10. (e)

Unit 3

Lesson **3** *Linearizing Data*

LESSON OVERVIEW   In this lesson, students will learn how a calculator or computer fits an exponential equation to a set of data. The method is based on the observation that if the original points are clustered near the graph of an exponential equation, then the points (*x, log y*) are clustered near the graph of a linear equation. The calculator first takes the logarithm of each value of *y*. Next, a least squares regression line is fitted to the transformed data (*x, log y*). Finally, the least squares regression equation, log *y* = *a* + *bx*, is solved for *y* giving an exponential function *y* = *abˣ*. Students will be surprised to learn that the exponential equation given by the exponential regression command on their calculators is not the exponential equation that gives the smallest sum of squared errors. When the linear equation that minimized the sum of squared errors is transformed to an exponential equation, the least squares property is lost.

Statisticians typically omit translating back into exponential form, preferring to analyze the data in the form (*x, log y*), since a linear relationship is easier to think about and easier to deal with mathematically.

In order to be successful with this lesson, students have to connect their understanding of "inverse" from this unit to their understanding of least squares from Course 2, Unit 3, "Patterns of Association." They must also be able to manipulate logarithmic and exponential expressions.

Lesson Objectives

■ To understand the importance of linearization and how to transform data in order to linearize it

■ To understand and apply the procedure for fitting nonlinear functions to data

■ To review least squares linear regression

Think About This Situation

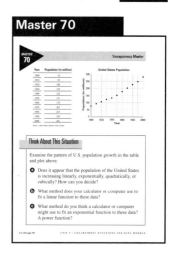

Master 70

See Teaching Master 70.

ⓐ At this stage, students should have a strategy other than just looking at the graph and saying that it appears to be linear, exponential, or quadratic. They should also know that using the calculator to fit each function to the data in order to find the largest value of the correlation coefficient *r* is not a good strategy. It's possible to get a large value of *r* even though the function does not have the same general shape as the data. Some students may think the graph looks linear. To have them test this, ask them to graph the equation of the least squares regression line on a plot of the data. Using years since 1900 for *x*, the regression equation is $y = 2.02x - 64.32$. They will see that even though *r* is very large, 0.991, the points follow a path that is slightly curved up. The points are above the regression line for small and large values of *x* and below the line for values in the middle.

Students also can see that the graph isn't linear by noticing that the differences aren't constant, but are increasing. The difference in population between 1900 and 1910 is 16 million. In the following ten-year intervals, the differences in millions are 14, 17, 9, 19, 28, 24, 24, 22, and 32. In general, the differences are growing.

Students may recall from Course 3, Unit 7, "Discrete Models of Change," that for a quadratic equation, the differences of the differences (that is, the second differences) are constant and for a cubic the differences of the differences of the differences (that is, the third differences) are constant. For this data, neither of these sets of differences looks constant. However, looking at the differences is a rather difficult way to decide on a function. The technique students learn in this lesson, linearization, is much more powerful.

From 1900 to 1910, the population increased by a factor of approximately 1.2. In the following ten-year intervals, the factors are approximately 1.2, 1.2, 1.1, 1.1, 1.2, 1.1, 1.1, 1.1, and 1.3. Since the factor is almost constant, it is reasonable to assume that the growth is close to exponential. If the students use their calculators to fit an exponential equation, they will get $y = 80.37(1.013^x)$ with $r = 0.997$. Graphing this equation on the scatterplot shows the points fall randomly on both sides of the graph.

Finally, students may want to explore the possibility that the data are piecewise linear, that is, the points follow the graph of a linear equation from 1900 to 1930 and another linear equation from 1930 to 2000.

ⓑ To fit a linear function, the calculator finds the equation that minimizes the sum of the squared errors or equivalently, the mean squared error (studied in Course 2, Unit 3, "Patterns of Association" and reviewed in Investigation 2 of this lesson).

ⓒ Most students will expect that the calculator will find the exponential function that minimizes the sum of the squared errors. That isn't quite the case. In this lesson, students will discover how calculators actually do fit exponential and power equations to data.

Unit 3

LAUNCH *continued*

This may also be a good time to remind students that changing the scales on a plot may change the visual impression of the data. For example, the points on the first plot below look quite linear. The points on the second plot look less linear. The only difference in the two plots is the length of the vertical scale.

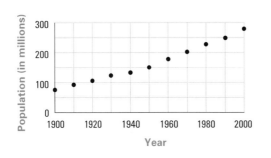
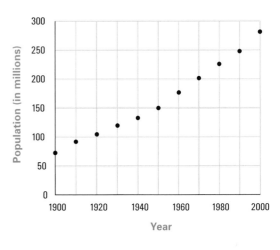

EXPLORE small-group investigation

INVESTIGATION 1 Straightening Functions

Transformation (statisticians sometimes say "re-expression") is a basic tool of statisticians, engineers, and scientists. This investigation will focus on transforming data so that it becomes linear. Why do statisticians, engineers, and scientists want their data to be linear? A linear relationship is the simplest relationship. Linear functions are easily understood and examined. The mathematics of least squares regression, for example, is easiest for linear functions.

Selecting the "best" transformation for a set of data is not an algorithmic procedure. It requires a combination of technical expertise and insight into the context from which the data came.

In this investigation, students will learn that some paired data can be transformed so that the points cluster about the graph of a linear equation. In some cases, this can be done by transforming each value of *y*. For example, if the points originally cluster about the graph of an exponential equation, transforming each value of *y* by taking its log (to any base) results in points (*x*, *log y*) that cluster about the graph of a linear equation.

NOTE: You may need to remind students that bivariate data are called "linear" if the points cluster tightly or loosely about a line that is, if they form an elliptical cloud. The points do not have to lie exactly on a line.

1. **a.** $\pi(15)^2 \approx 706.86$ square inches

   b. $y = \pi x^2, x \geq 0$

   The graph of this equation is part of a parabola.

EXPLORE *continued*

c. To transform square inches to square feet, divide by 144. The relationship between radius and surface area in square feet is also quadratic, $y = \frac{\pi}{144}x^2$, so the plot will still be part of a parabola.

Radius (in inches)	Surface Area (in square inches)	Surface Area (in square feet)
9	254.47	1.77
12	452.39	3.14
15	706.86	4.91
18	1,017.88	7.07
21	1,385.44	9.62
24	1,809.56	12.57

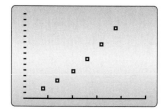

```
WINDOW
 Xmin =5
 Xmax=30
 Xscl =5
 Ymin =0
 Ymax=15
 Yscl =1
 Xres =1
```

Unit 3

d. No, if you transformed the surface area to square centimeters, the relationship would still be quadratic: $y = \frac{\pi}{0.155}x^2$. (1 cm^2 ≈ 0.155 in^2)

e. This type of transformation will lead to an equation of the form $y = ax^2$, which is a stretching or shrinking of the graph. The general shape of the graph remains parabolic.

2. a.

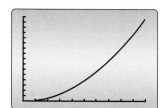

```
WINDOW
 Xmin =0
 Xmax=10
 Xscl =1
 Ymin =0
 Ymax=320
 Yscl =20
 Xres =1
```

b.

x	$y = \pi x^2$	$y^* = \sqrt{y}$
0	0	0
1	$\pi \approx 3.14$	$\sqrt{\pi} \approx 1.77$
3	$9\pi \approx 28.27$	$3\sqrt{\pi} \approx 5.32$
5	$25\pi \approx 78.54$	$5\sqrt{\pi} \approx 8.86$
10	$100\pi \approx 314.16$	$10\sqrt{\pi} \approx 17.72$
7 (for example)	$49\pi \approx 153.94$	$7\sqrt{\pi} \approx 12.41$

EXPLORE *continued*

c.

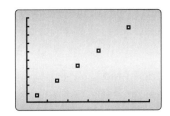

```
WINDOW
 Xmin =0
 Xmax=12
 Xscl =2
 Ymin =0
 Ymax=20
 Yscl =2
 Xres =1
```

Yes, they are collinear. The points (x, y^*) will fall on the graph of $y^* = \sqrt{\pi x^2}$ or $y^* = 1.77x$.

d. The slope is the square root of π or approximately 1.77. The slope is the square root of the coefficient of the x^2 term of the original function.

e. The original function operated on each value of x by squaring it and then multiplying by π. The linearizing transformation operated on each value of y by taking the square root. Squaring and taking the square root are inverse operations. (Note that you don't quite have inverse functions here because of the constant π. The inverse function of $y = \pi x^2$, $x \geq 0$ would be $y = \sqrt{\frac{x}{\pi}}$, not $y = \sqrt{x}$. If students had used the inverse function and plotted $\left(x, \sqrt{\frac{x}{\pi}}\right)$, the points would all lie on the graph of $y = x$.)

3. a.

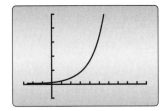

```
WINDOW
 Xmin =-3
 Xmax=10
 Xscl =1
 Ymin =-10
 Ymax=50
 Yscl =10
 Xres =1
```

b.

x	*y = 2^x*	*y* = log y*
0	1	0
1	2	0.3010
3	8	0.9031
5	32	1.5051
10	1,024	3.0103
7	128	2.1072

c.

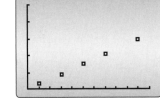

```
WINDOW
 Xmin =0
 Xmax=11
 Xscl =1
 Ymin =0
 Ymax=5
 Yscl =1
 Xres =1
```

Yes, they are collinear. The points (x, y^*) fall on the graph of $y^* = \log 2^x = x \log 2 \approx 0.3010x$.

EXPLORE *continued*

d. The slope of the linear function is log 2, and 2 is the base of the exponential function.

e. Exponentiation and taking the logarithm are inverse operations, but again the two functions are not inverses since the exponential function is base 2 and the log function is base 10.

4. a.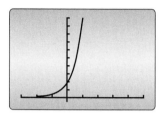

```
WINDOW
  Xmin =-3
  Xmax=5
  Xscl =1
  Ymin =-1
  Ymax=20
  Yscl =2
  Xres =1
```

b. Take the log (to any base) of each value of *y*. (Base 10 logarithms are used below.)

c. The operations of exponentiation and taking the logarithm are inverse operations. Again, the functions are not quite inverses.

d. The points $(x, \log y)$ will fall on the graph of $y^* = \log (4 \cdot 5^x) = \log 4 + x \log 5$. This is a linear equation of the form $y = a + bx$. (You may wish to point out that nothing is lost by leaving the coefficients in the form log 5 and log 4. Converting them to decimal form obscures the relationship between the coefficients of the original equation and these coefficients.)

e. The slope is the log of the 5 in the original equation. In general, if points on the graph of $y = a(b^x)$ are transformed by letting $y^* = \log y$, the slope of the linear equation that fits the transformed points $(x, \log y)$ will be log *b*. (The *y*-intercept is log *a*.)

5. a.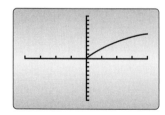

```
WINDOW
  Xmin =-1
  Xmax=1
  Xscl =.25
  Ymin =-10
  Ymax=10
  Yscl =1
  Xres =1
```

b. Square each value of *y*.

c. The original function is a square root function, and the linearizing function is a squaring function. Taking the square root and squaring are inverse operations. However, the two functions are not quite inverses of each other because of the constant 6.

d. The points (x, y^*) will fall on the graph of $y^* = (6\sqrt{x})^2 = 36x$. This is a linear equation.

e. The slope is 36. It is the square of the 6 in the original equation.

Unit 3

EXPLORE *continued*

6. **a.** A scatterplot of the data is shown below.

> **Some students may think the data are exponential, but they aren't. In the rest of this activity, students will see why an exponential function isn't a good fit. Some students may know a quadratic model is correct for equations of falling objects from previous work in science or mathematics.**

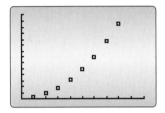 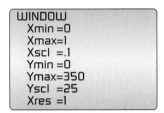

b. The relationship between time and distance fallen for free fall in a vacuum is given by the function $d = 0.5gt^2$, where $g = 980$ cm/sec^2 when the distance fallen is in centimeters and the time in seconds. This suggests a square root transformation. Such a transformation linearizes the data almost perfectly as seen below. (If students chose an exponential model, the linearizing transformation would be $y^* = \log y$. See the data, scatterplot, and discussion in Part c for why the data are not exponential.)

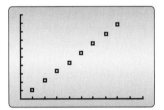

c.

Time (in seconds)	Distance Fallen (in centimeters)	Log (Distance Fallen)
0.1	5	0.6990
0.2	20	1.3010
0.3	44	1.6435
0.4	78	1.8921
0.5	122	2.0864
0.6	176	2.2455
0.7	240	2.3802
0.8	314	2.4969

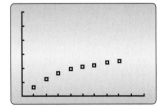 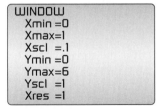

A log transformation did not linearize the data. The log transformation was "overkill"; instead of straightening the data, it made it bend the other way.

EXPLORE *continued*

d. Applying the power regression function to the data gives $d = 486t^{1.99} \approx 486t^2$, where d is measured in centimeters and t in seconds. To find the time it would take for the weight to fall 100 cm, solve the equation with $d = 100$.

$$100 = 486t^2$$
$$\frac{100}{486} = t^2$$
$$t \approx 0.45$$

It would take approximately 0.45 second for the weight to fall 100 cm.

7. a. The points will cluster on or about the graph of the linear equation $y^* = \log y = \log (ab^x) = \log a + x \log b$.

 b. The points will cluster on or about the graph of the linear equation $y^* = \sqrt{y} = \sqrt{ax^2} = \sqrt{a}x$.

SHARE AND SUMMARIZE full-class discussion

Checkpoint

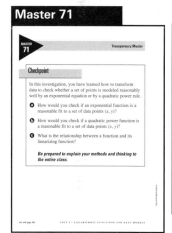

Master 71

See Teaching Master 71.

ⓐ If the original data follow an exponential pattern, the graph of $(x, \log y)$ should follow a linear pattern.

ⓑ If the original data are quadratic, then the graph of $(x, \sqrt{y})$ will be linear.

ⓒ The inverse function or a close relative has been used to linearize. In the examples in this investigation, the linearizing function differed from the inverse function by a constant or two. For example, the inverse of $y = 6\sqrt{x}$ is actually $y = \frac{x^2}{36}$ rather than $y = x^2$, the close relative used to linearize. In the case of the exponential and logarithmic functions, a different base may be used.

In this investigation, students have learned how to transform data to check if a set of points fits reasonably well to an exponential equation or to a quadratic equation. To summarize, make a plot of $(x, \log y)$. If this set of points is approximately linear, then an exponential function should be considered for the original data. This same principle applies with data that may be quadratic of the form $y = ax^2$, $x \geq 0$. In this case, make a plot of $(x, \sqrt{y})$ and see if it is linear. Note that the inverse function of $y = ax^2$, $x \geq 0$, is actually $y = \sqrt{\frac{x}{a}}$, but to linearize, the constant a can be ignored.

APPLY individual task

On Your Own

a. Some students may choose to represent the years by 0 to 350, but this will not affect the shape of the plot since it is a horizontal shift.

APPLY *continued*

Year	Estimated Population (in millions)	Log (Population)
1650	550	2.740
1750	725	2.860
1850	1,175	3.070
1900	1,600	3.204
1950	2,556	3.408
1980	4,458	3.649
2000	6,080	3.784

The plot for (x, *log y*) appears below.

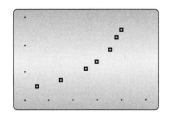

```
WINDOW
 Xmin =1600
 Xmax=2100
 Xscl =100
 Ymin =2.5
 Ymax=4
 Yscl =.5
 Xres =1
```

MORE
ASSIGNMENT *pp. 190–195*

Students can now begin
Modeling Task 3 or 4,
Organizing Task 1, Reflecting
Task 1 or 4, or Extending
Task 2 or 3 from the MORE
assignment following
Investigation 2.

b. The world population is increasing faster than exponentially. The scatterplot shows that a log transformation doesn't linearize the data. The scatterplot of the data still curves up. You can also see that the population is increasing faster than exponentially by observing that the multiplication factor is increasing. For the 100-year intervals from 1650–1950, the population increased by factors of approximately 1.3, 1.6, and 2.2, respectively.

As a follow-up to this task, you may wish to assign Reflecting Task 4 from the MORE set following Investigation 2.

EXPLORE small-group investigation

INVESTIGATION 2 Fitting Exponential Functions Using Log Transformations

In Activities 1 and 2 of this investigation, students review the idea of least squares regression. In Activity 3, students learn that the exponential regression function of their calculator does not produce the exponential function that is the best fit using the criterion of minimizing the sum of the squared residuals. After they complete these activities, you may want to check that all students understand this point.

EXPLORE *continued*

Activity 4 Part d will be difficult for many students and you may want to do a similar example with the whole class to help them learn how to do the necessary algebra.

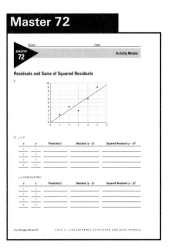

Master 72

TECHNOLOGY NOTE: The calculator only fits exponential functions of the form $y = a(b^x)$. If the data follow a function of the form $y = a(b^x) + c$, then the value c must first be subtracted from each value of y before fitting an exponential function. This will come up in Extending Task 3 on page 207, and may arise if students bring in their own data.

---

1. **See Teaching Master 72.**

    a. The residuals are 0.4, 0.8, −1.8, −0.4, and 1. Each residual should be shown on the plot as a vertical distance from the point to the line.

    b. The sum of the squared errors (residuals) is 5.2.

2. Line *A* has a sum of squared residuals of 4.8. Line *B* has a sum of squared residuals of 16. Line *A* has the smaller sum and thus must be the regression line. Some students may remember that the regression line must go through the point $(\bar{x}, \bar{y}) = (2.5, 3.5)$. Thus, again, line *A* must be the regression line.

3. a. Students should use their calculators to draw the plot and graph the functions. The graphs will be much more accurate. If they graph them by hand, they may not see any difference in the graphs.

    Both functions fit the points very well.

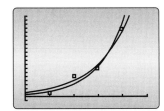

```
WINDOW
  Xmin =0
  Xmax=5
  Xscl =1
  Ymin =−1
  Ymax=20
  Yscl =1
  Xres =1
```

b. For $y = 2^x$, the sum of the squared residuals is 4.

x	y	Predicted $\hat{y}$	Residual $(y-\hat{y})$	Squared Residuals $(y-\hat{y})^2$
1	1	2	−1	1
2	5	4	1	1
3	7	8	−1	1
4	17	16	1	1
			Total	4

Unit 3

EXPLORE *continued*

For $y = 0.5423(2.4196^x)$, the sum of the squared residuals is 6.412.

x	*y*	**Predicted $\hat{y}$**	**Residual $(y - \hat{y})$**	**Squared Residual $(y - \hat{y})^2$**
1	1	1.312	−0.312	0.097
2	5	3.175	1.825	3.331
3	7	7.682	−0.682	0.465
4	17	18.587	−1.587	2.519
			Total	6.412

c. $y = 2^x$ (Note also that for this function, the sum of the residuals is 0.)

d. At this point, students will probably think that the calculator will give $y = 2^x$ since it has the smaller sum of the squared residuals and the sum of the residuals is 0.

e. $y = 0.5423(2.4196^x)$

Thus, the calculator does not give a function that minimizes the sum of the squared residuals.

4. In this activity, students find the exponential function in the same way that their calculator does. The most difficult part for them will be determining that the equation they get in Part d is equivalent to the one that the calculator got in Activity 3 Part e.

a. Taking the logarithm of each value of *y* would linearize the data.

b. The points seem to follow a linear pattern. See the plot at the right.

c. The least squares regression line for the points (x, y^*) is $y^* = -0.265739 + 0.383747x$.

d. $\log y = -0.265739 + 0.383747x$

$y = 10^{-0.265739 + 0.383747x}$

$= 10^{-0.265739} \cdot 10^{0.383747x}$

$= 0.5423(10^{0.383747})^x$

$= 0.5423(2.4196^x)$

This is the exponential function given by the calculator in Activity 3 Part e.

e. The calculator first takes the log of each value of *y*. Next, a least squares regression line is fit to the transformed data $(x, \log y)$. Finally, the least squares regression line $\log y = a + bx$ is solved for *y*.

SHARE AND SUMMARIZE full-class discussion

Checkpoint

See Teaching Master 73.

a First, by transformations, you can see if the proposed function is a reasonable fit. It is difficult to distinguish visually an exponential relationship from other relationships such as quadratic or cubic ones. If the original data follow an exponential relationship, the graph of (x, log y) should be linear. It is much easier to check visually that a graph is linear than exponential.

   Second, once you determine a reasonable model, the transformed data will follow a linear pattern. Linear models are the easiest to deal with both conceptually and computationally. For example, for data that follow a linear pattern, a least squares regression equation can easily be found using a calculator or computer.

b The calculator first finds $y^* = \log y$ for each value of y. It then computes a regression line $y^* = ax + b$ from the points (x, y^*), minimizing the sum of the squared residuals for those points. When the regression equation is solved for y, it becomes an exponential equation that isn't necessarily the one with the smallest sum of squared residuals for the original values.

CONSTRUCTING A MATH TOOLKIT: Students should describe how they can choose which type of function is a good fit to a given set of data. (See the Checkpoint on page T237 also.)

Unit 3

APPLY individual task

▶ On Your Own

a. See the table and plot. The scatterplot of the transformed data appears somewhat linear, so it is reasonable to consider an exponential model.

Year	Population (in millions)	Log (Population)
0	76	1.8808
10	92	1.9638
20	106	2.0253
30	123	2.0899
40	132	2.1206
50	151	2.1790
60	179	2.2529
70	203	2.3075
80	227	2.3560
90	249	2.3962
100	281	2.4487

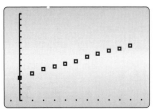

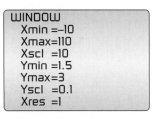

```
WINDOW
 Xmin =-10
 Xmax=110
 Xscl =10
 Ymin =1.5
 Ymax=3
 Yscl =0.1
 Xres =1
```

APPLY *continued*

b. If the years are entered as 0 to 100, the function is $y = 80.3741(1.0129^x)$. This function says the population of the United States in a given year is about 1.0129 times the population the previous year. In other words, the yearly growth rate in the United States is about 1.3%.

c. The linear equation fit to the points $(x, \log y)$ is $y^* = \log y = 0.00557x + 1.905116$. Solving this equation for y, gives the same equation as in Part b.

$$y = 10^{0.00557x + 1.905116}$$

$$= (10^{0.00557})^x \cdot 10^{1.905116}$$

$$= 80.3741(1.0129^x)$$

d. The estimates here use the rounded exponential regression equation above. According to this equation, the population was about 163 million in 1955 and about 329 million in 2010.

e. **Students could find these dates symbolically, graphically, or using tables. You may want to be sure they can find the dates symbolically since that skill is one of the objectives of this unit.**

$$50 = 80.3741(1.0129^x)$$

$$1.0129^x = 0.62209$$

$$x = \frac{\log 0.62209}{\log 1.0129} \approx -37 \text{ years or } 1863$$

To find the population in 2010, solve

$$140 = 80.3741(1.0129^x)$$

$$x = \frac{\log 1.74185}{\log 1.0129} \approx 43 \text{ years or } 1943$$

Therefore, the population of the United States was about 50 million in 1863 and about 140 million in 1943.

MORE
ASSIGNMENT *pp. 190–195*

Modeling: 2 and choice of one*

Organizing: 1, 3 or 4, and 5*

Reflecting: 1, 2, and 3

Extending: 2, and 3 or 4*

*When choice is indicated, it is important to leave the choice to the student. **NOTE:** It is best if Organizing tasks are discussed as a whole class after they have been assigned as homework.

MORE independent assignment

Modeling

1. a. The plot of (*year, number of deaths*) looks like it might be exponential.

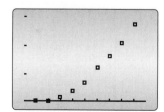

```
WINDOW
 Xmin =1980.2
 Xmax=1989.8
 Xscl =1
 Ymin =-4557.71
 Ymax=32376.71
 Yscl =10000
 Xres =1
```

MORE *continued*

However, the plot of (*year*, *log (number of deaths)*) is curved slightly downwards, indicating that the original data doesn't increase quite as fast as an exponential function.

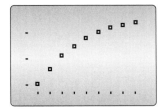

```
WINDOW
Xmin =1980.2
Xmax=1989.8
Xscl =1
Ymin =1.7102380...
Ymax=4.8393105...
Yscl =1
Xres =1
```

b. The number of deaths is clearly not increasing exponentially. See the plot of the (*year*, *number of deaths*) data below. A transformation is not needed to verify this.

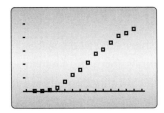

```
WINDOW
Xmin =1979.7
Xmax=1995.3
Xscl =1
Ymin =-7678.74
Ymax=53856.74
Yscl =10000
Xres =1
```

Note: This shape is sometimes called an *s*-curve or logistic curve. Such curves increase quickly at first, almost like an exponential curve, but then level off and approach a horizontal asymptote. (The leveling off is not apparent here.) These curves are characteristic of the population growth of animals in situations where there is a finite number of resources. They are also characteristic of phenomena like the spread of a rumor or of disease, where time is plotted on the *x*-axis and the percentage of the population that has heard the rumor or had the disease is plotted on the *y*-axis.

c. No, since the definition was expanded, that should make the number of cases relatively larger than before. But from 1992 on, the rate of increase is even less than before, so clearly the relationship isn't exponential.

2. a. The scatterplot of the (*time*, *relative activity*) data is below.

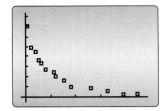

```
WINDOW
Xmin =-4.28
Xmax=49.48
Xscl =10
Ymin =-4.663
Ymax=40.763
Yscl =5
Xres =1
```

■ It appears that the data might follow an exponential pattern $y = a(b^x)$ with $b \leq 1$.

■ *a* would be approximately 35.

■ *b* would be less than 1 since the graph is decreasing.

Unit 3

MORE *continued*

b. The points on the plot of the (*time, log (relative activity)*) data below are approximately linear, so an exponential function appears to be a reasonable fit to these data.

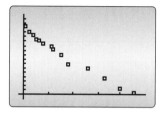
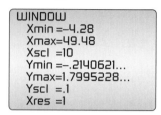

```
WINDOW
  Xmin =-4.28
  Xmax=49.48
  Xscl =10
  Ymin =-.2140621...
  Ymax=1.7995228...
  Yscl =.1
  Xres =1
```

c. $y = 27.12(0.9276^x)$

d. The linear regression equation is $y^* = \log y = -0.0326x + 1.4334$. Substituting $y^* = \log y$ and solving for y, gives $y = 27.12(0.9276^x)$, the same equation as the calculator computed in Part c.

If students want to do further analysis, have them look at a scatterplot of the residuals for the linear regression. The residuals from the linear regression are not as randomly scattered as one might like, indicating additional curvature in the data. The plot below is of the (*time, log y – predicted log y*) data.

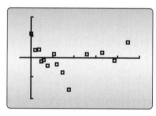
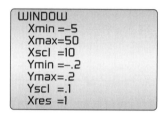

```
WINDOW
  Xmin =-5
  Xmax=50
  Xscl =10
  Ymin =-.2
  Ymax=.2
  Yscl =.1
  Xres =1
```

e. After 10 days, the function predicts relative activity of 12.79. After 47 days, it predicts relative activity of 0.7929.

3. a. As can be seen from the table or graph at the beginning of Lesson 3 on page 180 of the student text, the population of the United States increased almost linearly over the period 1960–1995, but the expenditures seem to increase faster than linearly. Factors about this context that might suggest exponential growth in these expenditures include the aging of the population (so that a larger percentage of the population receives Social Security and Medicare), the increase in life-span (so that people receive these benefits for more years), and the effect of inflation.

b. If the pattern of the data is exponential, then transforming the data by letting $y^* = \log y$ should linearize the data. This transformation does seem to linearize the data. A plot of (*x, log y*) using the **ZoomStat** window is shown at the right.

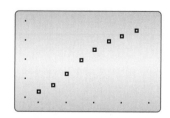

4. a. This looks something like a square root function, so perhaps squaring would linearize the data. It also looks something like a log function, so perhaps exponentiation would linearize the data.

MORE *continued*

b. First, try squaring the *y* values. The graph of (x, y^2), as shown below, is still concave down. This indicates that something stronger than squaring is needed.

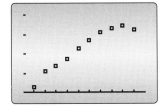

```
WINDOW
Xmin =.1
Xmax=10.9
Xscl =1
Ymin =-.025364
Ymax=.402364
Yscl =.1
Xres =1
```

Next, try exponentiation. The graph of $(x, 10^y)$, as shown below, is still concave down, but closer to linear.

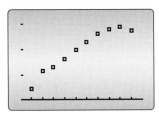

```
WINDOW
Xmin =.1
Xmax=10.9
Xscl =1
Ymin =1.0691800...
Ymax=4.30037977
Yscl =1
Xres =1
```

Since the points are not always increasing (the value of *y* for 10 choices is smaller than for 9 choices) the underlying continuous function fails the horizontal line test and has no inverse. Therefore, no transformation of *y* will linearize these data.

POSSIBLE PROJECT:
Designing and analyzing the results of an experiment to test reaction time versus number of choices would make a good project for students. It would be interesting to have data for large numbers of choices to see if the downward trend continues.

Organizing

1. a. The exponential function for these data is $y = 5.924(239.2312^x)$. The value of *r* for this regression is 0.959.

b. Students should know from their work in the investigation that an exponential model is not appropriate for these data which are quadratic. Thus, a large value of *r* does not always indicate that the model is appropriate for the data. However a large value of *r* does indicate that the points lie close to the graph of the exponential function.

2. You could square each value of *x* or you could divide each value of *y* by the corresponding value of *x*.

3. $y = a(b^x)$

$\log y = \log (a \cdot b^x)$

$\log y = \log a + \log b^x$

$\log y = \log a + x \log b = (\log b)x + \log a$

which is a linear relationship between *x* and $\log y$ with slope $\log b$.

4. a. $y = 10^{4x} = 10{,}000^x$

b. $y = 10^{-3x} = 0.001^x$

c. $y = 10^{ax} = (10^a)^x$, which is in the form k^x, where *k* is the constant 10^a.

Unit 3

MORE *continued*

5. **a.** $y = 10^{3x+2} = 10^{3x} \cdot 10^2 = 100(1,000^x)$

   b. $y = 10^{3x-4} = 0.0001(1,000^x)$

   c. $y = 10^{ax+b} = 10^{ax}10^b = 10^b(10^a)^x$, which is in the form $y = c(d^x)$, where $c = 10^b$ and $d = 10^a$ are constants.

Reflecting

1. The inverse will always work as a linearizing function since the points $(x, f^{-1}(f(x)))$ lie on the graph of $y = x$. However, a simplified version, with all constants set equal to 1 will also often work. If a non-constant function isn't one-to-one, there is no function of y that will linearize it.

TECHNOLOGY NOTE: On the TI calculators, the values of r and r^2 are displayed when **DiagnosticOn** is selected under **Catalog**.

2. As you have seen, the data are first linearized. The calculator then assumes a linear relationship between x and log y. At this stage, a least squares linear regression line is computed. The calculator also computes the value of r from these linearized data, using one of the equivalent standard formulas for the linear correlation coefficient r.

3. The search for a model should always be driven by scientific theory. The scientist should have some reasonable explanation for why the data might follow a certain kind of relationship before declaring a function a "model" of the phenomenon. If there aren't many points or if the scientist searches long enough, he or she will find a function that fits reasonably closely, but that doesn't mean that the function is a good "model" that can be used to further scientific inquiry.

4. Some examples of functions that (eventually) grow faster than an exponential function are $y = 2^{x^2}$, $y = x!$, and $y = x^x$.

Extending

1. **a.** The mean of the transformed data values is $\bar{x} + c$. (Students should know this from previous work.)

   b. The mean of the transformed data values is $c\bar{x}$.

   c. No, the mean of the transformed data is not equal to $\sqrt{\bar{x}}$. One counterexample is to let $x_1 = 1$ and $x_2 = 4$. Then $\bar{x} = 2.5$. The mean of the transformed data is $\frac{1+2}{2} = 1.5$, and $1.5 \neq \sqrt{2.5}$. In fact, the mean of the transformed data is never equal to $\sqrt{\bar{x}}$ for positive numbers.

   d. No, the mean of the transformed data is not equal to log $\bar{x}$. For example, let $x_1 = 10$ and $x_2 = 100$. Then $\bar{x} = 55$. Then the mean of the transformed data is $\frac{1+2}{2} = 1.5$, and $1.5 \neq \log 55$.

2. **a.** Instead of graphing $(x, \log y)$, the spreadsheet program has re-scaled the y-axis to get exactly the same effect. Notice that if the scale on the y-axis were written as powers of ten, it would be 10^0, 10^1, 10^2, 10^3, and 10^4. The base 10 logs of these numbers are 0, 1, 2, 3, and 4. Thus, this graph is designed to be linear in $(x, \log y)$.

MORE *continued*

b. It means that the population is increasing even faster than exponentially.

c. This plot curves down instead of up, indicating that the growth is not as fast as exponential growth. An exponential model is not appropriate for these data.

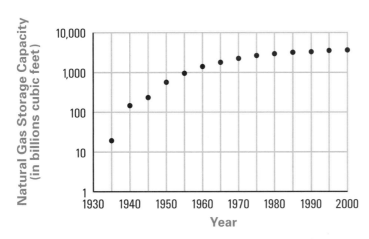

3. a. The residual for the point (2, 15) is $8 - 2a$.

The residual for the point (3, 21) is $14 - 3a$.

b.

x	y	$\hat{y}$	Residual	Squared Residual
1	12	$a + 7$	$5 - a$	$(5 - a)^2 = 25 - 10a + a^2$
2	15	$2a + 7$	$8 - 2a$	$64 - 32a + 4a^2$
3	21	$3a + 7$	$14 - 3a$	$196 - 84a + 9a^2$

c. The sum of the squared residuals is $14a^2 - 126a + 285$.

d. Think of $y = 14a^2 - 126a + 285$ as a function. Its graph is a parabola that opens up. The minimum occurs at the vertex with $a = \frac{-(-126)}{2(14)} = 4.5$.

e. $\hat{y} = 4.5x + 7$

The sum of the squared residuals is 1.5, the y-coordinate of the vertex of the parabola.

f. The calculator also gives $\hat{y} = 4.5x + 7$.

4. a.

x	y	$\hat{y} = ax^2$	Residual	Squared Residual
1	4	a	$4 - a$	$16 - 8a + a^2$
2	12	$4a$	$12 - 4a$	$144 - 96a + 16a^2$
3	26	$9a$	$26 - 9a$	$676 - 468a + 81a^2$

b. $98a^2 - 572a + 836$

c. Think of $y = 98a^2 - 572a + 836$ as a function. Its graph is a parabola that opens up. The minimum occurs at the vertex with $a = \frac{-(-572)}{2(98)} \approx 2.92$.

d. $\hat{y} = 2.92x^2$

REVIEW AND PRACTICE individual task

▶PUMP

Answers

1.	(c)	6.	(b)
2.	(e)	7.	(c)
3.	(c)	8.	(b)
4.	(d)	9.	(e)
5.	(c)	10.	(a)

EXPLORE small-group investigation

INVESTIGATION 3▶ Fitting Functions Using Log-Log Transformations

In this investigation, students study how a power function is fit to paired data. Suppose the data points (x, y) are clustered about the graph of a power function, $y = ax^b$. Note that if you take the logarithm of both sides of this equation, you get $\log y = \log a + b \log x$, which is linear in $\log x$ and $\log y$. Thus, taking the log of the values of x and the log of the values of y results in data that are linear. This is called a log-log transformation. Again, the calculator fits a linear equation to these transformed data and then "back-transforms" to get a power function.

One way to unify this lesson algebraically is to show students that if points fall near the graph of an exponential function $y = a(b^x)$ and they take the log of both sides, they will get $\log y = \log a + (\log b)x$, which is linear in x and $\log y$. If points fall near the graph of a power function $y = ax^b$ and they take the log of both sides, they will get $\log y = \log a + b \log x$, which is linear in $\log x$ and $\log y$. Thus, it isn't the act of taking the log of both sides of the equation that defines a log-log transformation. A log-log transformation consists of taking the log of each value of x and the log of each value of y in a set of bivariate data.

EXPLORE *continued*

1. **a.** *a*, *b*, and *x* will all be positive. Since *x* is in millions of miles, it will be positive. Since the points on the scatterplot follow a path that curves up, *b* will be positive and greater than 1. Since when *x* = 1, *y* should be positive, *a* will also be positive.

   b. To find the inverse function, exchange *x* and *y* and solve for *y*.

   $$y = ax^b$$
   $$x = ay^b$$
   $$\frac{x}{a} = y^b$$
   $$y = \sqrt[b]{\frac{x}{a}} = \left(\frac{x}{a}\right)^{\frac{1}{b}}$$

   c. In the inverse function, you don't know the values of *a* and *b*. If you try what worked before and ignore the constants, you can let *a* = 1. However, you don't have an obvious choice for *b*.

   d. No, a log transformation doesn't linearize the data. See the plot below.

   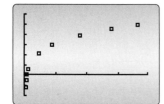

   ```
   WINDOW
    Xmin =0
    Xmax=4000
    Xscl =1000
    Ymin =-1
    Ymax=3
    Yscl =.5
    Xres =1
   ```

   e. Yes, a log-log transformation linearizes the data. See the following plot.

   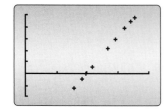

   ```
   WINDOW
    Xmin =0
    Xmax=4
    Xscl =1
    Ymin =-1
    Ymax=2.5
    Yscl =.5
    Xres =1
   ```

   f. $$y = ax^b$$
   $$\log y = \log (ax^b)$$
   $$\log y = \log a + \log x^b$$
   $$\log y = \log a + b \log x$$

   The final equation is linear in log *x* and log *y*.

   NOTE: Taking the log of both sides of an equation isn't the same thing as a log-log transformation. (See the last paragraph on page T248.)

   g. The scatterplot from Part e makes it easier to distinguish all of the points. In the original scatterplot, the points for the planets close to the Sun were plotted on top of each other. The log-log transformation "brings in" the larger points so that the smaller ones can also be seen.

Unit 3

EXPLORE *continued*

2. **a.** $y^2 = kx^3$, where x is half the length of the longer axis and y is the time the planet takes to orbit the Sun.

   b. Since y is positive, $y = \sqrt{kx^3} = \sqrt{k}x^{\frac{3}{2}} = \sqrt{k}x^{1.5}$.

   c. $y = (0.0011)x^{1.50015}$

   This is very close to Kepler's model of $y = \sqrt{k}x^{1.5}$.

3. **a.** The data were linearized by taking the square root of the distance: $y^* = \sqrt{y}$.

   b. Yes, it does. Since the basic model for free fall is $y = kx^2$, a power model, a log-log transformation will linearize the data. You can see this from both the graph and the equation.

   A plot of the transformed data (*log (time)*, *log (distance fallen)*) appears below.

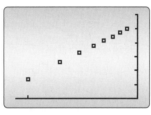

```
WINDOW
Xmin =-1.1
Xmax=0
Xscl =1
Ymin =0
Ymax=3
Yscl =.5
Xres =1
```

$y = kx^2$

$\log y = \log (kx^2)$

$\log y = \log k + \log x^2$

$\log y = \log k + 2 \log x$,

which is linear in $\log x$ and $\log y$.

SHARE AND SUMMARIZE full-class discussion

Checkpoint

See Teaching Master 74.

a To perform a log-log transformation, take the log (to any base) of each of the paired values. A log-log transformation is useful because it linearizes data that have a power relationship of the form $y = ax^b$. As seen with the planet data, graphing (*log x*, *log y*) has the effect of "bringing in" points that otherwise would be much larger than the other points that are clustered together near the origin. By using logarithms, the points with very large coordinates are proportionally not so much larger than the other points as they were before.

b *Step 1* Decide what models are suggested by scientific theory.

Step 2 For each possible model, perform the appropriate transformation that should linearize the data.

Step 3 Examine the scatterplot of the transformed data. The points should fall randomly about a straight line. (You may want to graph the least squares linear regression line on the plot of the transformed data to better observe the residuals.)

CONSTRUCTING A MATH TOOLKIT: Students should explain why a log-log transformation linearizes a power model. They should also describe the general steps to go through in order to determine an appropriate model for a set of data.

APPLY individual task

On Your Own

a.

Planet	Average Distance From the Sun (in millions of miles)	Length of a "Year" (in Earth days)	Log (Distance)	Log (Length of a "Year")
Mercury	36	88	1.556	1.945
Venus	67	225	1.826	2.352
Earth	93	365	1.969	2.562
Mars	142	687	2.152	2.837
Jupiter	484	4,333	2.685	3.637
Saturn	887	10,759	2.948	4.032
Uranus	1,783	30,685	3.251	4.487
Neptune	2,794	60,189	3.446	4.780
Pluto	3,661	90,465	3.564	4.957

b. See the plot below. You can see the points for all nine planets because the points for planets close to the Sun don't lie on top of each other. By using logs, the planets with very large distances and lengths of a year are proportionally not so much larger than the other planets. Yes, the log-log transformation linearized the data. (It is interesting that this plot shows the gap between Mars and Jupiter, where the asteroid belt is located.)

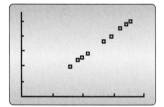
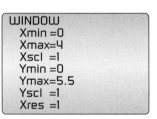

```
WINDOW
 Xmin =0
 Xmax=4
 Xscl =1
 Ymin =0
 Ymax=5.5
 Yscl =1
 Xres =1
```

c. $y = 0.4077x^{1.4999}$ A planet 600 million miles from the Sun would have an Earth year of about 5,988 days.

d. The first columns are two different ways of defining the distance of the planet from the Sun. One definition uses half of the major axis of the orbit; the other uses the average distance from the Sun. (The two numbers are so close that you should make a conjecture about the character of the elliptical orbits: They are almost circular.) The second columns give the same measurement, but in different units. One is the number of Earth years; the other is this number multiplied by 365 or the number of Earth days. Thus, the two power equations should be about the same. In Activity 2, the power function was $y = (0.0011)x^{1.50}$. In this "On Your Own," the power function is $y = 0.4077x^{1.4999}$. These are about the same since the exponents are very close and $0.0011(365) = 0.4015 \approx 0.4077$.

Unit 3

APPLY *continued*

If time permits, you may wish to illustrate and discuss the following questions: "Do the residuals from the power function follow a random pattern?" "What does this say about the appropriateness of a power function for these data?" The residuals aren't random, they tend to grow with *x*. Notice the large residual for Pluto. This is a common phenomenon and one reason statisticians prefer to do their analysis entirely with (*log x*, *log y*), where the residuals from the linear equation do not grow with *x*.

Planet	x	y	$\hat{y}$	$y - \hat{y}$
Mercury	36	88	88.05	−0.05
Venus	67	225	223.55	1.45
Earth	93	365	365.58	−0.58
Mars	142	687	689.74	−2.74
Jupiter	484	4,333	4,340.02	−7.02
Saturn	887	10,759	10,767.02	−8.03
Uranus	1,783	30,685	30,684.71	0.29
Neptune	2,794	60,189	60,190.02	−1.022
Pluto	3,661	90,465	90,277.28	187.72

Note that the sum of the residuals isn't 0. This is because the calculator linearizes the data using a log-log transformation and uses least squares to compute a linear regression equation in (*log x*, *log y*). The sum of the residuals from that equation, log *y* = 1.4999*x* − 0.3896, is 0.

MORE

ASSIGNMENT *pp. 203–207*

Modeling: Choose two*
Organizing: 1, 2, and 4
Reflecting: 4 and choice of one*
Extending: 1 and choice of one*

*When choice is indicated, it is important to leave the choice to the student.
NOTE: It is best if Organizing tasks are discussed as a whole class after they have been assigned as homework.

MORE independent assignment

Modeling

1. **a.** A log-log transformation linearizes these data so that the pattern is no longer curved down. See the plot below. The three smallest and youngest trees don't seem to follow quite the same linear relationship as the rest of the trees.

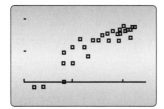

```
WINDOW
  Xmin =.49994106...
  Xmax=1.72536822
  Xscl =.5
  Ymin =-.2669100...
  Ymax=1.0730899...
  Yscl =.5
  Xres =1
```

MORE *continued*

b. Since a log-log transformation linearizes the data, find a power function: $y = 0.285x^{0.911}$. Note that the exponent is not too much less than 1, indicating that the curvature of the plot of the data was only slightly downward. Perhaps the three smallest trees should be eliminated from this analysis as the linear relationship may hold only for medium- and larger-sized trees.

c. A 15-year-old chestnut tree planted on a poor site would have about a 3.4-inch diameter.

d. Assume the trees have circular cross sections. Since the circumference is a multiple of the diameter ($C = \pi d$), the circumference would increase according to the power function $C = 0.285\pi \cdot x^{0.911}$.

e. Again assuming circular cross sections, the cross-sectional area A would be modeled by the power function below.

$$A = \pi r^2$$
$$= \tfrac{\pi}{4}d^2$$
$$= \tfrac{\pi}{4}(0.285x^{0.911})^2$$
$$= 0.020\pi \cdot x^{1.822}$$

2. a. You cannot conclude much from looking at the given plot except that there are two animals much larger than the rest. The other points are all clustered on top of each other near the origin.

b. Below is a plot of (*log x, log y*). A log-log transformation linearized the data, so a power equation should fit the points well. The power function is $y = 0.1966x^{1.1056}$.

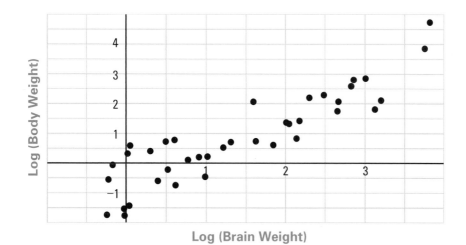

3. a. A log-log transformation linearizes the data. This indicates that a power function would be a good fit for the data.

MORE *continued*

b. The general form of the power function is $y = ax^b$. First use (1, 588). Then, $588 = a \cdot 1^b = a$. Now, substitute this value for a and use the point (9, 121,072):

$$121{,}072 = 588(9^b)$$

$$\frac{121{,}072}{588} = 9^b$$

$$\frac{\log\left(\frac{121{,}072}{588}\right)}{\log 9} = b$$

$$2.425 \approx b$$

Thus, an approximate power function is $y = 588(x^{2.425})$.

Some students might choose to find the equation of the line through the two points after applying a log-log transformation and then rewrite that equation as a power function.

The equation found using the power regression feature is $y = 433.27(x^{2.534})$.

c. The predicted number of AIDS deaths by the year 2000 is $y = 433.27(19^{2.534}) \approx 753{,}564$ people. This prediction assumes that the pattern of change in total number of AIDS deaths remains the same from 1993 to 2000.

Organizing

1. a. Responses will vary. For example, the points below lie exactly on the graph of $y = 2^x$. The linear correlation is $r \approx 0.91$.

x	y
0	1
1	2
2	4
3	8
4	16
5	32

b. Responses will vary. The student's set of points should form an elliptical cloud.

2. a. $y = 10^{\log x + 2} = x \cdot 10^2 = 100x, \; x > 0$

b. $y = 10^{-2 \log x + 3} = 1{,}000x^{-2}, \; x > 0$

MORE *continued*

    c. $y = 1,000x^2,\ x > 0$

    d. $y = 10^{a \log x + b} = 10^b x^a,\ x > 0$

3. **a.** Take the log of both sides to get $\log y = \log 2 + x \log 3$, which is linear in x and $\log y$.

    b. First, subtract 5 from both sides and then take the log of both sides to get $\log (y - 5) = x \log 2$, which is linear in x and $\log (y - 5)$.

    c. Take the square root of both sides to get $\sqrt{y} = \sqrt{3}x$, which is linear in x and $\sqrt{y}$.

4. **a.** $d = kt^2$

    b. $v = kr^3$

    c. $s = k\sqrt{l}$

    d. $l = ks^2$

Reflecting

1. Linear equations are the simplest and the easiest to understand. For example, you can interpret the slope of a line: for every increase of 1 unit in x, you expect that y will increase by m units (where m is the slope of the regression line). It is also easier to determine visually if a relationship is linear than it is to verify other relationships.

2. Perhaps this can be explained best by an example. Scientists often speak of one phenomenon being an "order of magnitude larger than another." When they say this they are thinking in terms of a logarithmic scale. One example is the Richter scale for earthquakes. On this scale, an earthquake with intensity 10 times larger than another is reported as one unit larger. For example, a 7.0 earthquake is ten times as intense as a 6.0 earthquake. Scientists find such a scale more useful.

    (You might mention to students that a second example comes from the field of psychology. One of the characteristics of perception is that in order for a person to sense a linear increase in the magnitude of a stimulus, the strength of the stimulus must be increasing exponentially. Such an exponential relationship is called Fechner's Law and is taught in many introductory college psychology courses. So the intensity of the stimulus could be reported in the actual physical units or in the units in which people perceive it, the log of physical units. See Activity 1 on page 169.)

3. The path of a comet is distinctly elliptical. It is clearly not circular with the Sun at the center.

4. The value of r indicates how closely the data points cluster around the least squares regression line. (Recall that r is the linear correlation coefficient.) It does not indicate how adequate the equation is as a model of the data. That depends on whether the equation flows from scientific theory and on whether the points are scattered randomly about the graph of the equation. If there is a pattern to the residuals, the model is probably inadequate, no matter how large r is.

Unit 3

MORE *continued*

Extending

1. A log-log transformation will not linearize data that have an exponential relationship. For example, consider the following points, which lie on the graph of $y = 2^x$. The plot of (*log x*, *log y*) is clearly not linear; in fact, it is exponential.

x	y	log x	log y
1	2	0	0.301
2	4	0.301	0.602
3	8	0.477	0.903
4	16	0.602	1.204
5	32	0.699	1.505

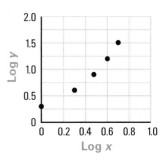

You can see algebraically that this transformation results in another exponential equation:

$y = 2^x$

$\log y = \log (2^x)$

$\log y = x \log 2$

$\log y = (\log 2)(10^{\log x})$

This is an exponential equation in *log y* and *log x*.

2. **a.** ■ The table below shows the values of (*log (distance)*, *log (length of a year)*).

Planet	Average Distance From the Sun (in millions of miles)	Length of a "Year" (in Earth days)	Log (Distance)	Log (Length of a "Year")
Mercury	36	88	1.556	1.945
Venus	67	225	1.826	2.352
Earth	93	365	1.969	2.562
Mars	142	687	2.152	2.837
Jupiter	484	4,333	2.685	3.637
Saturn	887	10,759	2.948	4.032
Uranus	1,783	30,685	3.251	4.487
Neptune	2,794	60,189	3.446	4.780
Pluto	3,661	90,465	3.564	4.957

■ Fitting a linear equation to (*log (distance)*, *log (length of a year)*), gives $\log y = -0.3896 + 1.4999 \log x$.

MORE *continued*

■ Solve for *y*:

$$y = 10^{(-0.3896 + 1.4999 \log x)}$$
$$= 10^{-0.3896} \cdot 10^{1.4999 \log x}$$
$$= 0.4078(10^{\log x})^{1.4999}$$
$$= 0.4078x^{1.4999}$$

b. The equation in Part a should be almost the same equation that the calculator gives for the power regression equation based on the original data.

3. a. From the fact that $y = 1.6$ when $x = 0$, you know that $1.6 = a \cdot 0^b + c$, so $c = 1.6$. Since $y = 3.9$ when $x = 1$, you have $3.9 = a \cdot 1^b + 1.6$, or $a = 2.3$. Finally, using the fact that $y = 5.3364$ when $x = 2$, you have $5.3364 = 2.3 \cdot 2^b + 1.6$, or $3.7364 = 2.3 \cdot 2^b$ or $1.624521739 = 2^b$. Solving for b by taking the log of both sides, gives $b = 0.7$. The equation is $y = 2.3x^{0.7} + 1.6$. This can be checked using $(3, 6.5626)$, the final (x, y) pair.

b.

t (in seconds)	*d* (in feet)
1	516
2	564
3	644
4	756
5	900

A log-log transformation gives the values in the following table.

log *t*	log *d*
0	2.71265
0.30103	2.75128
0.47712	2.80889
0.60206	2.87852
0.69897	2.95424

The points (*log t*, *log d*) follow a pattern that is curved upwards. A log-log transformation did not linearize these points.

c. $\log y = \log (16x^2 + 500)$. This cannot be simplified. It is not an equation linear in $\log x$ and $\log y$.

d. The transformed values are

t	*d* − 500
1	16
2	64
3	144
4	256
5	400

Unit 3

Assessments 91–93

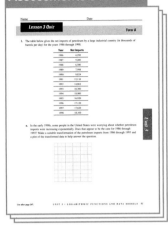

MORE *continued*

A log-log transformation gives the values

log t	log $(d - 500)$
0	1.20412
0.30103	1.80618
0.47712	2.15836
0.60206	2.40824
0.69897	2.60206

Yes, a log-log transformation linearizes the points. This should be the case because the points $(t, d - 500)$ fall on the graph of the power function

$$d = 16t^2 + 500 - 500 = 16t^2.$$

Alternatively, students may note the following sequence of equivalent equations for $t > 0$ and $d > 500$:

$$d = 16t^2 + 500$$
$$d - 500 = 16t^2$$
$$\log (d - 500) = \log (16t^2)$$
$$\log (d - 500) = \log 16 + \log t^2$$
$$\log (d - 500) = \log 16 + 2 \log t$$

The last equation is linear in log t and log $(d - 500)$.

e. Subtract the value of the constant c from each of the values of y.

See Assessment Resources pages 91–96.

Assessments 94–96

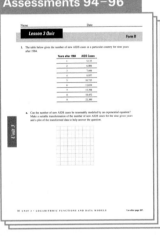

REVIEW AND PRACTICE individual task

▶**PUMP**

Answers

1.	(e)	6.	(c)
2.	(a)	7.	(e)
3.	(a)	8.	(a)
4.	(c)	9.	(b)
5.	(d)	10.	(d)

Lesson **4** *Looking Back*

SYNTHESIZE UNIT IDEAS   small-group activity

1. **a.** $f(20)$ is the population in thousands of the town in the year 2000. $f^{-1}(20)$ is the number of years after 1980 when the population reached 20,000.

    b. After t years, the population of the town was 32,000. The equation can be rewritten as $f^{-1}(32) = t$.

2. Both the graphs of the given function and the inverse function are shown on the graphs below.

    a.

    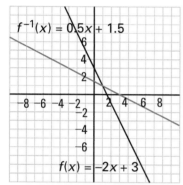

    The function has an inverse because it is one-to-one.

    b.

    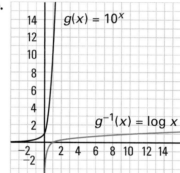

    The function has an inverse because it is one-to-one.

    c.

    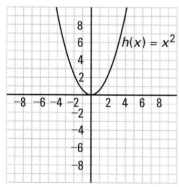

    The function doesn't have an inverse because it is not one-to-one.

    d.

    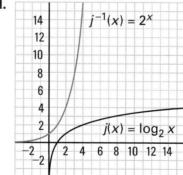

    The function has an inverse because it is one-to-one.

SYNTHESIZE *continued*

3. The letters on the scale below correspond to the letters in the far right-hand column of the table.

Type of Wave		Log (Frequency)	Label on Chart
Alternating current		1.78	*a*
AM radio	ranges from	5.73	*b*
	to	6.20	*c*
Television and FM radio	range from	7.73	*d*
	to	8.33	*e*
Light	ranges from infrared	14.59	*f*
	to ultraviolet	14.89	*g*
X-rays	range from	16.48	*h*
	to	20	*i*

Frequency

i — 10^{20}
— 10^{19}
— 10^{18}
h — 10^{17}
— 10^{16}
g, f — 10^{15}
— 10^{14}
— 10^{13}
— 10^{12}
— 10^{11}
— 10^{10}
— 10^{9}
e — 10^{8}
d — 10^{7}
c — 10^{6}
b — 10^{5}
— 10^{4}
— 10^{3}
a — 10^{2}
— 10^{1}
— 10^{0}

4. **a.** $f^{-1}(x) = \frac{1}{3}x + \frac{2}{3}$

   b. $h^{-1}(x) = 10^x$

   c. $i^{-1}(x) = \log_7 x = \frac{\log x}{\log 7}$

5. The algorithm with time given by $g(n) = n \log n$ is faster. This can be seen by looking at the graphs of $f(n)$ and $g(n)$. Numerically, students may observe that, for example, if $10^2 \le n \le 10^3$, then $2 \le \log n \le 3 < \frac{10^2}{2} \le \frac{n}{2}$. It is clear that for all $n > 0$, $\frac{1}{2}n^2 > n \log n$, indicating that the second method requires less time. (A proof using calculus is based on the facts that $\frac{1}{2}n^2 > n \log n$ for $n = 1, 2, 3, 4, 5$ and $\frac{d}{dx}\frac{1}{2}x = \frac{1}{2} > \frac{1}{x}\ln 10 = \frac{d}{dx}\log x$ for $x \ge 5$. Since $\frac{1}{2}n$ "starts out" larger, and for $n \ge 5$, increases faster, it is always greater than $\log n$.)

6. **a.** $x = \log 2.75 \approx 0.439$ Check: $10^{0.439} \approx 2.75$

   b. There is no solution since 10^x is always positive.

   c. $\log 16.2 = \log 9.3^x$

   $\log 16.2 = x \log 9.3$

   $x = \frac{\log 16.2}{\log 9.3}$

   $x \approx 1.25$ Check: $16.2 \approx 9.3^{1.25}$

   d. $\log\left(\frac{16.2}{2}\right) = \log 3.7^x$

   $\frac{\log 8.1}{\log 3.7} = x$

   $x \approx 1.60$ Check: $16.2 \approx 2(3.7)^{1.6}$

   e. $x = 10^{-2.3} \approx 0.005$ Check: $\log(0.005) \approx -2.3$

SYNTHESIZE *continued*

7. **a.** Yes, it looks like this is reasonable. The scatterplot indicates a pattern of the form $y = x^k$ where $0 \le k \le 1$.

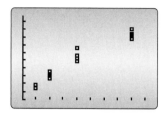

```
WINDOW
 Xmin =0
 Xmax=9
 Xscl =1
 Ymin =260
 Ymax=365
 Yscl =10
 Xres =1
```

b. $y = kx^{\frac{1}{9}}$

c. Since the suggested model is a power function, a log-log transformation should linearize the data. A log-log transformation produces the following data:

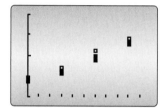

```
WINDOW
 Xmin =-.09
 Xmax=1
 Xscl =.1
 Ymin =2.4
 Ymax=2.6
 Yscl =.05
 Xres =1
```

Log *x*	Log *y*
0	2.4456
0	2.44091
0	2.43933
0	2.4456
0.30103	2.46389
0.30103	2.4609
0.30103	2.45788
0.30103	2.46982
0.60206	2.49969
0.60206	2.49415
0.60206	2.48996
0.60206	2.51322
0.90309	2.53275
0.90309	2.52892
0.90309	2.53529
0.90309	2.54283

Yes, the transformed data appear linear.

d. Using a calculator to find the least squares linear regression line gives the equation $y^* = 0.1038x^* + 2.438$.

Solve for *y*:

$\log y = 0.1038 \log x + 2.438$

$y = 10^{0.1038 \log x + 2.438}$

$y = (10^{\log x})^{0.1038} \cdot 10^{2.438}$

$y = 274.1574x^{0.1038}$

e. From the calculator, the power function is $y = 274.2769x^{0.1038}$, which is almost the same.

Unit 3

SYNTHESIZE *continued*

8. **a.** The equation of the line containing the two points is $\log N = 0.3566t + 2.3387$. (Be sure that students write the equation using the appropriate variables.)

Next, express N as a function of t:

$$N = 10^{(0.3566t + 2.3387)}$$

$$N = (10^{0.3566t})(10^{2.3387})$$

$$N = 218.12(2.273^t)$$

All three of the equations above express N as a function of t. In the unit, students have been asked to write exponential equations in the form $y = a(b^x)$, which corresponds to the last equation above.

b. The equation of the line containing the two given points is $\log N = 2.655 \log t + 2.3607$. (Be sure students write this equation using $\log N$ and $\log t$.) This equation can be rewritten as follows:

$$N = 10^{(2.655 \log t + 2.3607)}$$

$$N = (10^{\log t})^{2.655}(10^{2.3607})$$

$$N = (t^{2.655})(229.456)$$

$$N = 229.456t^{2.655}$$

c. The function in Part b is a better fit to the data in Plot I because the least squares regression line in Plot III is a better fit to the transformed data than is the least squares regression line in Plot II.

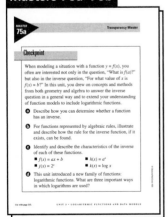

Masters 75a–75b

SHARE AND SUMMARIZE full-class discussion

Checkpoint

See Teaching Master 75a and 75b.

ⓐ A function has an inverse if and only if it is one-to-one. This can be determined from the graph of the function using the horizontal line test. It can be determined from the table of all values of the function by noting whether there are any duplicate y values. It can be determined from the equation by interchanging x and y, solving for y, and checking to be sure a function results.

ⓑ Given $y = f(x)$, the inverse is found by interchanging x and y and solving for y. The resulting function is the inverse $f^{-1}(x)$.

ⓒ ■ $f^{-1}(x) = \dfrac{x - b}{a} = \dfrac{1}{a}x - \dfrac{b}{a}$

The graphs of both $f(x)$ and $f^{-1}(x)$ are lines. The slope of the graph of $f^{-1}(x)$ is $\dfrac{1}{a}$.

SHARE AND SUMMARIZE *continued*

The y-intercept of $f^{-1}(x) = -\frac{b}{a}$.

- $h^{-1}(x) = \log_a x$

  $h^{-1}(x)$ is defined only for positive x.

  $h^{-1}(x)$ is increasing at a decreasing rate. It is asymptotic to the y-axis.

- $j^{-1}(x) = \log_2 x$

  $j^{-1}(x)$ is defined for $x > 0$.

  $j^{-1}(x)$ is increasing at a decreasing rate. It is asymptotic to the y-axis.

- $k^{-1}(x) = 10^x$

  $k^{-1}(x)$ is defined for all x.

  $k^{-1}(x)$ is asymptotic to the x-axis and is increasing at an increasing rate.

ⓓ (1) Logarithms are used to make logarithmic scales. (2) Logarithms are used to solve exponential equations. (3) Logarithms are used to transform data to help determine the appropriate function family to model a given data set.

ⓔ ■ True

  $\log (M \cdot N) = \log M + \log N$ is the Product Property of logarithms.

  ■ False

  $\log M^N = N \log M$, not $(\log M)^N$.

  ■ True

  $\log_a M = \frac{\log M}{\log a}$

  ■ True

  If $\log y = 3x + 2$, then

  $10^{3x + 2} = y$

  $100(10^{3x}) = y$

  $100(1{,}000^x) = y$.

ⓕ The goal of using logarithms to transform data is to be able to fit a linear function to the transformed data. Then the linear equation (using transformed variables) can be solved to get an exponential or power function that models the original data. Before transforming data, you should consider the context, and from the data and the context choose an appropriate transformation to try to linearize the data. If an exponential model seems appropriate, then the transformation that should linearize the data is $y^* = \log y$. If a power model seems appropriate, then to linearize the data, both the x and y values need to be transformed with $x^* = \log x$ and $y^* = \log y$.

ⓖ The calculator first "linearizes" the data by making the transformation that is appropriate for the function you select. For example, if you ask for an exponential regression, the calculator makes the transformation $y \rightarrow \log y$. It then finds the linear equation that minimizes the sum of the squared residuals. Finally, the calculator solves the linear equation for the original y.

See Teaching Masters 76a–76c.

Responses will vary. Above all, this should be something that is useful to the individual

Unit 3

Masters 76a–76c

On Your Own

student. You may wish to have students use the Teaching Master 76a–76c, "Logarithmic Functions and Data Models" Unit Summary, to help them organize the information.

Optional Habits of Mind Master:

See Teaching Master 77.

You may wish to use this master as a transparency to facilitate a class discussion that raises student awareness of the thinking skills they are learning.

See Assessment Resources 97–113.

Looking Back, Looking Ahead

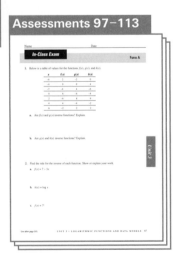

Master 77

Assessments 97–113

The extensive work that students have done developing a well-defined sense of function, as well as the technical skills required to create and use function models to answer questions about pat-

▶Reflecting on Mathematical Content

terns relating variable quantities, rates of change, motion, and optimization has positioned them well for the mathematics in this unit. Here, the graphical and symbolic sense that they have developed with a variety of families of functions was extended to logarithmic functions.

Students' evolving understanding of the concept of function inverse from Course 2, "Matrix Models" and "Patterns of Location, Shape, and Size"; Course 3, "Families of Functions" and "Discrete Models of Change"; and Course 4, "Modeling Motion" was formalized in this unit. The inverse of a function is like the inverse of a number when addition or multiplication is the operation in question. For functions, the operation is composition; the composition of a function and its inverse is the identity function. A key idea relating functions and their inverses is the connection between their graphs. The graph of the inverse is the image of the graph of the function when reflected across the line $y = x$. This gives an easily used visual check of whether a graph represents the inverse of a function. The coordinate representation of this reflection, $(x, y) \rightarrow (y, x)$, provides a systematic way to construct an equation for the inverse function.

The idea of inverse was then used to introduce logarithmic functions, the inverses of exponential functions. Properties of common (base 10) logarithms were studied and logarithmic scales were introduced as a precursor to the use of the logarithm function as a means to linearize data. The unit culminated by using a logarithmic transformation of one or both variables of a set of data to help determine whether or not an exponential or a power function is an appropriate model for the data.

The operation of composition will recur in this course in Unit 7, "Functions and Symbolic Reasoning," when they study the geometry of the complex numbers. Students who study calculus will use function composition extensively with applications of the chain rule. Logarithmic functions form a family of functions that are used throughout mathematics and mathematical modeling. Unit 7 of this course also revisits logarithms, extending to natural logarithms, to ensure that the fundamentals of this topic are well understood.

Unit 3 Assessment

Unit 3

Counting Models

UNIT OVERVIEW This unit provides an introduction to combinatorics. It continues and formalizes the previous informal work that students have done with systematic counting in earlier courses. Students learn fundamental concepts and methods used to solve combinatorial problems. Counting concepts and techniques that are developed include the Multiplication Principle of Counting, combinations, and permutations. Related topics include the Binomial Theorem and Pascal's triangle. Also, two new methods of mathematical reasoning are developed, combinatorial reasoning and mathematical induction.

In the first investigation of Lesson 1, students engage in counting by careful thinking, without use of formal counting formulas. This is important for developing basic skills and perspectives on combinatorial problems. Counting tools developed in this investigation include the Multiplication Principle of Counting, tree diagrams, and systematic lists. Students explore situations that anticipate the more formal work they will do in the following lessons. In the second investigation, students develop the concepts and formulas for combinations and permutations.

In Lesson 2, students investigate how counting methods can be applied to problems involving probability, geometry, discrete mathematics, and algebra. In the first investigation, they explore and use the General Multiplication Rule for probability. In Investigation 2, students consider the Binomial Theorem and Pascal's triangle and are introduced to proof by combinatorial reasoning.

Lesson 3 is an optional lesson on the Principle of Mathematical Induction. In this lesson, students learn how to do proofs by mathematical induction in a precise yet sense-making way.

Note: As indicated in the Preface to this *Teacher's Guide*, it is suggested that Lessons 1 and 2 be studied by all students. In addition, Lesson 3 should be studied by students planning to pursue mathematics or computer science in college. For these students, "Counting Models" should be studied after Unit 7, "Functions and Symbolic Reasoning." (See Preface p. xix.)

Unit 4 Objectives

- ■ To develop the skill of careful counting in a variety of contexts
- ■ To understand and apply a variety of counting techniques, including the Multiplication Principle of Counting, tree diagrams, and systematic lists
- ■ To solve counting problems involving combinations and permutations
- ■ To understand and apply the General Multiplication Rule for probability
- ■ To understand and apply the Binomial Theorem
- ■ To understand and apply connections among combinations, the Binomial Theorem, and Pascal's triangle
- ■ To develop the ability to prove statements using combinatorial reasoning and the Principle of Mathematical Induction

Unit 4 Planning Guide

Lesson Objectives	Assignments	Suggested Pacing	Materials
Lesson 1 *Methods of Counting* • To develop the skill of systematic counting by thinking carefully about the number of possibilities in a variety of contexts • To understand and apply basic counting strategies, such as making tree diagrams, making systematic lists, and using the Multiplication Principle of Counting • To understand and apply concepts, techniques, and formulas related to combinations and permutations	**MORE** **after page 222** Students can begin Modeling Task 1, 2, or 4; Organizing Task 1 or 2; or Reflecting Task 3 from p. 232. **after page 229** Students can begin Extending Task 1, 2, 3, or 4 from p. 232. **page 232** **Modeling:** 1, 3, and 2 or 4* **Organizing:** 2, 4, and choice of one* **Reflecting:** 1, 2, and choice of one* **Extending:** Choose one* **PUMP** **pages 238–239**	**Path A:** 6 days **Path B:** 9 days	• Teaching Resources 78–83 • Assessment Resources 114–119
Lesson 2 *Counting Throughout Mathematics* • To use counting methods to solve probability problems in situations where all outcomes are equally likely • To understand and apply the General Multiplication Rule for probability • To understand and apply the Binomial Theorem. • To understand and apply the connections among the Binomial Theorem, Pascal's triangle, and combinations	**MORE** **after page 245** Students can begin Modeling Task 1, 2, or 3; Organizing Task 1, 4, or 5; Reflecting Task 1; or Extending Task 1 from p. 250. **page 250** **Modeling:** 3, 4, and choice of one* **Organizing:** Choose two* **Reflecting:** 1, 3, and 4 **Extending:** 4 and choice of one* **PUMP** **pages 256–257**	**Path A:** 5 days **Path B:** 7 days	• Teaching Resources 84–87 • Assessment Resources 120–125
Lesson 3 *The Principle of Mathematical Induction* • To understand and use the Principle of Mathematical Induction • To develop the skill of proof by mathematical induction	**MORE** **page 264** **Modeling:** Choose two* **Organizing:** 1 and choice of two* **Reflecting:** 1 and 4 **Extending:** Choose one* **PUMP** **pages 268–269**	**Path A:** 3 days **Path B:** omit	• Set of dominoes (optional) • Towers of Hanoi game (optional) • Teaching Resources 88–91 • Assessment Resources 126–131
Lesson 4 *Looking Back* • To review and test the major objectives of the unit		**Path A:** 3 days **Path B:** 3 days	• Teaching Resources 92–93 • Assessment Resources 132–155

When choice is indicated, it is important to leave the choice to the student.
Note: *It is best if Organizing tasks are discussed as a whole class after they have been assigned as homework.*

Unit 4

Lesson 1 *Methods of Counting*

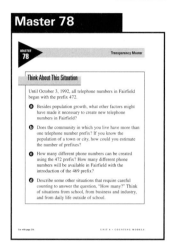

LESSON OVERVIEW In this lesson, students will first engage in counting by careful thinking, without using explicit counting formulas. Then they will develop and use formulas for permutations and combinations. It is important that students have an opportunity to make sense of counting situations before they get too many formal and technical details, since otherwise there is the danger that they will simply try to memorize formulas, rather than apply concepts to solve problems. Counting methods that students will learn and use include the Multiplication Principle of Counting, general counting problem solving strategies (making a list, drawing a tree diagram, considering a simpler case, making a table, and looking for patterns, including recursive patterns), and techniques and formulas related to combinations and permutations. Another fundamental counting principle that is implicitly embedded in this lesson is the Addition Principle of Counting. (See Part b of the Checkpoint at the end of Investigation 1.)

Lesson Objectives

- To develop the skill of systematic counting by thinking carefully about the number of possibilities in a variety of contexts
- To understand and apply basic counting strategies, such as making tree diagrams, making systematic lists, and using the Multiplication Principle of Counting
- To understand and apply concepts, techniques, and formulas related to combinations and permutations

LAUNCH full-class discussion

Think About This Situation

See Teaching Master 78.

ⓐ More than one prefix is often necessary in order to accommodate all the telephone numbers needed in a community. The discussion should include how population might affect the number of phones needed. Other factors to consider include the average number of people in a household, the economics of the community which might influence the number of lines to a house for fax or for Internet use, and cellular phone use. You might also consider the types of local businesses such as industrial, service, or telecommunications.

Unit 4

LAUNCH *continued*

(b) Many communities will have more than one prefix; some will have recently added prefixes. If students realize that each prefix creates 10,000 numbers (see Part c), then they could get a rough estimate of the number of prefixes needed by dividing the population by 10,000. Of course, a more accurate count would require considering many variables, such as number of business phones, number of people at a residence, and so on.

(c) **Student answers to this question will give you some idea how much students may already know about systematic counting and, in particular, the Multiplication Principle of Counting.**

There are 4 digits following each prefix, so there are 10,000 possible phone numbers for each prefix. This allows for 20,000 different phone numbers using the two prefixes.

(d) Some possible counting questions are: How many ways can the school trophies be arranged in the case? How many ways can six students be seated on stage at an awards assembly? How many different ATM codes are possible? How many pants-shirt combinations are possible? How many different pizzas can be ordered? How many different committees can be formed? How many times is a line of code in a computer program executed? Encourage students to think of many counting situations.

EXPLORE small-group investigation

INVESTIGATION 1 Careful Counting

This investigation might be informally called, "counting without formulas," or "careful counting by careful thinking." In this investigation, students will use the Multiplication Principle of Counting, tree diagrams, and systematic lists to solve counting problems.

1. **a.** Twelve different passwords are possible. Students might make a list of all possible passwords, use the Multiplication Principle of Counting (whether they explicitly know it or not), or draw a diagram, such as a tree diagram.

   b. Twelve different passwords are not enough to be practical because not enough users could be assigned different passwords and because it would be too easy for somebody to get into the system just by trying all 12 possible passwords.

   c. $10^3 \times 26^2 = 676,000$ different passwords are possible. It would take someone about $\frac{676,000}{3,600} = 187.78$ hours or approximately 7.82 days, working nonstop, to check all possible passwords.

   d. There are 10,000 possible different PINs. Although this is a reasonably large number, it would be possible for an unauthorized user to try many PINs in a short period of time and maybe get the right one. An ATM machine might be programmed to confiscate a card whenever several wrong entries are made in a row in order to prevent someone from trying to use a stolen ATM card by trying many possible PINs.

EXPLORE *continued*

2. **a.** Twenty-four different jackets could be displayed. (Students may use a variety of methods to get this answer. In the next activities, they will examine several fundamental methods.)

b. Sam's, Billie's, and Dwight's methods do not work. The others are valid. Notice that Dwight's disorganized list missed three possibilities: M-p-m, W-y-l, and M-b-m. A disorganized list may work sometimes, but, in general, it is not a good method.

c. Jackie's method is very similar to Antonio's. One more step could be added to Jackie's tree diagram: she could list the different types of jackets by following each of the 12 branches of the tree. This would create the same list that Antonio has. Each factor in Marsha's multiplication method corresponds to one branching of Jackie's tree. Students may see other connections among the three correct methods.

d. Responses will vary according to student preference. Some students may prefer Jackie's visual approach, Antonio's organized list of all possibilities, or Marsha's quick multiplication method. Students should describe any other counting methods they can think of for this situation. One method could involve doing half the tree or list and then doubling the result.

e. In this case, there are 32 different jackets that could be displayed. Each method would need to be modified as follows:

Jackie's method: Modify the last step of the tree, so that each color branches into 4 sizes: s, m, l, xl.

Antonio's method: Modify the systematic list. After every combination ending with "l," add another ending in "xl." For example, directly below W-b-l insert W-b-xl.

Marsha's method: Since there are now 4 choices for size, this method would find the total by changing the 3 to a 4. This gives $2 \times 4 \times 4$ or 32 different jackets.

3. **This activity gets students thinking about some slightly more complicated counting problems. They will refine their understanding of the Multiplication Principle of Counting, which will be defined in the next activity. They will investigate the "Addition Principle" in Part c, although it is not necessary that students name this principle. They will be introduced to the notion of repetition in Parts d and e, which will be further studied in the next investigation.**

a. Jackie's method: Draw a tree that first branches into 4 possibilities, labeled A, B, C, and D, and then branches again to 3 possibilities, labeled 0, 1, 2.

Antonio's method: Make a systematic list: A0, A1, A2, B0, B1, B2, C0, C1, C2, D0, D1, D2.

Marsha's method: $4 \times 3 = 12$

Unit 4

EXPLORE *continued*

b. For Part c of Activity 1, there are too many possibilities to list them all or to draw a complete tree diagram, although students might make an outline without creating the complete list or diagram. Thus, Marsha's method is the most efficient: $10 \times 10 \times 10 \times 26 \times 26 = 676,000$.

c. **This activity involves breaking the problem into two distinct parts. Students may use the "Addition Principle," in which the possibilities in two disjoint sets are added. This is an important principle. Since it is quite intuitive, it is not explicitly taught as part of this lesson.**
There are $3 \times 2 = 6$ letter-digit passwords, plus 6 more digit-letter passwords, for a total of 12 different passwords.

d. **This activity introduces the important idea of repetition, which will be systematically investigated in the next investigation. For now, students should just count by careful thinking and application of the Multiplication Principle of Counting.**
For the first question, there is no restriction concerning repeated letters or digits, so the number of possible passwords is $26^7 \times 10^2 = 803,181,017,600$. If no letters or digits can be repeated, then the number of possible passwords is $26 \times 25 \times 24 \times 23 \times 22 \times 21 \times 20 \times 10 \times 9 = 298,378,080,000$.

e. In this activity, students must first determine the different possible password configurations, and then count the number of possible passwords for each configuration. In a 5-character password, there are 5 possible positions for the single digit (which will be seen as $C(5, 1)$ in the next investigation). The number of possible passwords for each of these 5 password configurations is $26^4 \times 10 = 4,569,760$. To get the total number of possible passwords of any configuration, multiply by 5: $4,569,760 \times 5 = 22,848,800$

4. a. In Activity 2, the events are gender, color, and size. The sequence of events is gender-color-size. In Activity 3, the events are letters and digits, and the sequence of events is the sequence of letters and digits.

b. **It is quite likely that students will have used the Multiplication Principle of Counting in Activity 3, without yet knowing the name. In case they have not, it is important for them to go back and see how it could be applied. In particular, for Parts a and c of Activity 3 students may have used a tree diagram or a list, rather than the Multiplication Principle of Counting, since the number of possibilities is small. If so, they should realize that the Multiplication Principle will give them the same answer.**

Unit 4

EXPLORE *continued*

5. **a.** The second digit of a new area code is any digit from 2 through 9. The old area codes always used 0 or 1 for the second digit.

b. A new area code has the form ABC, where A and B are any digits from 2 through 9 and C is any digit from 0 through 9. So, using the Multiplication Principle of Counting, the number of possible new area codes is $8 \times 8 \times 10$ or 640. This is the same as the number reported in the article.

6. **a.** 10^{10} possible telephone numbers (10 billion)

b. The possibilities for each digit of an area code were: 2–9, 0–1, 0–9. The possibilities for each digit of a local prefix were: 2–9, 2–9, 2–9. Any number 0–9 could be used for the digits of the local number. Thus, the number of possible phone numbers was:

Area Code		Local Prefix		Local Number
$8 \times 2 \times 10$	$\times$	$8 \times 8 \times 8$	$\times$	$10 \times 10 \times 10 \times 10$ = 819,200,000

SHARE AND SUMMARIZE   full-class discussion

Checkpoint

See Teaching Master 79.

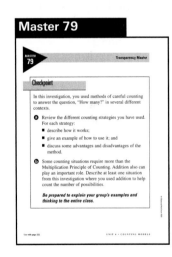

Master 79

a Tree diagram:

- Draw a tree with a branch for each possibility.
- To count types of jackets or different passwords, you could have branches for gender-color-size or letter-digit.
- It is visual and concrete, but cumbersome for large problems.

Systematic list:

- Make an ordered list that includes all the possibilities.
- For example, list passwords by first listing all the passwords that begin with 0, then those that begin with 1, and so on.
- It shows all the possibilities in a clear and systematic manner, but it is cumbersome for large problems.

Multiplication Principle of Counting:

- Count the number of possibilities for each event and then multiply all those numbers.
- For example, to count the number of possible area codes, multiply the number of digits possible for the first digit by the number of digits possible for the second digit by the number of digits possible for the third digit.

Unit 4

SHARE AND SUMMARIZE *continued*

■ This is an efficient method that works even for very large problems. However, it does not show the actual possibilities, as do the tree diagram and list methods. Also, you must be careful to apply it correctly. (See Billie's and Sam's methods in Activity 2 for an incorrect application.)

b This task implicitly brings out another fundamental counting principle—the Addition Principle of Counting. This principle states that the number of elements in two disjoint sets is the sum of the number of elements in each set. This is such an intuitive principle that you may decide not to explicitly state it. Students should identify places where they counted by adding the possibilities in different cases, as in the case of passwords that begin with a letter or those that begin with a digit.

CONSTRUCTING A MATH TOOLKIT: Students should record the Multiplication Principle of Counting in their Math Toolkits along with an example illustrating its use.

MORE

ASSIGNMENT *pp. 232–237*

Students can now begin Modeling Task 1, 2, or 4; Organizing Task 1 or 2; or Reflecting Task 3 from the MORE assignment following Investigation 2.

APPLY individual task

On Your Own

a. $10^3 \times 26^3 = 17,576,000$

b. $10 \times 9 \times 8 \times 26 \times 25 \times 24 = 11,232,000$

c. This would allow only $10 \times 10 \times 10 \times 1 = 1,000$ different license plates, which may not be enough for all the vehicles in the county.

d. Responses will vary depending on the local license plate configuration.

EXPLORE small-group investigation

INVESTIGATION 2 Permutations and Combinations

In the first investigation, students learned and applied several fundamental methods of counting, including the Multiplication Principle of Counting. They studied concepts and techniques of combinatorics informally, without using specific counting formulas. In this investigation, students will formalize some of the work they did in the previous investigation. In particular, they will study the issues of order and repetition (repetition can also be thought about in terms of replacement), they will define permutations and combinations, and they will develop and apply formulas for counting the number of combinations or permutations.

1. a. Both order and repetition are important issues when counting the number of choices of three side dishes. It makes a difference whether or not the order of the side dishes matters and whether or not repetition of side dishes is possible. Students should

EXPLORE *continued*

conclude that it does not matter in which order the side dishes appear, and that the three side dishes could include a repeated dish.

b. There are 16 side dishes, so applying the Multiplication Principle of Counting gives $16 \times 15 \times 14 = 3,360$. This probably accounts for the claim that "more than 3,000 combinations can be created." However, this method and answer are incorrect, as will be seen later in this lesson.

c. Students may suggest that 3,000 is too high because this counts different orderings of side dishes as different, when in fact the order in which the side dishes appear does not matter. **Note:** Students will further analyze this problem in Extending Task 5 on page 237 and in Lesson 4 Activity 1 Part c on page 271.

2. **In this activity, students will explore four different ways order and repetition can be involved in a problem.**

a. ■ Yes, repetitions are allowed.

■ No, two different orderings should not be counted as different possibilities, since John doesn't care about order.

■ John has 15 different ice cream choices. The possibilities are CC, VV, FF, MM, DD, CV, CF, CM, CD, VF, VM, VD, FM, FD, MD.

b. ■ No, repetitions are not allowed.

■ Yes, two different orderings should be counted as different possibilities.

■ Shrita has 20 different ice cream cone choices. The possibilities are CV, CF, CM, CD, VC, VF, VM, VD, FC, FV, FM, FD, MC, MV, MF, MD, DC, DV, DF, DM.

c. ■ No, repetitions are not allowed.

■ No, two different orderings should not be counted as different possibilities.

■ Jeong-Woo has 10 different ice cream cone choices. The possibilities are: CV, CF, CM, CD, VF, VM, VD, FM, FD, MD.

d. ■ Yes, repetitions are allowed.

■ Yes, two different orderings should be counted as different possibilities.

■ Deborah has 25 different ice cream cone choices. The possibilities are: CC, VV, FF, MM, DD, CV, CF, CM, CD, VC, VF, VM, VD, FC, FV, FM, FD, MC, MV, MF, MD, DC, DV, DF, DM.

e. Deborah has the most choices and Jeong-Woo has the fewest. This makes sense because allowing repetition and having order matter will always give the greatest number of possibilities. On the other hand, not allowing repetition and not caring about order both decrease the number of possibilities.

Unit 4

Master 80

Master 80

Name _____ Date _____

MASTER
80

Activity Master

Analyzing Counting Situations

	No Repetitions	Repetitions OK
Different Orderings Count as Different Possibilities.		
Different Orderings Do Not Count as Different Possibilities.		

Use with page 226.

UNIT 4 • COUNTING MODELS

EXPLORE *continued*

3. **See Teaching Master 80.**

    In this table, students will keep track of the four different types of problems with respect to order and repetition. By the end of the unit, the table should be filled out completely. For now, students should be able to fill in appropriate names from Activity 2 and, depending on how they solved each of the problems in Activity 2, possibly some of the computations shown below.

    Analyzing Counting Situations

	No Repetitions	**Repetitions OK**
Different Orderings Count as Different Possibilities.	Shrita $5 \times 4 = 20$	Deborah $5 \times 5 = 25$
Different Orderings Do Not Count as Different Possibilities.	Jeong-Woo $\frac{(5)(4)}{2} = 10$	John

    In the activities regarding the French Club election (Activities 4–8), students investigate permutations. In the activities regarding the Ski Club election (Activities 9 and 10), they investigate combinations. In both situations, students first solve the counting problem any way they can. Factorial notation and specific formulas for permutations are developed in Activities 5–8, and combinations formulas are developed in Activities 9 and 10 and the subsequent Checkpoint. It is best not to require or use these formulas until they arise in the appropriate activity.

4. **a.** Enter "P-VP-T" in the cell corresponding to "No Repetitions" and "Order Counts."

    b. Students should figure this out any way they can, and explain how they did it. For example, using the Multiplication Principle of Counting, the answer is $15 \times 14 \times 13 = 2,730$.

5. **a.** Students should verify that the strategy presented here yields the same answer as they got in Activity 4. If the answers are not the same, then they should make the necessary corrections.

    b. $20 \times 19 \times 18 = 6,840$

    c. $15 \times 14 \times 13 \times 12 = 32,760$

6. **a.** The method in Activity 5 used the beginning part of 15!. It is a factorial-type computation, but the multiplication stops after the first three factors.

    b. $30 \times 29 \times 28 \times 27$, which starts out like 30! but stops after four factors.

7. **a.** In the counting problem in Part b of Activity 5, $n = 20$, $k = 3$, and $n - k + 1 = 18$, so the answer is $20 \times 19 \times 18 = 6,840$. In the counting problem in Part c of Activity 5, $n = 15$ and $k = 4$, so the answer is $15 \times 14 \times 13 \times 12 = 32,760$. These answers should match the ones obtained in Activity 5.

Unit 4

EXPLORE *continued*

b. This formula is a generalization of the method in Activity 5 because you do the same kind of factorial-type multiplication, but with general n and k. In particular, you use the first k factors of $n!$, just as in Activity 5 you used the first 3 factors of 15!. If students do not mention the number of factors, k, here, they will be explicitly asked for this number in Part c.

c. There are k factors in this product.

d. By using the distributive property, students can see that $n - (k - 1) = n - k + 1$. This equivalence may help students better understand where the factorial-type computation ends, and it may help them to complete the proof in Part b of Activity 8.

TECHNOLOGY NOTE: On the TI-82 and TI-83, the factorial symbol is located in the [MATH] **PRB** menu.

8. a. In the counting problem in Part b of Activity 5, $n = 20$ and $k = 3$, so the answer is $\frac{20!}{(20-3)!} = \frac{20!}{17!} = 20 \times 19 \times 18 = 6{,}840$. This is the same answer as in Activity 5. In the counting problem in Part c of Activity 5, $n = 15$ and $k = 4$, so the answer is $\frac{15!}{(15-4)!} = \frac{15!}{11!} = 15 \times 14 \times 13 \times 12 = 32{,}760$. This is also the same answer as in Activity 5.

b. $\dfrac{n!}{(n-k)!} = \dfrac{n(n-1)(n-2)\cdots(n-(k-1))(n-k)\cdots(2)(1)}{(n-k)(n-k-1)(n-k-2)\cdots(2)(1)}$

$$= n(n-1)(n-2)\cdots(n-(k-1))$$

$$= n(n-1)(n-2)\cdots(n-k+1)$$

c. There are n choices for the first officer, then $(n-1)$ choices for the second officer, and so on. So $n!$ is a good way to start this computation. But you want the computation to stop after k factors since there are k officers. Thus, you do not want the tail end of the $n!$ computation. This can be achieved by dividing by $(n-k)!$.

9. So far, students have been exploring permutations. Now they will begin investigating combinations. The terms "permutation" and "combination" will be introduced and defined after the Checkpoint. It is best not to introduce these terms until then. A good "benchmark" for students to establish as they work with combinations and permutations is knowledge of whether there are more permutations or combinations.

a. The number of three-person committees is less than the number of three-person P-VP-T groups. Students may not have detailed reasons for this fact yet, but they should be able to provide some plausible arguments. They might say that this is because one given committee of three people could be rearranged in different ways to yield several different P-VP-T groups. More specifically, they may say that one given committee of three people can be rearranged in 3! ways and thus yield 3! different P-VP-T groups.

EXPLORE *continued*

b. In both the French Club and Ski Club elections, repetition is not allowed. The difference is that in the French Club election order matters, but in the Ski Club election order does not matter.

c. Enter "committee" in the cell corresponding to "No Repetitions" and "Order Does Not Count."

NOTE: As the unit progresses, it may be helpful for students to refer back and think about combinations in terms of committees.

---

d. Students should figure this out any way they can, and explain how they did it. They should get 455 committees. Specific formulas will be developed in Activity 10 and the Checkpoint.

10. a. The 6 different orderings are *ABC, ACB, BAC, BCA, CAB, CBA*. Using the Multiplication Principle of Counting, this number can be calculated as $3 \times 2 \times 1$.

b. If a student's answer in Activity 9 does not match the answer given in the strategy description, then the student should go back to Activity 9 and correct that solution.

c. $\frac{24 \times 23 \times 22}{6} = 2{,}024$ different committees

d. **In Parts d and e, students will analyze their work carefully so that they can generalize their thinking and develop general formulas in the following Checkpoint.**

- The number of executive committees is $\frac{15 \times 14 \times 13 \times 12}{24} = 1{,}365$.
- You divide by 24. This number can be computed using the Multiplication Principle of Counting: $4 \times 3 \times 2 \times 1$, which students may represent as 4!.

e.
- There are 15 members in the club, so start carrying out a factorial-type computation beginning with 15. Since 3 people will be elected, stop the factorial-type computation after 3 factors. But now you've counted too many because you have included all orderings of each group of 3 people, so divide by 3!.

- To find the number of different 5-person committees that can be chosen from a 30-member club, proceed as follows. Start carrying out a factorial computation beginning with 30. Since 5 people will be elected, stop the factorial-type computation after 5 factors. But now you've counted too many, because you have included all orderings of each group of 5 people, so divide by 5!. This method is summarized by the following computation: $\frac{30 \times 29 \times 28 \times 27 \times 26}{5!} = \frac{30 \times 29 \times 28 \times 27 \times 26}{120} = 142{,}506$.

SHARE AND SUMMARIZE full-class discussion

Checkpoint

See Teaching Master 81.

a In both types of problems, repetition is not allowed. For the ranked-officer problem, order counts; for the committee problem, order does not count.

b Dividing each of the two general formulas for the ranked-officer problem by $k!$ will give general formulas for the committee problem.

$$\frac{n(n-1)(n-2)\cdots(n-k+1)}{k!} \text{ and } \frac{n!}{(n-k)!k!}$$

c In this case, $n = 30$ and $k = 5$. Thus, the number of 5-person executive committees that can be chosen from a club with 30 members is $\frac{(30)(29)(28)(27)(26)}{5!}$ or $\frac{30!}{(30-5)!5!}$. Both computations give 142,506. (This is the same as the answer in Part e of Activity 10.)

d
$$\frac{n!}{(n-k)!k!} = \frac{n(n-1)(n-2)\cdots(n-(k-1))(n-k)\cdots(2)(1)}{(n-k)(n-k-1)(n-k-2)\cdots(2)(1)k!}$$

$$= \frac{n(n-1)(n-2)\cdots(n-(k-1))}{k!}$$

$$= \frac{n(n-1)(n-2)\cdots(n-k+1)}{k!}$$

The word "arrangement" is used in the paragraph following the Checkpoint as a generic term. Terminology is not completely standardized in combinatorics, and sometimes "arrangement" is used with a specific technical meaning. That is not the case here.

CONSTRUCTING A MATH TOOLKIT: Students should describe the difference between permutations and combinations.

APPLY individual task

▶On Your Own

a. In this case, $n = 27$ and $k = 4$. Thus, the number of 4-person executive committees that can be chosen from a club with 27 members is $\frac{(27)(26)(25)(24)}{4!}$ or $\frac{27!}{(27-4)!4!}$. Both computations give 17,550.

b. The number of possibilities for four people who will be President, Vice-President, Treasurer, and Secretary in a 27-member club is $(27)(26)(25)(24) = 421,200$.

ASSIGNMENT *pp. 232–237*

Students can now begin Extending Task 1, 2, 3, or 4 from the MORE assignment following Investigation 2.

Unit 4

EXPLORE *continued*

11. **a.** Shrita's ice cream cone problem is an example of a permutation. Jeong-Woo's ice cream cone problem is an example of a combination.

b. "Permutation" goes into Shrita's cell and "combination" goes into Jeong-Woo's cell.

c. Permutations yield a greater number of possibilities. This can be understood by combinatorial reasoning, that is by just thinking about how the arrangements are formed and counted. Permutations count order, therefore, there are more possibilities. This can also be understood by reasoning with the formulas. The formula for permutations has the same numerator as the formula for combinations, but the denominator is smaller in the permutation formula, and thus the number is larger.

12. **a.** In order for students to understand how the factorials in the formulas work, they should first compute permutations and combinations without using calculators.

■ $P(9, 2) = \frac{9!}{(9-2)!} = \frac{9!}{7!} = 9 \times 8 = 72$

$C(9, 2) = \frac{9!}{(9-2)!2!} = \frac{9!}{7!2!} = \frac{9 \times 8}{2 \times 1} = 36$

■ The permutation and combination features on TI-calculators are found on the $\boxed{\text{MATH}}$ **PRB** menu. Using these features, $P(9, 2) = 72$ and $C(9, 2) = 36$.

b. Students should correct their formulas from the Checkpoint if one is not the same as the formula given here.

c. Both n and k must be nonnegative integers, with $n \geq k$.

d. $C(n, k) = \frac{P(n, k)}{k!}$

13. **a.** Think about having a blank for each of the ranked club officer positions, with multiplication signs between them. Fill in the first blank with the number of choices for the first position, then fill in the second blank with the number of choices for the second position (this will be one less), and so on. This yields a factorial-type computation with one factor for each of the k positions. In terms of the formula, the denominator "cancels out" all factors after the kth factor.

b. Start making choices for each position, just as you did with permutations in Part a. This gives, as before, a factorial-type computation with k factors. However, each k-person group can be arranged in $k!$ orderings, and all these orderings are included so far. Correct the overcount by dividing by $k!$, since different orderings are not counted in a combination problem.

14. **a.** For most card games you may note that order does not matter. Combinations: $C(52, 13) = \frac{52!}{39!13!} = 635,013,559,600$

b. Combinations: $C(7, 3) = \frac{7!}{4!3!} = 35$

c. Permutations: $P(7, 3) = \frac{7!}{4!} = 210$ (It is assumed here that the order of the seating makes a difference.)

APPLY *continued*

d. ■ This situation involves neither permutations nor combinations because repetition is allowed. There are $2^8 = 256$ different bytes possible.

■ Six of the bits will be 1s and two will be 0s. Thus, you need to choose where to place the two 0s among the eight bits. Therefore, the answer is $C(8, 2) = 28$. Equivalently, you could choose where to place the six 1s among the eight bits. This yields $C(8, 6) = 28$. (This interesting "symmetry" will be investigated in more detail in Lesson 2.)

15. $C(12, 5) = 792$ subsets. This is an important way to think about combinations and it will be revisited in the Checkpoint.)

SHARE AND SUMMARIZE   full-class discussion

Checkpoint

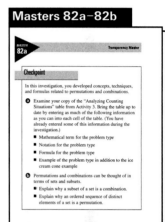

Masters 82a–82b

See Teaching Masters 82a and 82b.

ⓐ Note that the right-hand cells of the table are explored in Lesson 4 and the Extending tasks in the MORE set. At this time, students should only be required to enter formulas for the left-hand cells of the table (combinations and permutations).

	No Repetitions	**Repetitions OK**
Different Orderings Count as Different Possibilities.	Shrita $5 \times 4 = 20$ **Permutations** $P(n, k) = \frac{n!}{(n-k)!}$ P–VP–T seating in a row (Activity 14 Part c)	Billie $5 \times 5 = 25$
Different Orderings Do Not Count as Different Possibilities.	Jeong-Woo $\frac{(5)(4)}{2} = 10$ **Combinations** $C(n, k) = \frac{n!}{(n-k)!k!}$ Committee card hands (Activity 14 Part a)	John

ⓑ The context of sets and subsets is a classic context in which to think about combinations and permutations. In fact, some combinatorics texts define permutations and combinations in terms of subsets. In this curriculum, permutations and combinations are defined in terms of order and repetition (see page **228** of the student text). From these definitions, students can see how to view permutations and combinations in terms of subsets, as explained on the next page.

Unit 4

CONSTRUCTING A MATH TOOLKIT: Students should explain strategies they use for determining if a given situation involves combinations, permutations, or neither. They should also include the counting formulas, along with examples and notation.

SHARE AND SUMMARIZE *continued*

■ A subset is a combination because in a subset, repetition of elements is not allowed and the order in which the elements are listed does not matter.

■ An ordered sequence of distinct elements of a set is a permutation because elements cannot be repeated (since they are distinct) and different orderings of elements do count as different possibilities (since you are considering ordered sequences of elements).

c Similarities: Neither allows repetitions. Both use "modified factorial" computations to find the number of permutations or combinations.

Differences: Order counts in permutations, but not in combinations. The combination formula has an extra divisor of *k*!.

APPLY individual task

On Your Own

a. In this problem, repetition is not allowed and order does matter. Thus, this is a permutation problem. There are $P(11, 4) = 7{,}920$ seating arrangements possible.

b. In this problem, repetition is allowed and order does matter. Since there are 10 choices for each digit of the combination, the Multiplication Principle of Counting can be used to determine that there are $10^4 = 10{,}000$ different lock combinations. These are *not* "combinations" in the mathematical sense of the word since repetitions are allowed (and neither are they permutations).

ASSIGNMENT *pp. 232–237*

Modeling: 1, 3, and 2 or 4*
Organizing: 2, 4, and choice of one*
Reflecting: 1, 2, and choice of one*
Extending: Choose one*

*When choice is indicated, it is important to leave the choice to the student.
NOTE: It is best if Organizing tasks are discussed as a whole class after they have been assigned as homework.

MORE independent assignment

Modeling

1. Students should be careful to notice that an *n*-dot set of dominos has 0 to *n* dots in each square, so that there are $(n + 1)$ different numbers possible for each square. This problem could be done by examining sequentially larger domino sets and finding a pattern, or by reasoning as below.

Standard set: The number of dominos that have different numbers of dots on the two squares is $(7)(6) = 42$, but this counts each such domino twice. For example, the 3–4 domino would be counted as different from the 4–3 domino, even though they are really the same. Therefore, divide 42 by 2 to get the number of dominos with different numbers of dots on each square: $\frac{42}{2} = 21$. Now count the number of dominos that have the same numbers of dots on each square. There are 7 of these. Thus, the total number of standard dominos is $21 + 7 = 28$.

MORE *continued*

Deluxe set: $\frac{(10)(9)}{2} + 10 = 55$

n dots: Note that each square has 0 to *n* dots, so there are $(n + 1)$ possibilities for each square. Thus, the number of different *n*-dot dominos is

$$\frac{(n + 1)(n)}{2} + (n + 1) = \frac{(n + 2)(n + 1)}{2}$$

2. **a.** $(1 \times 26 \times 26) + (1 \times 26 \times 26 \times 26) = 18{,}252$ different sets of such call letters are possible.

b. $(2 \times 26 \times 26) + (2 \times 26 \times 26 \times 26) = 36{,}504$ different sets of radio call letters are possible.

3. **a.** The "ballpark" figure is definitely too low, because even if only 1 pizza were chosen with 1 topping, there would be 11 different possibilities.

b. $C(11, 5) = 462$

c. $C(11, 3) = 165$

d. $C(11, 0) + C(11, 1) + C(11, 2) + C(11, 3) + C(11, 4) + C(11, 5) = 1 + 11 + 55 + 165 + 330 + 462 = 1{,}024$ (This is an example of an interesting pattern of combinations. See Modeling Task 5 on page 251.)

e. The 4-year-old boy has an incorrect answer. It appears that he determined his answer using the following incorrect reasoning: There are 1,024 ways to order one pizza, so the number of ways to order two pizzas is $(1{,}024)^2 = 1{,}048{,}576$. One reason that this argument is incorrect is that it counts different orderings of the two pizzas as different two-pizza combinations, but that is not correct. For example, a cheese pizza and olive pizza is the same as an olive pizza and cheese pizza.

   The correct answer can be determined as follows. For two pizzas, they are either both the same or they are different. There are 1,024 possibilities if they are the same. If they are different, the number of possibilities is $C(1{,}024, 2) = \frac{1{,}024 \times 1{,}023}{2} = 523{,}776$. Thus, the total number of possibilities is $1{,}024 + 523{,}776 = 524{,}800$.

f. Jeremy's answer is not correct either. Jeremy partially corrects the 4-year-old boy's reasoning by dividing $(1{,}024)^2$ by 2. This takes care of double counting due to counting different orderings as different two-pizza combinations. But it reduces the answer by too much because it also takes the 1,024 legitimate possibilities where the two pizzas are the same and divides that number by 2 as well. Thus, it is 512 too low.

4. **a.** $8 \times 10 \times 10 \times 10 \times 10 \times 10 \times 10 = 8{,}000{,}000$ seven-digit phone numbers.

b. $640 \times 8{,}000{,}000 = 5{,}120{,}000{,}000$

This number is about 5 billion, which agrees with the information given in the newspaper article.

Unit 4

MORE *continued*

Organizing

1. **a.** Since there are 6 entries in a 3×2 matrix and each entry is a 0 or 1, there are 2^6 or 64 different matrices.

   b. Since there are $n \times m$ entries in each matrix and two choices for each entry, there are 2^{nm} different matrices.

2. There are $2 \times 2 \times 3$ or 12 different types of uniforms that the boys could be wearing, so if there are 13 boys, at least two must be wearing the same type of uniform. In order to guarantee that three boys would be wearing the same type of uniform, the group would need to have $(12)(2) + 1$ or 25 boys in it. (Note that this problem involves the Pigeonhole Principle: If there are more pigeons than pigeonholes, then some pigeonhole must contain at least two pigeons.)

3. **a.** The number of segments connecting n points is $\frac{n(n-1)}{2}$. It makes no difference if the points are not in the same plane, because any two points in space determine a line.

   b. Every line has to intersect every other line (since no two are parallel), and they have to intersect in pairs (since no three intersect in one point), so the number of points of intersection of n lines is $\frac{n(n-1)}{2}$.

   c. Parts a and b are essentially the same because in each case you are choosing two objects from a group of n objects (points or lines). This can happen in $C(n, 2)$ ways. The conditions in Part b assure us that every two lines will have a unique point of intersection.

4. $C(12, 5) = \frac{12!}{7!5!} = 792$

   $_8C_3 = \frac{8!}{5!3!} = 56$

   $\binom{12}{7} = \frac{12!}{5!7!} = 792$

Reflecting

1. Often the first step in solving a problem is understanding and interpreting the conditions of the problem. In many counting problems, it is necessary to decide how the issues of order and repetition are involved in the problem. Sometimes such decisions are "obvious" and other times it is more difficult to decide. For example, when counting the ways to seat people on stage, questions arise such as: "Will they be seated in a line?" "If so, does it matter who sits at which end of the line?" "Does it matter how they are lined up?" Answers to these questions will help determine whether or not order is important. When counting how many license plate numbers are possible, questions arise such as: "Are all letters and numbers allowed?" "Can you use the same letter or number more than once?" Answers to these questions will help determine whether or not repetition is possible.

MORE *continued*

In general, order should be considered in counting situations if different orderings are counted as different possibilities. To decide if repetitions are involved, you must decide if objects can be used more than once.

When order matters (and repetition is not allowed), then possible choices can be counted using permutations. When order does not matter (and repetition is not allowed), then possible choices can be counted using combinations. If repetition is allowed, then you can think about modifying the combination and permutation formulas (for example, see the selection problem formulas in Extending Task 4), or you can start by counting combinations and permutations and then figure out how to add the possibilities where repetition is allowed.

2. Responses will vary. The formulas and methods students have investigated in this lesson allow students to determine the number of possibilities under given circumstances without actually listing (or counting) all of them.

3. $(12 \times 1) + (11 \times 2) + (10 \times 3) + (9 \times 4) + (8 \times 5) + (7 \times 6) + (6 \times 7) + (5 \times 8) + (4 \times 9) + (3 \times 10) + (2 \times 11) + (1 \times 12) = 364$.

4. Responses will vary.

Extending

1. This book has many interesting stories related to counting. Most concern counting strategies related to fair division problems. Student responses will vary depending upon which counting feat they choose to describe. One of the early counting feats is an application of the Multiplication Principle of Counting to count the leaves of a tree, by first counting the number of branches and the average number of leaves per branch.

2. **a.** CG   UUG   G   AUCG   AU

b. The G-enzyme breaks the chain after each G. Thus, at every break, the fragment to the left must end in G. The only fragment that might not end in G is the last one. Thus, if there is a fragment that does not end in G, then it must be the last fragment.

c. There is one fragment that does not end in G, namely, AAC. Thus, AAC must be the last fragment of the chain. The other 3 fragments could occur in any order. Thus, there are $3! = 6$ possible chains.

MORE *continued*

 d. The 3 fragments could be combined in any way. Thus, there are 3! = 6 possibilities.

 e. The only possibility that works is AGAU-GC-GAAC. Students may use a variety of ways of reasoning. From Part c, you know that the chain must end in AAC. By examining the fragments in Part d, this means that the chain ends in GAAC. There are only two fragments left in Part d. Try them in both possible orders in front of GAAC and see which one gives the correct G-enzyme fragments in Part c. The AGAUGCGAAC chain will be broken by a G-enzyme just as in Part c, and it will be broken by a U-C enzyme just as in Part d. The only other possibility does not work.

 3. a. Yes, because each number appears 8 times, the dominos can be matched in pairs. An example of such a chain is 0–1, 1–1, 1–2, 2–2, 2–3, 3–1, 1–4, 4–5, 5–1, 1–6, 6–2, 2–4, 4–4, 4–6, 6–6, 6–3, 3–5, 5–5, 5–6, 6–0, 0–0, 0–2, 2–5, 5–0, 0–3, 3–3, 3–4, 4–0.

 b. For example, a 2-3 domino would correspond to an edge from the vertex representing 2 to the vertex representing 3. Since the numbers go from 0 to n, there are $(n + 1)$ vertices. Since there is a domino having each pair of numbers, there is an edge between each pair of vertices, and a loop at each vertex. Thus, the graph is a complete graph on $(n + 1)$ vertices with a loop at each vertex. A chain of dominos that uses each domino exactly once corresponds to a path through the graph that uses each edge exactly once, that is, an Euler path. For an n-dot set of dominos, there are $(n + 1)$ different numbers (0 to n), so there are $(n + 1)$ vertices, each of which has degree $(n + 2)$. This is because the degree of every vertex in a complete graph is one less than the number of vertices, but then you add 2 to the degree to account for the loop. If n is even, then $(n + 2)$ is also even, so every vertex has even degree and thus there is an Euler path (in fact, an Euler circuit). If n is odd, then each vertex has odd degree and thus there is no Euler path. Therefore, there is a chain of dominos for an n-dot set if and only if n is even.

 4. Out of the first 10 positive integers, that is, 0 to 9, 9 integers do *not* contain the digit 3. Out of the first 100 positive integers, that is, 0 to 99, 81 integers do not contain the digit 3. Out of the integers 0 to $(10^n - 1)$, 9^n do not contain the digit 3. Thus, the proportion that do not contain the digit 3 is $\left(\frac{9}{10}\right)^n$. As n gets larger, the proportion of integers that do not contain the digit 3 gets smaller and smaller, approaching 0. Thus, you could say that of all positive integers, the proportion that contain the digit 3 is 1. Students may find this answer to be quite surprising!

 5. a. Repetitions are allowed since you can order more than one of the same side dish. Order does not matter since it does not matter in what order the side dishes appear. Because repetitions are allowed, this situation involves neither permutations nor combinations.

MORE *continued*

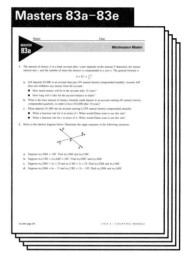
b. You want to count the number of different 3-side-dish selections chosen from 16 side dishes. Consider three cases: (1) If all three side dishes are different, then there are $C(16, 3) = 560$ selections. (2) If exactly two of the side dishes are the same, then there are $16 \times 15 = 240$ selections. (3) If all three side dishes are the same, then there are 16 selections. These three cases cover all possibilities. Thus, there are $560 + 240 + 16 = 816$ different 3-side-dish selections.

Here is another way to solve this problem: Think about taking a customer's order for three side dishes. Suppose you have an order form with room for all 16 side dishes and you put an "X" for the dishes ordered. Thus, an order form for two of side dish B and one of side dish M would look like this:

To help in the counting process, think about this order form as a sequence of marks. Each mark is either a dividing line to separate the different side dishes or an "X" to indicate a selection. For example, the following sequence of marks corresponds to ordering side dishes A, M, and O.

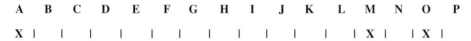

You can count the number of ways to choose 3 side dishes from 16 by counting the number of possible sequences of marks. A sequence of marks is completely determined by where the 3 "Xs" appear. So you only need to count the number of ways you can choose 3 marks from all the marks. In a system like this, there are 15 dividing lines and 3 "Xs", for a total of 18 marks. Thus, the answer to this counting problem is $C(18, 3) = 816$.

In general, if there are *n* side dishes available and you choose *k* side dishes, then the total number of marks (dividing lines and "Xs") is $(n - 1) + k = n + k - 1$; and the number of ways to choose the *k* side dishes is $C(n + k - 1, k)$.

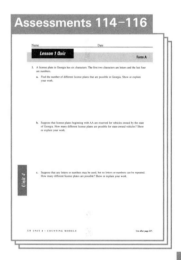
Counting problems in which repetitions are allowed and order does not matter are sometimes called *selection* problems. Although these problems can be solved by careful counting, without any new formulas, they can also be solved by the general formula developed above. That is, the number of selections of *k* objects from *n* objects when repetition is allowed and order does not matter is $C(n + k - 1, k)$. For this side dish problem, $n = 16$ and $k = 3$. Thus, the answer is $C(16 + 3 - 1, 3) = C(18, 3) = 816$.

See Masters 83a–83e for Maintenance tasks students can work on following Lesson 1.

See Assessment Resources pages 114–119.

REVIEW AND PRACTICE individual task

▶ PUMP

Answers

1. (d)
2. (e)
3. (e)
4. (a)
5. (c)

6. (a)
7. (a)
8. (d)
9. (e)
10. (a)

Unit 4

Lesson **2** *Counting Throughout Mathematics*

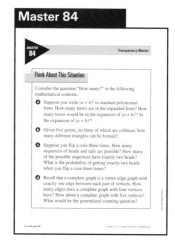

Master 84

In the last lesson, students learned and applied several fundamental methods of counting, including the Multiplication Principle of Counting, and permutations and combinations. In this lesson, students will study some important applications of counting throughout the major strands of high school mathematics. In the first investigation, students use counting to solve probability problems, and in the process they learn about the General Multiplication Rule for probability. In Investigation 2, the focus shifts to algebra, as students learn about the connections among combinations, the Binomial Theorem, and Pascal's triangle. Applications of counting in geometry and discrete mathematics are investigated in the MORE tasks.

Lesson Objectives

■ To use counting methods to solve probability problems in situations where all outcomes are equally likely
■ To understand and apply the General Multiplication Rule for probability
■ To understand and apply the Binomial Theorem
■ To understand and apply the connections among the Binomial Theorem, Pascal's triangle, and combinations

LAUNCH full-class discussion

Think About This Situation

See Teaching Master 84.

Briefly discuss these counting problems and some possible solutions. Complete solutions will be developed in the lesson.

ⓐ There are three terms in the expanded form of $(a + b)^2$. The expansion of $(a + b)^3$ has four terms. The expansion of $(a + b)^n$ has $(n + 1)$ terms.

ⓑ Ten different triangles can be formed. This boils down to the question: "How many ways can you choose three points out of five points?"

ⓒ If you flip a coin three times, eight sequences of heads and tails are possible. Three of the sequences have exactly two heads. The probability of getting exactly two heads when you flip a coin three times is $\frac{3}{8}$.

ⓓ A complete graph with 4 vertices has 6 edges. A complete graph with 5 vertices has 10 edges. The generalized counting question is, "How many ways can you choose 2 vertices out of n vertices?"

Unit 4

EXPLORE small-group investigation

INVESTIGATION 1 Counting and Multiplication Rules for Probability

In this investigation, students will use counting methods to solve probability problems in which all outcomes are equally likely. In the process, they will review the Multiplication Rule for independent events, and they will learn the General Multiplication Rule for any two events. The definition of probability given in the introduction to the investigation should be familiar to students, since they have used it in previous units and courses, but they may not have yet seen it explicitly stated.

1. **This activity should be review for students. It serves as a familiar context in which to make sure that they understand the idea of equally-likely outcomes and that they can apply the definition of probability given before Activity 1.**

   a. All outcomes are equally likely. The total number of possible outcomes is 36.

   b. There are six favorable outcomes for the event of doubles: (1, 1), (2, 2), (3, 3), (4, 4), (5, 5), and (6, 6).

   c. The probability of getting doubles is $\frac{6}{36}$ or $\frac{1}{6}$.

2. a. For the 5 regular numbers, repetition is not allowed and order does not matter. Thus, this part of the problem is a combinations problem. This answer then needs to be multiplied by 45 (using the Multiplication Principle of Counting) to account for the PowerBall number. Thus, there are $C(45, 5) \times 45 = 54,979,155$ different ways to fill out a ticket. (Note that these are the outcomes in this situation and they are all equally likely to be drawn.)

   b. There is only one way to fill out a "Match 5 + 1" winning ticket. Combining this information with that in Part a, the probability of the event "Match 5 + 1" is $\frac{1}{54,979,155}$. (Note that "Match 5 + 1" is the event in this situation, and there is one outcome that is favorable to this event.)

   c. There are 44 possible ways to fill out a "Match 5" winning ticket. The player must match the five regular numbers (only 1 way to do this), but the PowerBall number can be anything except the correct PowerBall number (44 ways to do this). Thus, the probability of the event "Match 5" is $\frac{44}{54,979,155}$. (Note that "Match 5" is the event in this situation, and there are 44 outcomes that are favorable to this event.)

   d. Four of the regular numbers are correct and one is wrong. If you think of filling 5 slots for the 5 numbers, then there is only one choice for each of 4 slots (the correct numbers). There are 40 choices for the slot containing the incorrect number, since 4 numbers have already been used and you can't choose the correct number.

EXPLORE *continued*

The incorrect number could be in any one of the 5 slots. There is only one choice for the correct PowerBall number. Thus, there are $40 \times 1 \times 1 \times 1 \times 1 \times C(5, 1) \times 1 = 200$ different ways to fill out a "Match 4 + 1" winning ticket. Another way to think about this is to use $C(5, 4)$ for the number of ways to arrange the 4 correct numbers to obtain $40 \times C(5, 4) \times 1 = 200$. Thus, the probability of the event "Match 4 + 1" is $\frac{200}{54,979,155}$.

3. **a.** An outcome in this situation is a sequence of heads and tails. There are 16 possible outcomes. This number could be determined by making a counting tree, by making a systematic list of possibilities, or by using the Multiplication Principle of Counting. All outcomes are equally likely.

   b. ■ $P(\text{four heads}) = \frac{1}{16}$

   ■ $P(\text{exactly one head}) = \frac{4}{16} = \frac{1}{4}$

   ■ $P(\text{at least three heads}) = P(\text{exactly three heads}) + P(\text{four heads}) = \frac{4}{16} + \frac{1}{16} = \frac{5}{16}$

   c. ■ When thinking about using the Multiplication Rule for independent events in this situation, you can break up the single combined event of "four heads" into four separate events, one for each toss. Thus, the four events in this situation are: "H on first toss," "H on second toss," "H on third toss," and "H on fourth toss." These are independent events since getting heads or tails on a given toss does not affect the probability of getting heads or tails on another toss. Thus, $P(\text{four heads}) = P(\text{head on first toss and head on second toss and head on third toss and head on fourth toss}) = P(\text{head on first toss}) \times P(\text{head on second toss}) \times P(\text{head on third toss}) \times P(\text{head on fourth toss}) = \frac{1}{2} \times \frac{1}{2} \times \frac{1}{2} \times \frac{1}{2} = \frac{1}{16}$.

   ■ Getting exactly one head means getting three tails and one head. The one head could occur on any one of the four tosses, so this probability can be found by finding the probability of H-T-T-T and multiplying by 4. $P(\text{H-T-T-T}) = P(\text{head on first toss and tail on second toss and tail on third toss and tail on fourth toss}) = P(\text{head on first toss}) \times P(\text{tail on second toss}) \times P(\text{tail on third toss}) \times P(\text{tail on fourth toss}) = \frac{1}{2} \times \frac{1}{2} \times \frac{1}{2} \times \frac{1}{2} = \frac{1}{16}$. Thus, $P(\text{exactly one head}) = 4 \times \frac{1}{16} = \frac{4}{16} = \frac{1}{4}$.

   ■ $P(\text{at least three heads}) = P(\text{three heads or four heads}) = P(\text{three heads}) + P(\text{four heads}) = \left(4 \times \frac{1}{2} \times \frac{1}{2} \times \frac{1}{2} \times \frac{1}{2}\right) + \frac{1}{16} = \frac{5}{16}$.

4. **a.** Yes, you can use the Multiplication Rule for independent events. The events in this case are "girl's name on first draw" and "boy's name on second draw." These events are independent because the first slip of paper is returned to the hat before the second slip is drawn, and therefore the result of the first draw does not affect the probability for the second draw. Thus, $P(\text{girl's name on first draw and boy's name on second draw}) = P(\text{girl's name on first draw}) \times P(\text{boy's name on second draw}) = \frac{4}{10} \times \frac{6}{10} = \frac{24}{100} = 0.24$.

   b. Using the definition of probability given at the beginning of this investigation, you can compute the probability by counting outcomes. An outcome in this situation is a possible result of drawing two slips of paper; that is, an outcome is a sequence of two names drawn. Each outcome is equally likely since each slip of paper is just as likely to be drawn as any other. The total number of possible outcomes is $10 \times 10 = 100$.

Unit 4

EXPLORE *continued*

The number of outcomes favorable to the event of "girl's name on first draw and boy's name on second draw" is $4 \times 6 = 24$. Thus, P(girl's name on first draw and boy's name on second draw) = $\frac{\text{number of favorable}}{\text{total number}} = \frac{24}{100} = 0.24$.

5. **a.** You cannot use the Multiplication Rule for independent events because the events are not independent. The events in this analysis are "girl's name on first draw" and "boy's name on second draw." These events are not independent because the first slip of paper is not returned to the hat before the second slip is drawn; therefore, the result of the first draw affects the probability for the second draw.

   b. ■ Event A is "girl's name on first draw"; $P(A) = \frac{4}{10}$.
   ■ Event B is "boy's name on second draw." $P(B|A) = \frac{6}{9}$.
   ■ The probability is $\frac{4}{10} \times \frac{6}{9} = \frac{24}{90} \approx 0.267$.

   c. Using the definition of probability given at the beginning of this investigation, you can compute the probability by counting outcomes. An outcome in this situation is a possible result of drawing two slips of paper when the first is drawn without replacement. That is, an outcome is a sequence of two names drawn. Each outcome is equally likely since each slip of paper is just as likely to be drawn as any other. Since the first slip of paper is not replaced before drawing the second, the total number of possible outcomes is $10 \times 9 = 90$. The number of outcomes favorable to the event of "girl's name on first draw and boy's name on second draw" is $4 \times 6 = 24$. Thus, P(girl's name on first draw and boy's name on second draw) = $\frac{\text{number of favorable}}{\text{total number}} = \frac{24}{90}$.

   d. In Activity 4, you draw with replacement, while in Activity 5 you draw without replacement. In both situations, the probability of a girl's name on the first draw is the same (0.4). However, the probability of a boy's name on the second draw is larger if there is no replacement, as in Activity 5, because in that case the number of slips of paper with boys' names is the same as in Activity 4 but there are fewer total slips from which to choose, and thus the probability of drawing a boy's name is larger. Thus, it makes sense that the probability in Activity 5 should be larger than in Activity 4.

   e. Using the extended General Multiplication Rule:

   $\frac{4}{10} \times \frac{3}{9} \times \frac{2}{8} \times \frac{1}{7} = \frac{24}{5,040} \approx 0.0048$.

   Using the Multiplication Principle of Counting and the definition at the beginning of this investigation: $\frac{\text{number of favorable}}{\text{total number}} = \frac{4 \times 3 \times 2 \times 1}{10 \times 9 \times 8 \times 7} = \frac{24}{5,040} \approx 0.0048$.

6. **a.** $\frac{15}{50} \times \frac{14}{49} \approx 0.086$

b. $\frac{35}{50} \times \frac{34}{49} \approx 0.486$

c. This probability can be found in two different ways:

$\frac{35}{50} \times \frac{15}{49} + \frac{15}{50} \times \frac{35}{49} \approx 0.429$ or $1 - (0.086 + 0.486) = 0.428$.

SHARE AND SUMMARIZE   full-class discussion

Checkpoint

a When all the outcomes are equally likely, you can define the probability of an event to be $\frac{\text{number of favorable outcomes}}{\text{total number of possible outcomes}}$.

b "With replacement" means that after any item is selected during a trial, it is returned to the population and could be selected again. "Without replacement" means that if an item is selected during a trial, it cannot be selected again. "With replacement" has the same effect as "with repetition," and in this case trials are independent. "Without replacement" has the same effect as "no repetition," and in this case trials are not independent.

c The Multiplication Rule $P(A \text{ and } B) = P(A) \times P(B)$ can be used when events A and B are independent, as when sampling with replacement. If the events are not independent, as when sampling without replacement, the General Multiplication Rule must be used.

d When comparing the Multiplication Rule or the General Multiplication Rule to the Multiplication Principle of Counting, you see that the same numbers are multiplied. When using the probability rules, you multiply separate fractions. When computing probabilities using the Multiplication Rule for Counting, you perform numerator multiplications and denominator multiplications separately and then form the ratio of those results.

APPLY   individual task

▶On Your Own

a. ■ $\frac{3}{6} \times \frac{2}{6} \times \frac{5}{6} = \frac{30}{216} \approx 0.139$ (See above for how to use the Multiplication Rule for independent events to find this probability.)

■ To use the Multiplication Principle of Counting, proceed as follows:

$$\frac{\text{number of favorable}}{\text{total number}} = \frac{3 \times 2 \times 5}{6 \times 6 \times 6} = \frac{30}{216}.$$

b. $\frac{\text{number of favorable}}{\text{total number}} = \frac{5 \times 4 \times 3 \times 26 \times 25 \times 24}{10 \times 9 \times 8 \times 26 \times 25 \times 24} = \frac{936{,}000}{11{,}232{,}000} \approx 0.083$

Using the General Multiplication Rule: $\frac{5}{10} \times \frac{4}{9} \times \frac{3}{8} = \frac{60}{720} \approx 0.083$.

Master 85

MASTER 85   Transparency Master

Checkpoint

In this investigation, you used counting methods to help calculate probabilities.

a Under what conditions can you calculate the probability of an event by using the following ratio?

$\frac{\text{number of favorable outcomes}}{\text{total number of possible outcomes}}$

b What is the difference between "with replacement" and "without replacement" in a probabilistic (chance) situation? What is the connection to independent trials? What is the connection to "repetition" and "no repetition"?

c When can you calculate probabilities using the Multiplication Rule $P(A \text{ and } B) = P(A) \times P(B)$? When do you need to use the General Multiplication Rule?

d How are the Multiplication Rule and the General Multiplication Rule for probability similar to the Multiplication Principle of Counting? How are they different?

Be prepared to explain your thinking to the entire class.

Use with page 244   UNIT 4 • COUNTING MODELS

CONSTRUCTING A MATH TOOLKIT: Students should record the General Multiplication Rule and an explanation of when it is necessary to use it rather than the Multiplication Rule for independent events.

ASSIGNMENT *pp. 250–255*

Students can now begin Modeling Task 1, 2, or 3; Organizing Task 1, 4, or 5; Reflecting Task 1; or Extending Task 1 from the MORE assignment following Investigation 2.

Unit 4

EXPLORE small-group investigation

INVESTIGATION 2 Combinations, the Binomial Theorem, and Pascal's Triangle

In this investigation, students will study and apply the Binomial Theorem and Pascal's triangle. They will see that these topics are closely related to each other and that both are related to combinations.

1. **a.** Students should expand $(a + b)^n$ by hand for $n = 0, 1, 2, 3$, and 4. This will give them enough practice and examples so that they may see some patterns and the connections to combinations.

    $(a + b)^0 = 1$. The coefficient is 1.

    $(a + b)^1 = a + b$. The coefficients are 1 and 1.

    $(a + b)^2 = a^2 + 2ab + b^2$. The coefficients are 1, 2, and 1.

    $(a + b)^3 = a^3 + 3a^2b + 3ab^2 + b^3$. The coefficients are 1, 3, 3, and 1.

    $(a + b)^4 = a^4 + 4a^3b + 6a^2b^2 + 4ab^3 + b^4$. The coefficients are 1, 4, 6, 4, and 1.

    b. Specific patterns and connections will be explored in the following activities. For now, students may notice some of the following:

    ■ Each list of coefficients begins and ends with 1.

    ■ There is one more coefficient each time the power increases by 1.

    ■ The number of coefficients is one more than the power.

    ■ The sum of the coefficients is 2^n.

    ■ For a given power, some of the coefficients are the sum of consecutive coefficients for the previous power. (This leads to a connection to Pascal's triangle.)

    ■ The coefficients for a given power n are the values of $C(n, k)$.

2. **a.** Coefficients from $(a + b)^5$: 1, 5, 10, 10, 5, 1

    Coefficients from $(a + b)^6$: 1, 6, 15, 20, 15, 6, 1

Master 86

MASTER
86   Transparency Master

Pascal's Triangle

| | | | | | | | | | | | | | | |
row 0 | | | | | | | 1 | | | | | | | |
row 1 | | | | | | 1 | | 1 | | | | | | |
row 2 | | | | | 1 | | 2 | | 1 | | | | | |
row 3 | | | | 1 | | 3 | | 3 | | 1 | | | | |
row 4 | | | 1 | | 4 | | 6 | | 4 | | 1 | | | |
row 5 | | 1 | | 5 | | 10 | | 10 | | 5 | | 1 | | |
row 6 | 1 | | 6 | | 15 | | 20 | | 15 | | 6 | | 1 | |
row 7 | 1 | 7 | 21 | 35 | 35 | 21 | 7 | 1 |

Use with page 246.   UNIT 4 • COUNTING MODELS

b. Students may notice that the number in any row (other than the 1s at the ends of the rows) can be computed by adding the numbers that are slightly to the left and to the right in the row just above.

c. According to the pattern in Part b, the coefficients in $(a + b)^7$ are 1, 7, 21, 35, 35, 21, 7, 1. Students should verify this by expanding $(a + b)^7$ to get $a^7 + 7a^6b + 21a^5b^2 + 35a^4b^3 + 35a^3b^4 + 21a^2b^5 + 7ab^6 + b^7$.

3. **See Teaching Master 86.**

    In this activity, students practice constructing Pascal's triangle and verify that the coefficients they found for $(a + b)^5$ and $(a + b)^6$ in Part a of Activity 2 are the same as the entries in rows 5 and 6 of Pascal's triangle.

EXPLORE *continued*

Activities 4–6 develop connections among the coefficients in the expansion of $(a + b)^n$, numbers in Pascal's triangle, and values of $C(n, k)$. Some confusion can arise due to slightly different notation used by different calculators, computers, and textbooks. Most computers, calculators and textbooks give the expansion of $(a + b)^n$ with a^n first, then descending powers of a and ascending powers of b. Also, a row in Pascal's triangle is read left to right from entry 0 to entry n. To make all this compatible as students explore connections among $C(n, k)$, row n, entry k in Pascal's triangle, and the coefficients of $(a + b)^n$, the activities below will focus on b^n, rather than a^n, and the Binomial Theorem will be stated from $k = 0$ to $k = n$ where k is the exponent on b.

4. **a.** $C(4, 2) = \frac{4!}{2!2!} = 6$. $C(4, 2)$ is entry 2 in row 4 of Pascal's triangle. The coefficient of the a^2b^2 term in $(a + b)^4$ is 6 or $C(4, 2)$.

    b. $C(6, 4) = \frac{6!}{2!4!} = 15$. $C(6, 4)$ is entry 4 in row 6 of Pascal's triangle. The coefficient of the a^2b^4 term in $(a + b)^6$ is 15 or $C(6, 4)$.

    c. $C(n, k)$ is entry k in row n of Pascal's triangle. The coefficient of the $a^{n-k}b^k$ term in $(a + b)^n$ is also entry k in row n of Pascal's triangle.

    $C(n, k)$ is also entry $(n - k)$ in row n. For example, $C(6, 4)$ is also entry 2 in row 6, since $C(6, 4) = C(6, 2)$. Let students briefly discuss this if they discover it, but don't spend too much time on it. This important symmetry in Pascal's triangle will be specifically studied in Activity 8.

5. **a.** There are 100 factors of $(a + b)$ in $(a + b)^{100}$. To get $a^{29}b^{71}$, you need to multiply by b in 71 of the factors, that is, you must choose 71 of the 100 factors to be those where you use b as the multiplier (and in the other factors a will be the multiplier). So the total number of ways to get $a^{29}b^{71}$ is the number of ways of choosing 71 of the 100 factors, that is, $C(100, 71)$.

    b. After students have understood how to use the reasoning in Part a, they should be encouraged to discuss the reasoning so that it makes sense to them. To test it, they should find the coefficients of $(a + b)^5$ using combinations and then verify their results against the display on student page 245.

    c. To get a^3b^5, you must choose 5 of the 8 factors of $(a + b)^8$ to be those where you use b as the multiplier. Thus, the coefficient of the a^3b^5 term in $(a + b)^8$ is the number of ways of choosing 5 factors from 8 factors, which is $C(8, 5) = 56$.

    d. $C(n, k)$ is the coefficient of the $a^{n-k}b^k$ term in $(a + b)^n$. To get $a^{n-k}b^k$, you choose k of the n factors to be those in which you use b as the multiplier.

6. **a.** $(a + b)^4 = C(4, 0)a^4 + C(4, 1)a^3b + C(4, 2)a^2b^2 + C(4, 3)ab^3 + C(4, 4)b^4$

    $\qquad\quad = a^4 + 4a^3b + 6a^2b^2 + 4ab^3 + b^4$

Unit 4

EXPLORE *continued*

b. According to the Binomial Theorem, the coefficient of a^3b^5 in $(a + b)^8$ is $C(8, 5) =$ 56. This is the same answer as in Part c of Activity 5.

c. The exponents of a and b in any term sum to n because to get each term you must multiply through all n factors of $(a + b)^n$. Thus, each term in the expansion will consist of n factors of a and b combined, so the exponents of a and b will sum to n. For example, consider $(a + b)^8$. To get b^5 when expanding $(a + b)^8$, you choose 5 of the 8 factors to be those where b is the multiplier. This leaves 3 factors where a is the multiplier, so whenever you get b^5, you also get a^3 $(5 + 3 = 8)$.

d. To get $a^{n-k}b^k$ you choose k of the n factors where b is the multiplier, which yields $C(n, k)$ as the coefficient. The same argument for a as the multiplier yields $C(n, k)$ for the coefficient of the a^kb^{n-k} term. A similar argument yields $C(n, n-k)$ as the coefficient in each case. Thus, the coefficient of the a^kb^{n-k} term is the same as the coefficient of the $a^{n-k}b^k$ term.

This will be seen more compactly in Activity 8, where students explore the identity $C(n, k) = C(n, n-k)$.

e. For $(2x - 3y)^5$, $a = 2x$ and $b = -3y$. Thus, using the Binomial Theorem,
$(2x - 3y)^5 = (2x)^5 + (5)(2x)^4(-3y)^1 + (10)(2x)^3(-3y)^2 + (10)(2x)^2(-3y)^3 +$
$(5)(2x)^1(-3y)^4 + (-3y)^5 = 32x^5 - 240x^4y + 720x^3y^2 - 1{,}080x^2y^3 + 810xy^4 - 243y^5$.

7. There are many patterns in Pascal's triangle that students may detect and describe. They should state all patterns in terms of properties of combinations, and formulate the properties using the $C(n, k)$ notation. Here are three fundamental patterns and corresponding properties that students may describe:

- $C(n, k) = C(n, n-k)$. This property is evident in the vertical line symmetry of Pascal's triangle.

- $C(n, k) = C(n-1, k-1) + C(n-1, k)$. This property is a restatement of the defining rule for construction of Pascal's triangle.

- $C(n, 0) + C(n, 1) + \dots + C(n, n) = 2^n$. This property is a statement of the fact that the sum of the entries in row n of Pascal's triangle is 2^n.

The first property listed above is explored and proved in Activity 8. The second property is proved in Extending Task 4 in this lesson. The last property is investigated in Activity 5 of Lesson 4.

8. Students may have seen and described this pattern in Activity 7. They should be encouraged to examine a few special cases using specific values of n and k. They should conjecture that $C(n, k) = C(n, n-k)$.

a.
- Using the factorial formula for combinations, $C(8, 3) = \frac{8!}{5!3!} = \frac{8!}{3!5!} = C(8, 5)$.
- $C(8, 3)$ is the number of ways of choosing 3 objects from 8 objects. By choosing 3 objects to take, you have implicitly chosen 5 objects to leave behind. Thus, just by changing your perspective from taking objects to leaving objects behind, you can see that the number of ways of choosing 3 objects from 8 is the same as the number of ways of choosing 5 objects from 8. Thus, $C(8, 3) = C(8, 5)$.

EXPLORE *continued*

b. ■ $C(n, k) = \frac{n!}{(n-k)!k!}$

$C(n, n-k) = \frac{n!}{[n-(n-k)]!(n-k)!} = \frac{n!}{k!(n-k)!} = \frac{n!}{(n-k)!k!}$

Thus, $C(n, k) = C(n, n-k)$.

■ $C(n, k)$ = the number of ways of choosing k objects to take from n objects

= the number of ways of choosing $(n-k)$ objects to leave behind

= $C(n, n-k)$

c. Responses will vary. Some students may prefer or be more convinced by the first proof, which uses algebraic reasoning based on the factorial formula for $C(n, k)$. Other students may prefer or be more convinced by the combinatorial reasoning about how to choose and count combinations.

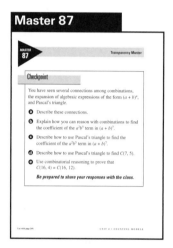

Master 87

SHARE AND SUMMARIZE   full-class discussion

Checkpoint

See Teaching Master 87.

Ⓐ Values of $C(n, k)$ are the coefficients in the expansion of $(a + b)^n$, and they are also the entries in Pascal's triangle. In particular, the coefficient of the b^k term in the expansion of $(a + b)^n$ is the same as entry k in row n of Pascal's triangle, both of which are also equal to $C(n, k)$. (Remember that rows and entries in Pascal's triangle are numbered starting at 0.)

Ⓑ There are 7 factors of $(a + b)$ in $(a + b)^7$. To get a^2b^5 in the expansion of $(a + b)^7$, you must multiply by b in exactly 5 of these 7 factors. Thus, the coefficient of the a^2b^5 term in the expansion of $(a + b)^7$ is equal to the number of ways of choosing 5 of the 7 factors, that is, $C(7, 5)$.

Ⓒ The coefficient of the a^2b^5 term in $(a + b)^7$ can be found in Pascal's triangle as entry 5 in row 7.

Ⓓ $C(7, 5)$ is entry 5 in row 7 of Pascal's triangle.

Ⓔ $C(16, 4)$ is the number of ways of choosing 4 objects to take from 16 objects. But choosing 4 objects to take from 16 is the same as choosing 12 objects not to take. Thus, $C(16, 4) = C(16, 12)$.

CONSTRUCTING A MATH TOOLKIT: In their Math Toolkits, students should describe the connections between the coefficients of $(a + b)^n$, $C(n, k)$, and the nth row of Pascal's triangle.

Unit 4

APPLY individual task

On Your Own

a. ■ $(x + 2)(x + 2)(x + 2) = (x + 2)(x^2 + 4x + 4) = x^3 + 6x^2 + 12x + 8$

   ■ Using row 3 of Pascal's triangle, the coefficients are 1, 3, 3, and 1.
   $$(x + 2)^3 = x^3 + 3(x^2)(2) + 3(x)(2^2) + 1(2^3)$$
   $$= x^3 + 6x^2 + 12x + 8$$

   ■ $(x + 2)^3 = C(3, 0)(x^3) + C(3, 1)(x^2)(2) + C(3, 2)(x)(2^2) + C(3, 3)(2^3)$
   $$= x^3 + 3(x^2)(2) + 3(x)(4) + 8 = x^3 + 6x^2 + 12x + 8$$

b. ■ To get a^4b^2, you must choose 2 of the 6 factors of $(a + b)^6$ to be those in which you use b as the multiplier, so the coefficient of the a^4b^2 term is the number of ways of choosing 2 objects from 6 objects, which is $C(6, 2) = 15$.

   ■ In Pascal's triangle, the coefficient is entry 2 in row 6, so the coefficient of b^2 is 15.

   ■ According to the Binomial Theorem, the coefficient is $C(6, 2) = 15$.

MORE

ASSIGNMENT *pp. 250–255*

Modeling: 3, 4, and choice of one*

Organizing: Choose two*

Reflecting: 1, 3, and 4

Extending: 4 and choice of one*

*When choice is indicated, it is important to leave the choice to the student.
NOTE: *It is best if Organizing tasks are discussed as a whole class after they have been assigned as homework.*

Unit 4

MORE independent assignment

Modeling

1. a. The number of three-initial monograms is $26 \times 26 \times 26$ or 17,576, so the number in the ad is correct.

   b. $P(\text{all three initials the same}) = \frac{26}{26 \times 26 \times 26} = \frac{26}{17,576} \approx 0.001$

   c. ■ If the first two initials are the same and the other is different, there are 26 choices for the letter that will be the first two initials, and then 25 choices for the third initial. Thus, there are $26 \times 25 = 650$ possible three-initial monograms.

   ■ If any two initials are the same and the third is different, then the different initial could be in any of the three positions. Thus, there are $3 \times 650 = 1,950$ possible three-initial monograms.

   ■ $P(\text{two initials the same and one different}) = \frac{3 \times 650}{26 \times 26 \times 26} = \frac{1,950}{17,576} \approx 0.111$

   d. $P(\text{all three initials different}) = \frac{26 \times 25 \times 24}{26 \times 26 \times 26} = \frac{15,600}{17,576} \approx 0.888$

   e. In Parts b, c, and d, all cases have been covered, so the sum of all three probabilities should be 1. Adding the three probabilities does indeed yield 1.

2. a. $\frac{10}{18} \times \frac{10}{18} = \frac{100}{324} \approx 0.309$

MORE *continued*

b. $\frac{10}{18} \times \frac{9}{17} = \frac{90}{306} \approx 0.294$

c. Compare this task to Activity 5 Part d in Investigation 1 of this lesson. In that case, you were drawing one of each (girl's name and boy's name), and it is easy to see that drawing *without* replacement gives a larger probability (because the second fraction in the probability computation has the same numerator but smaller denominator). The reasoning in this case is more subtle. Here you are drawing two of the same (two blue socks). In this case, when drawing without replacement, the second fraction in the probability computation has a smaller numerator and a smaller denominator. This makes it less clear whether the resulting fraction is smaller or larger. In fact, since the numerator is less than the denominator and you are reducing both numerator and denominator by 1, you will get a smaller resulting fraction. (For example compare $\frac{10}{18}$ to $\frac{9}{17}$.) Thus, the first fractions in the computations for "with replacement" and "without replacement" are the same, but the second fraction is smaller for "without replacement." Therefore, drawing *with* replacement gives a larger probability when both socks are blue.

3. a. $\frac{6}{17} \times \frac{5}{16} = \frac{30}{272} \approx 0.110$

b. There are $6 \times 5 = 30$ ways to select a president and secretary from the 6 seniors. There are $17 \times 16 = 272$ ways to select a president and secretary from the 17 people in the club. Thus, the probability they are both seniors is $\frac{\text{number of favorable}}{\text{total number}} = \frac{30}{272} \approx 0.110$.

4. This task introduces an important connection between combinations and binomial probability distributions. This connection will be revisited in Unit 5, "Binomial Distributions and Statistical Inference."

a. There are 16 possible sequences of heads and tails. Students might conclude this by using the Multiplication Principle of Counting ($2 \times 2 \times 2 \times 2 = 16$), by making a tree diagram, or by making a systematic list. In any case, 1 sequence contains no heads, 4 contain exactly one head, 6 contain exactly two heads, 4 contain exactly three heads, and 1 contains four heads.

b. These numbers are in row 4 of Pascal's triangle. Note that the coin is flipped 4 times.

c. You could find these numbers by combinatorial reasoning as follows: Consider the situation of having exactly one head. You can think about this in terms of choosing which flip yields heads. That is, of the four coin flips, you must choose one flip to be heads. You can choose one flip from four in $C(4, 1)$ ways. $C(4, 1) = 4$, which is the same answer found in Part a. Similar reasoning shows that the number of possible sequences from 4 flips that contain exactly k heads is $C(4, k)$.

d. $P(\text{more than three heads}) = P(4 \text{ heads}) = \frac{1}{16}$

5. a. The sums are 1, 2, 4, 8, and 16. This is a geometric sequence where the common multiplier is 2. Note also that each sum is a power of 2.

Unit 4

MORE *continued*

b. The sum of row n is 2^n.

c. $C(3, 0) + C(3, 1) + C(3, 2) + C(3, 0) =$ sum of row $3 = 2^3$

In general, $C(n, 0) + C(n, 1) + \ldots + C(n, n) = 2^n$. (This conjecture is proved in Activity 5 in Lesson 4.)

Organizing

1. a. The General Multiplication Rule, $P(A \text{ and } B) = P(A) \cdot P(B|A)$, can be written as

$$P(B|A) = \frac{P(A \text{ and } B)}{P(A)} \text{ provided } P(A) \neq 0.$$

b. If A and B are independent, then $P(A \text{ and } B) = P(A) \cdot P(B)$. Thus,

$$P(B|A) = \frac{P(A) \cdot P(B)}{P(A)} = P(B).$$

2. a. $C(2n, 2) = \frac{(2n)!}{2!(2n-2)!} = \frac{(2n)(2n-1)(2n-2)!}{2!(2n-2)!} = n(2n-1) = 2n^2 - n$ and

$2C(n, 2) + n^2 = 2\left(\frac{n!}{2!(n-2)!}\right) + n^2 = n(n-1) + n^2 = n^2 - n + n^2 = 2n^2 - n$

Thus, $C(2n, 2) = 2C(n, 2) + n^2$.

$C(n, 2)$ is undefined for $n = 1$, so the statement is true for integers greater than or equal to 2.

b. One possible way of reasoning: If you want to choose 2 objects from a set of $2n$ objects, you can first divide the sets into two subsets each containing n objects. There are $C(n, 2)$ ways of choosing 2 objects from each subset, so there are $C(n, 2) + C(n, 2) = 2C(n, 2)$ ways of choosing 2 objects, where both come from the same subset. There are n^2 ways of choosing two objects, one from the first subset and one from the second subset. So there are $2C(n, 2) + n^2$ ways of choosing 2 objects from a set of $2n$ objects.

3. a. $C(4, 0) \quad C(4, 1) \quad C(4, 2) \quad C(4, 3) \quad C(4, 4)$

For Parts b and c, the commands for the TI-83 are given here.

b. `seq(4nCrX,X,0,4)`

c. `seq(10nCrX,X,0,10)`

You may wish to ask students to find a way to use the function capabilities of the calculator to produce the rows of Pascal's triangle. For example, let Y = 4nCrX and set the table to start at 0 and increase by 1 unit.

4. a. If no three of the n points are collinear, you can choose any three to make a triangle. This can be done in $C(n, 3)$ ways, since order does not matter. It makes no difference if all points are not in the same plane, because the three points chosen to make a triangle will all lie in a plane.

Unit 4

MORE *continued*

b. Since no four of the points are coplanar, then no three are collinear, and you can choose any four points to make a tetrahedron. This can be done in $C(n, 4)$ ways, since order does not matter.

c. The fewest number of colors needed is two. There are several ways to think about this. Students might experiment with several lines and see that two colors are always enough, but they should be encouraged to give an explanation for this fact. Two different explanations follow.

Explanation 1: Think of sequentially adding lines to the plane, so that each new line is parallel to no existing line, and intersects each existing line at a point where no other line already intersects it. The first line defines two regions. Color each region a different color. Two colors have now been used. Each succeeding line either divides any given region in two parts, or leaves it untouched. On one side of the new line, each color remains as it was, and on the other side of the new line every region changes color, so you still need only two colors for up to n lines.

Explanation 2: Because of the requirements of the problem, each intersection point is the intersection of exactly two lines. Thus, if you look at each intersection point, you will find two pairs of vertical angles. Each of the four angles corresponds to a region in the "map." Color each pair of vertical angles the same color. This will color all regions using only two colors.

5. a. A complete graph with 5 vertices has 10 edges. A complete graph with n vertices has $\frac{n(n-1)}{2}$ edges.

b. A cycle graph with an odd number of vertices can be edge-colored with three colors. If a cycle graph has an even number of vertices, then it can be edge-colored with two colors.

c. If n is even, then the fewest number of colors needed to color the edges is $n - 1$. If n is odd, the fewest number of colors is n. Students may conjecture this after trying several graphs. Proving it is difficult. (See, for example, Robin Wilson and John Watkins, *Graphs: An Introductory Approach*, New York: John Wiley and Sons, 1990.)

Reflecting

1. The General Multiplication Rule must be used in situations that do not have replacement. This rule must be used because the events will not be independent if there is no replacement.

Unit 4

MORE *continued*

2. **a.**

$\left(-\right)$ represents 1 $\qquad$ $\left(=\right)$ represents 2

$\left(\equiv\right)$ represents 3 $\qquad$ $\left(\underline{\equiv}\right)$ represents 4

$\left(\overline{\underline{\equiv}}\right)$ represents 5 $\qquad$ $\left(\vdash\right)$ represents 6

$\left(\underline{\varphi}\right)$ represents 10

b. Student ideas will vary. The "mirror" in the title may refer to the symmetry of the pattern, and the four elements may have to do with the pattern of connections: Four symbols are connected in diamond patterns.

3. Responses will vary. One connection that students may mention has to do with the notion of repetition or replacement. The General Multiplication Rule for probability is needed when events are not independent, which corresponds to drawing without replacement, which corresponds to no repetition. Similarly, for permutations and combinations, repetition is not allowed.

4. **a.** The correct answer is "equal to"; $C(10, 2) = C(10, 8)$.

b. Responses will vary. Maybe some students in the survey thought that since 2 is such a small part of 10, compared to 8, there should be more ways of choosing 2 from 10 than there are ways of choosing 8 from 10.

Extending

1. Answers will depend on each particular class. In this sample answer, suppose that there are 30 students in the class and 12 have been to the movies in the past week.

a. Without replacement, the probability is $\frac{12}{30} \times \frac{11}{29} = \frac{132}{870} \approx 0.152$.

With replacement, the probability would be $\frac{12}{30} \times \frac{12}{30} = \frac{144}{900} = 0.16$.

b. Responses will vary. Students may suspect that the first-draw probability is different than the second-draw probability. However, they will see that the probabilities are the same.

c. $\frac{12}{30} = 0.4$

d. $\frac{18}{30} \times \frac{12}{29} = \frac{216}{870} \approx 0.248$

e. $\frac{12}{30} \times \frac{11}{29} = \frac{132}{870} \approx 0.152$

f. $\frac{18}{30} \times \frac{12}{29} + \frac{12}{30} \times \frac{11}{29} = \frac{216}{870} + \frac{132}{870} = \frac{348}{870} = 0.4$. This is the same answer as in Part c. Thus, the probability of selecting a student who has been to the movies in the last week is the same on the first draw as on the second draw.

Unit 4

MORE *continued*

2. a. $rC(n, r) = \frac{(r)(n!)}{r!(n-r)!} = \frac{n!}{(r-1)!(n-r)!} = \frac{n(n-1)!}{(r-1)!(n-r)!} =$

$n\left(\frac{(n-1)!}{(r-1)!((n-1)-(r-1))!} \right) = nC(n-1, r-1)$

Note that $n - r = n - 1 - r + 1 = (n-1) - (r-1)$.

b. Count how many ways there are to choose a committee of r people and a chairperson from a group of n people. One way is to choose the committee first and then the chair; there are $C(n, r)$ ways to choose the committee and then r ways to choose the chair, which gives $rC(n, r)$ choices. Alternatively, you could choose the chair first and then the remaining members of the committee; there are n ways to choose the chair and then $C(n-1, r-1)$ ways to choose the remaining $(r-1)$ members of the committee. Other answers are possible.

3. a. $C(4, 2) + C(3, 2) + C(2, 2) = \frac{4!}{2!2!} + \frac{3!}{2!1!} + \frac{2!}{2!0!} = 6 + 3 + 1 = 10 = C(5, 3)$

b. $C(n, m) = C(n-1, m-1) + C(n-2, m-1) + \ldots + C(m-1, m-1)$

c. Choose any entry in Pascal's triangle. Move to the number just diagonally up and to the left. From there, go diagonally up to the right. The sum of all the numbers in this upward-right diagonal equals the entry originally chosen.

d. $C(n, m)$ is the number of ways of choosing an m-member committee from n people. You could choose an m-member committee by reasoning as follows: First, you could either choose the first of the n people or not. If you choose the first of the n people, then you can choose $(m-1)$ of the remaining $(n-1)$ in $C(n-1, m-1)$ ways. If you do not choose the first of the n people, then you could either choose the second person or not. If you choose the second of the n people (remembering that you are not choosing the first person), then you could choose $(m-1)$ of the remaining $(n-2)$ in $C(n-2, m-1)$ ways. Continue reasoning like this until there are $(m-1)$ people left, that is, you are at person number $n - (m-1)$, and you have not chosen any of the previous people. Now, reasoning as before, you could either choose this person or not. But in this case, there is no such choice. You must choose this person and take all of the remaining $(m-1)$ people. This can be done in $C(m-1, m-1)$ ways.

e. In the general case, $C(n, m) = C(n-1, m-1) + C(n-2, m-1) + C(n-3, m-1) + \ldots + C(m-1, m-1)$. $C(n, m)$ is the coefficient of the b^m term in the expansion of $(a + b)^n$. To generate one of the b^m terms in the expansion of $(a + b)^n$, take b from the first factor in $(a + b)^n$ and $(m-1)$ bs from the other $(n-1)$ factors; or take b from the second factor and $(m-1)$ bs from the remaining $(n-2)$ factors; continue this process.

4. a. $C(n-1, k-1)$ is the entry one to the left of entry k in the row that is one above row n, thus it corresponds to the "number above and to the left" of $C(n, k)$.

$C(n-1, k)$ is in the row just above row n, and entry k in that row is just to the right of entry k in row n. Thus, $C(n-1, k)$ corresponds to the "number above and to the right" of $C(n, k)$.

MORE *continued*

b. For example,

$$C(5, 3) = \frac{5!}{(5-3)!3!} = 10$$

$$C(4, 2) = \frac{4!}{(4-2)!2!} = 6$$

$$C(4, 3) = \frac{4!}{(4-3)!3!} = 4$$

Thus, $C(5, 3) = C(4, 2) + C(4, 3)$.

c. Two proofs are shown here—one using factorials and algebraic reasoning, and the other using combinatorial reasoning.

Algebraic Proof:

$$C(n, k) = \frac{n!}{(n-k)!k!}$$

$$C(n-1, k-1) = \frac{(n-1)!}{[(n-1)-(k-1)]!(k-1)!} = \frac{(n-1)!}{(n-k)!(k-1)!}$$

$$C(n-1, k) = \frac{(n-1)!}{(n-1-k)!k!} = \frac{(n-1)!}{(n-k-1)!k!}$$

In order to add $C(n-1, k-1)$ and $C(n-1, k)$, a common denominator is needed. Observe that $k! = k(k-1)!$ and $(n-k)! = (n-k)(n-k-1)!$. Thus, the common denominator is $(n-k)!k!$.

$$
\begin{aligned}
C(n-1, k-1) + C(n-1, k) &= \frac{(n-1)!}{(n-k)!(k-1)!} + \frac{(n-1)!}{(n-k-1)!k!} \\
&= \frac{k(n-1)!}{k(n-k)!(k-1)!} + \frac{(n-k)(n-1)!}{(n-k)(n-k-1)!k!} \\
&= \frac{k(n-1)!}{(n-k)!k!} + \frac{(n-k)(n-1)!}{(n-k)!k!} \\
&= \frac{k(n-1)! + (n-k)(n-1)!}{(n-k)!k!} \\
&= \frac{(n-1)![k + (n-k)]}{(n-k)!k!} \\
&= \frac{(n-1)!(n)}{(n-k)!k!} \\
&= \frac{n!}{(n-k)!k!} \\
&= C(n, k)
\end{aligned}
$$

Combinatorial Proof:

$C(n, k)$ = number of k-member committees chosen from a group of n people: $\{1, 2, 3, …, n\}$. (This statement is the definition of combinations in the context of forming committees.)

= number of k-member committees that include person n + number of k-member committees that do not include person n

= number of $(k-1)$-member committees chosen from the people $\{1, 2, 3, …, n-1\}$ (and automatically include person n in each of these committees) + number of k-member committees chosen from the people $\{1, 2, 3, …, n-1\}$.

= $C(n-1, k-1) + C(n-1, k)$

MORE *continued*

5. Reports will vary.

See Assessment Resource pages 120–125.

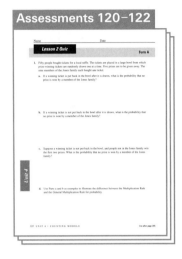

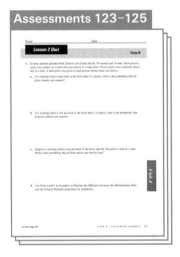

Unit 4

REVIEW AND PRACTICE individual task

▶ **PUMP**

Answers

1.	(d)	**6.**	(b)
2.	(a)	**7.**	(c)
3.	(d)	**8.**	(e)
4.	(e)	**9.**	(e)
5.	(d)	**10.**	(e)

Lesson **3** *The Principle of Mathematical Induction*

LESSON OVERVIEW The material in this lesson is important for students planning to major in mathematics or computer science in college. However, the lesson can be omitted for other students as it is independent of the remaining units in Course 4.

In this lesson, students will learn how to do proof by mathematical induction. This is a fundamental proof technique used throughout mathematics and also in computer science. You will probably find that this traditionally difficult topic is accessible to more students because of students' previous work with recursion in the *Contemporary Mathematics in Context* curriculum and the sense-making development of the lesson.

Students will build on their previous work with recursion to help them understand and carry out proof by mathematical induction. They will tackle problems in which they must first find patterns and then prove them. The patterns include recursive formulas and function rules. Students will come to recognize that the type of problem to which proof by mathematical induction might be successfully applied is one in which you know a recursive pattern and you have a good conjecture for a closed-form pattern (e.g., a function rule). In this type of problem, you use the recursive pattern to help you prove the conjectured closed-form pattern using the Principle of Mathematical Induction. The lesson emphasizes geometrical problems, since these problems are often most illustrative of the process of proof by mathematical induction. Some typical algebraic problems involving finite sums are included at the end of the lesson.

The Principle of Mathematical Induction can be equivalently formulated in terms of moving from the n case to the $(n + 1)$ case, or from the $(n - 1)$ case to the n case. Because of a more natural development that avoids some common notational and conceptual confusions, the development in this lesson is based on moving from the $(n - 1)$ case to the n case. This development focuses on the "looking back" or "stepping back" approach that should be familiar to students because of their extensive work with recursion in the *Contemporary Mathematics in Context* curriculum. It also avoids introducing another variable, k, which is used in the traditional treatment of induction proofs and is often confusing to students.

You may also notice that the two steps of the Principle of Mathematical Induction are presented in the opposite order from most textbooks. This is done to fit nicely with the domino analogy that is used to introduce and motivate this topic. When you reach this point of the lesson, you may wish to ask students if they have ever set up an extensive domino display or have seen this done in person or in contests shown on television. Then ask the students what the contestant must do first. (Set up the dominos spaced so that each will knock over the next one, but so that they will remain standing until the first domino is knocked over.) What does the

Unit 4

contestant do next? (Knock over the first domino.) The result that all the dominos fall over is equivalent to the *conclusion* of the proof (that the statement is true for all integers greater than or equal to the initial value).

However, in writing their proofs, some students may prefer to follow the traditional approach of verifying that the statement to be proved is true for the initial value first, perhaps because this is the easiest step, and, if it fails, there is no need to continue with the other step. This is fine. In this lesson, the two steps are referred to by the names "induction step" and "base step," rather than "Step 1," "Step 2," to get away from the idea that one of these steps must be done before the other.

Lesson Objectives

- ■ **To understand and use the Principle of Mathematical Induction**
- ■ **To develop the skill of proof by mathematical induction**

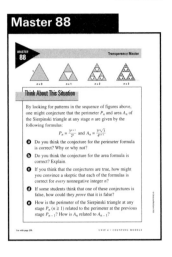

Master 88

LAUNCH full-class discussion

Think About This Situation

See Teaching Master 88.

ⓐ Students will probably try the formula for perimeter for several values of n, see that the values agree with the diagrams, and conclude that the formula is probably correct. $P_0 = 3$, $P_1 = \frac{9}{2}$, $P_2 = \frac{27}{4}$, $P_3 = \frac{81}{8}$. Some may see that the pattern is to multiply by $\frac{3}{2}$ each time, starting with 3.

ⓑ Students will find making sense of the area formula more difficult. They may see that each time one-fourth of each triangle is cut out, but they may have a difficult time finding the area of the initial triangle. $A_0 = \frac{\sqrt{3}}{4}$, $A_1 = \frac{3\sqrt{3}}{4^2}$, $A_2 = \frac{9\sqrt{3}}{4^3}$ so that you are multiplying by $\frac{3}{4}$ each time. Don't spend too much time here. The point is to give students a context in which to think about Part c.

ⓒ Showing that the formulas work for the given diagrams does not prove that the formulas are correct for every nonnegative integer n. The key step in proving the formulas are correct is finding the recursive pattern, in this case finding the constant multiplier, as noted in Parts a and b. Once you know for sure that the constant multipliers are correct, which could be established by geometric reasoning, then you could prove that the formulas are correct by, for example, appealing to previous knowledge about geometric sequences, or using mathematical induction. All these ideas will be carefully studied in the lesson.

ⓓ Disproving either conjecture would require finding only one value of n for which the conjecture is not true (i.e., finding a counterexample).

ⓔ If students did not discuss this previously, it will be worthwhile to find these patterns now. The perimeter is multiplied by $\frac{3}{2}$ each time (it gets longer), so $P_n = \frac{3}{2}P_{n-1}$.

NOTE: Teaching Master 91 could be used for a transparency of the Sierpinski Triangles.

Unit 4

LAUNCH *continued*

The area gets smaller each time, multiplying by $\frac{3}{4}$, so $A_n = \frac{3}{4}A_{n-1}$. As noted in Part c, finding the recursive pattern is crucial for proving the formulas, particularly for proofs by mathematical induction.

EXPLORE small-group investigation

INVESTIGATION 1 Infinity, Recursion, and Mathematical Induction

In this investigation, students will carry out and develop an understanding of induction proofs. Sometimes, before the proof begins, students need to decide what to prove. This is often done by experimenting and looking for a pattern. There are typically two relevant patterns—a recursive pattern (sometimes expressed as a recursive formula) and a closed-form pattern (sometimes expressed as a function rule). It is the closed-form pattern that is proven with mathematical induction. The recursive pattern is essential for the induction step in the induction proof. It is important to note that the recursive pattern must also be proven, but this must be done by reasoning about the context, and it must be done before using the recursive relationship in the induction proof. All of these points will be investigated carefully in this lesson.

1. The goal of this activity is for students to realize that when checking the validity of a statement that is claimed for infinitely many values of *n*, it is not enough to simply check a few, or even many, values of *n*. A statement may be true for many values of *n*, but may not be true for *all n*, as in Part a below. On the other hand, a statement may be false for finitely many values of *n*, but true for infinitely many other values of *n*, as in Part b.

   a. This conjecture is false, but the statement $5^n > n!$ is true for $n = 1, 2, 3, 4, ..., 11$. Thus, when students check small values of *n* the conjecture may appear to be true. Students should realize that a statement about *n* may be true for many values of *n*, but it might not be true for all *n*.

   b. The conjecture that $n! > 5^n$ for $n \geq 1$ is false, since it fails for $n = 1, 2, ..., 11$. However, the statement $n! > 5^n$ is true for $n \geq 12$.

   c. The conjecture that $n! > 5^n$ for $n \geq 12$ is true. Students may suggest that they know this for sure because they tried many numbers, but this is not a sufficient method for establishing that it is true for all $n \geq 12$. They may suggest that the conjecture is true because they have seen a pattern, but students must be wary of patterns since they can hold for a long while and then fail. Students may try to reason from the graphs that the conjecture is true. This is a better argument than those possible arguments given above, but it still would need more explanation about the behavior of the functions involved. Ultimately a rigorous proof is needed. Mathematical induction will be seen to be a method of proof that can be used to establish this conjecture.

Unit 4

EXPLORE *continued*

2. **a.** Set the dominos upright on edge in a line just far enough apart so that when one falls over it will knock over the next one in line.

   b. All the dominos will fall over.

   c. The conditions are: each domino must be positioned to knock the next one over, and the first domino must be knocked over. Both conditions are needed. If the dominos are positioned correctly but the first domino is not knocked over, then all the dominos will not fall over. Likewise, if the first domino is knocked over but the dominos are not set up correctly, then they won't all fall over.

   d.

Dominos	**Principle of Mathematical Induction**
(a) Set up the dominos in such a way that whenever any given domino falls over, it will knock over the next domino.	**(a)** Show that whenever a statement is true for $n - 1$, it is also true for n.

   The statements for each value of n are like dominos. Setting up the dominos so that if one falls over, then it will knock over the next is like the situation where if the statement is true for $n - 1$, then it is also true for n.

(b) Knock over the first domino.	**(b)** The statement is true for some initial value of n.

   Knocking over the first domino is like proving the first instance of the conjecture, that is, proving that the statement is true for the first value of n.

Result	*Conclusion*
All the dominos fall over.	The statement is true for all values of n greater than or equal to the initial value.

   Mathematical induction can be used to prove a statement that is to be true for all integer values of n greater than or equal to some initial value. Such a statement is really an infinite sequence of statements. This is like an infinite line of dominos. To prove that the statement is true for all values of n, you must in effect prove infinitely many statements. This is like knocking over all the dominos. The way to do this is to first show that if the statement is true for one value of n, then the statement is true for the next value of n (set up the dominos so that they will sequentially knock each other over); then prove the statement for the first value of n (knock over the first domino). These two steps will prove that the statement is true for all values of n (all the dominos will fall over).

Unit 4

EXPLORE *continued*

3. Students may have worked on this problem previously (for example, see Organizing Task 5 in Lesson 2). In any case, they should experiment with several complete graphs, look for patterns, and figure out some conjectures for the number of edges. In this activity, they are exploring. In the next activity, they will be guided to find specific equations that will be used in an induction proof. They may find a recursive formula, like $E_n = E_{n-1} + (n-1)$, or they may find a function rule, like $E_n = \frac{n(n-1)}{2}$, but if they don't find those particular equations in this activity, they will in Activity 4.

4. **a.** $E_n = E_{n-1} + (n-1)$

Some students may have found this equation in Activity 3. In any case, it is important for students to justify (prove) this recursive pattern. This relationship holds because to go from a complete graph on $(n-1)$ vertices to a complete graph on n vertices you must add one vertex and an edge to each of the $(n-1)$ vertices that were in the complete graph on $(n-1)$ vertices. Thus, $E_n = E_{n-1} + (n-1)$.

b. Some students may have already found a function rule in Activity 3, in which case they can go directly to Part c. In Part c, they focus on the specific function rule that will be proven using mathematical induction.

c. Some students may have found this function rule in activities above. In any case, all students should now have the function rule, $E_n = \frac{n(n-1)}{2}$. This is what will now be proven by mathematical induction.

NOTE: The Principle of Mathematical Induction refers to a statement about integers, $S(n)$. In this case, $S(n)$ is the statement $E_n = \frac{n(n-1)}{2}$.

5. **a.**
■ $E_{n-1} = \frac{(n-1)(n-2)}{2}$

■ $E_n = E_{n-1} + (n-1)$

$= \frac{(n-1)(n-2)}{2} + (n-1)$ You assume that the statement is true in the $(n-1)$ case. Thus, you may assume the function rule for E_{n-1}. Thus, substitute for E_{n-1} using the result from above.

$= \frac{n^2 - 3n + 2}{2} + (n-1)$ Use the distributive property to rewrite $(n-1)(n-2)$.

$= \frac{n^2 - 3n + 2}{2} + \frac{2(n-1)}{2}$ Rewrite using a common denominator.

$= \frac{n^2 - n}{2}$ Add the fractions.

$= \frac{n(n-1)}{2}$ Factor the numerator.

(There is more than one way to carry out the algebraic reasoning and simplification in this proof.)

b. It is obvious that a complete graph with 1 vertex has 0 edges, and in fact this is what you get when you substitute 1 into $\frac{n(n-1)}{2}$. This step corresponds to knocking over the first domino.

Unit 4

EXPLORE *continued*

6. a. Students should experiment by drawing lines and looking for patterns. They might make a table. Their conjecture should be $R_n = 2n$, where R_n is the number of regions formed by n lines.

b. Since a new line will divide two of the already existing regions, it will create two new regions. Thus, $R_n = R_{n-1} + 2$.

c. Induction Step: Show that the n case of the function rule is true if the $(n-1)$ case is true. A good way to do this is to start trying to prove the n case. Then (often in the first step) use the recursive formula to step back to the $(n-1)$ case, which you are assuming is true. By using this assumption, and typically doing some algebraic manipulation, you arrive at the desired n case. Thus:

$$R_n = R_{n-1} + 2$$
$$= 2(n-1) + 2$$
$$= 2n - 2 + 2$$
$$= 2n$$

Base Step: Show that the statement is true for $n = 1$. That is, you must show that the number of regions formed by n lines is $2n$, where $n = 1$. Do this by reasoning as follows: If there is 1 line, then 2 regions are formed, and in fact if you substitute $n = 1$ into $2n$, you get 2.

   Thus, the two steps of a proof by mathematical induction have been completed and the conjecture has been proven.

7. a. $S_1 = 1$, $S_2 = 4$, $S_3 = 9$, $S_4 = 16$, ..., $S_n = n^2$. Thus, $S_n = n^2$ is the conjecture that you now need to prove.

b. First, find and justify the recursive pattern that will be the key to the induction proof. In this case, the statement of the problem says that you add the next odd integer, $(2n - 1)$, at each step, so the recursive formula that describes this situation is $S_n = S_{n-1} + (2n - 1)$. Now the induction proof proceeds with the usual two steps.

Induction Step: Show that the $(n-1)$ case implies the n case. Do this by starting to prove the n case and using the $(n-1)$ case as needed. The $(n-1)$ case of the conjecture is $S_{n-1} = (n-1)^2$. Thus,

$$S_n = S_{n-1} + (2n - 1)$$
$$= (n-1)^2 + (2n-1)$$
$$= n^2 - 2n + 1 + 2n - 1$$
$$= n^2$$

Base Step: Now show that the statement is true for the first value of n, $n = 1$. When $n = 1$, you are looking for the sum of the first odd integer, that is, start with 1 and add no further. Thus, the sum is 1, and in fact when you substitute $n = 1$ into n^2, you get 1.

   Thus, the two steps of an induction proof have been completed successfully and therefore the proof is complete.

Unit 4

Masters 89a–89c

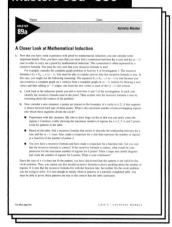

Master 90

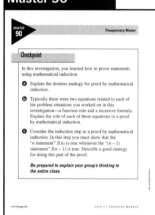

CONSTRUCTING A MATH TOOLKIT: Students should write an explanation of when to use the Principle of Mathematical Induction and how to prove statements using mathematical induction.

EXPLORE *continued*

See Teaching Masters 89a–89c.

Students who successfully complete this lesson will have a good basic understanding of proof by induction. You may choose to push some students a bit farther by having them consider two important details:

(1) You must prove that the recursive formula used in an induction proof is true.

(2) You must carefully identify the initial value(s) of *n*.

To address these two important details, you could have the students do the activities found on Teaching Masters 89a and 89b, "A Closer Look at Mathematical Induction." Solutions for the activities on these activity masters are given in Teaching Master 89c. You may use these solutions to check students' work, or you may wish to duplicate this master so that students can check their own work.

SHARE AND SUMMARIZE full-class discussion

Checkpoint

See Teaching Master 90.

During the discussion of this Checkpoint, you may wish to help students think about the types of situations in which considering proof by mathematical induction is appropriate. Students should consider proof by mathematical induction when they know a recursive pattern (like a recursive formula) and they have a conjecture for a closed-form pattern (like a function rule.)

a Mathematical induction may be used to prove a statement that is supposed to be true for all integer values of *n* greater than or equal to some initial value. Such a statement is really an infinite sequence of statements. This is like an infinite line of dominos. To prove that the statement is true for all values of *n*, you must in effect prove infinitely many statements. This is like knocking over all the dominos. The way to do this is to first show that if the statement is true for one value of *n*, then the statement is true for the next value of *n* (set up the dominos so that they will sequentially knock each other over), then prove the statement for the first value of *n* (knock over the first domino). These two steps will prove that the statement is true for all values of *n* (all the dominos will fall over).

b The function rule is the conjecture to be proved by mathematical induction. The recursive formula is essential for the induction step in the proof, because it lets you step back from the *n* statement to the $(n - 1)$ statement.

c You start trying to prove the *n* statement. At some point (often in the first step, as in the proofs in this lesson), you use a recursive pattern to step back to the $(n - 1)$ statement, which you are assuming is true. By using this assumption, and typically doing some algebraic rearrangement, you arrive at the desired *n* statement.

▶On Your Own

Let D_n be the number of diagonals in a regular n-gon. Students should experiment with this situation to find a recursive formula that shows the relationship between D_n and D_{n-1}. The recursive formula is $D_n = D_{n-1} + (n-2)$. This is true because you can form an n-gon from an $(n-1)$-gon as follows: Add a vertex off one side, erase that side, and add two new edges from the new vertex to the vertices of the edge you erased. Now, all the diagonals of the old $(n-1)$-gon are still diagonals of the new n-gon. In addition, the erased edge is now a diagonal. You can also draw diagonals from the new vertex to all the non-adjacent vertices; there are $(n-3)$ such diagonals. Thus, you have added $1 + (n-3)$ new diagonals, so $D_n = D_{n-1} + 1 + (n-3) = D_{n-1} + (n-2)$. Now the induction proof can begin.

Induction Step: Assume that the formula holds for the $(n-1)$ case. Then prove the n-case by using the recursive formula and the $(n-1)$ case as needed. Assuming the $(n-1)$ case is true gives

$$D_{n-1} = \frac{(n-1)(n-4)}{2}. \text{ Thus,}$$

$$D_n = D_{n-1} + (n-2)$$

$$= \frac{(n-1)(n-4)}{2} + (n-2)$$

$$= \frac{(n-1)(n-4)}{2} + \frac{2(n-2)}{2}$$

$$= \frac{n^2 - 5n + 4 + 2n - 4}{2}$$

$$= \frac{n^2 - 3n}{2}$$

$$= \frac{n(n-3)}{2}$$

Base Step: You must also show that the statement is true for the first n value, in this case $n = 3$. A 3-gon is a triangle, which has 0 diagonals, and in fact if you substitute $n = 3$ into $\frac{n(n-3)}{2}$, you get 0.

Thus, the two steps of a proof by mathematical induction have been completed and the conjecture has therefore been proven.

Modeling

1. To get the maximum number of regions, each new line should intersect each of the previous lines. Thus, the nth line will intersect the previous $(n-1)$ lines and create n new regions. That is, if R_n is the number of regions formed by n lines, then $R_n = R_{n-1} + n$. By examining a table, using statistical regression, or using the method of finite differences, students should conjecture a rule equivalent to the following function rule: $R_n = \frac{n(n+1)}{2} + 1$.

MORE
ASSIGNMENT *pp. 264–267*

Modeling: Choose two*
Organizing: 1 and choice
of two*
Reflecting: 1 and 4
Extending: Choose one*

When choice is indicated, it is important to leave the choice to the student.
NOTE: *It is best if Organizing tasks are discussed as a whole class after they have been assigned as homework.*

Unit 4

MORE *continued*

Proof that $R_n = \frac{n(n+1)}{2} + 1$:

Induction Step: Assume the formula is true for the $(n-1)$ case, that is $R_{n-1} = \frac{(n-1)(n)}{2} + 1$. Thus

$$R_n = R_{n-1} + n$$
$$= \frac{(n-1)(n)}{2} + 1 + n$$
$$= \frac{n^2 - n}{2} + 1 + \frac{2n}{2}$$
$$= \frac{n^2 + n}{2} + 1$$
$$= \frac{n(n+1)}{2} + 1.$$

Base Step: For 1 line, there are $2 = \frac{1(2)}{2} + 1$ regions.

From the two steps, you can conclude that the maximum number of regions formed by n lines is $R_n = \frac{n(n+1)}{2} + 1$, for $n \geq 1$.

2. **a.** The fewest number of moves needed with 2 disks is 3. The fewest number of moves needed with 3 disks is 7. The fewest number of moves needed with 4 disks is 15.

   b. $M_n = 2^n - 1$

   Students should conjecture this rule based on their experimentation in Part a.

   c. First find a recursive pattern: To move n disks, first move $(n-1)$ disks to a new peg, then move the largest disk onto the third peg, and then move the $(n-1)$ disks on top of the largest disk. Thus, the number of moves to move n disks is

   $$M_n = M_{n-1} + 1 + M_{n-1} = 2M_{n-1} + 1.$$

   Induction Step: Now assume that the formula in Part b is true for the $(n-1)$ case and show that it is true for the n case. Note that $M_{n-1} = 2^{n-1} - 1$. Then use the recursive pattern: $M_n = 2M_{n-1} + 1 = 2(2^{n-1} - 1) + 1 = 2^n - 2 + 1 = 2^n - 1$

   Base Step: To finish a game with 1 disk requires 1 move and $1 = 2^1 - 1$.

   From the two steps, you can conclude that a game with n disks requires $2^n - 1$ moves, that is, $M_n = 2^n - 1$, for $n \geq 1$.

   d. $2^{64} - 1 = 1.844674407 \times 10^{19}$ moves are needed for a game with 64 disks. If a move is made every second, it will take approximately 584,942,417,400 years for the game to be finished. There is no need to worry about the world ending soon!

3. To find the recursive pattern, note that for a tree with n vertices, you can take off a dangling vertex and its adjacent edge, getting a new tree with $(n-1)$ vertices and one less edge.

   Induction Step: Assume the statement is true for a tree with $(n-1)$ vertices. That is, assume that a tree with $(n-1)$ vertices has exactly $(n-2)$ edges. Let T be a tree with n

MORE *continued*

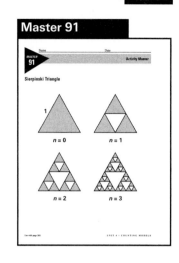

vertices. You are given the fact that *T* has at least one dangling vertex. Remove a dangling vertex and its adjacent edge. This creates a tree with $(n-1)$ vertices. Thus, by the induction hypothesis it has $(n-2)$ edges. Now, restore the vertex and edge to get back to *T*. Thus, *T* has $(n-2)+1 = (n-1)$ edges.

Base Step: For a tree with 1 vertex, there are $1-1 = 0$ edges. (Since no initial value is given, you could decide to start the induction at $n = 2$. For a tree with 2 vertices, there is $2-1 = 1$ edge.)

From these two steps, you can conclude that a tree with *n* vertices has $(n-1)$ edges, for $n \geq 1$.

4. **See Teaching Master 91.**

    a. The conjecture is $A_n = \frac{3^n\sqrt{3}}{4^{n+1}}$, and the $(n-1)$ case is $A_{n-1} = \frac{3^{n-1}\sqrt{3}}{4^n}$. The recursion equation is $A_n = \frac{3}{4}(A_{n-1})$. This represents the situation accurately, because each time the Sierpinski triangle is cut, you lose one-fourth of the existing area. The new area is then $\frac{3}{4}$ times the old area. The induction proof follows:

    Induction Step: $A_n = \frac{3}{4}(A_{n-1})$
    $$= \frac{3}{4} \cdot \frac{3^{n-1}\sqrt{3}}{4^n}$$
    $$= \frac{3^n\sqrt{3}}{4^{n+1}}$$

    Base Step: The first triangle $(n = 0)$ has area $\frac{\sqrt{3}}{4}$. Substituting $n = 0$ yields $\frac{3^0\sqrt{3}}{4^{0+1}} = \frac{\sqrt{3}}{4}$. Thus, by the Principle of Mathematical Induction, the area of the Sierpinski triangle is

    $A_n = \frac{3^n\sqrt{3}}{4^{n+1}}$ for $n \geq 0$.

    b. The conjecture is $P_n = \frac{3^{n+1}}{2^n}$, and the $(n-1)$ case is $P_{n-1} = \frac{3^n}{2^{n-1}}$.

    The recursion equation is $P_n = \frac{3}{2}(P_{n-1})$. This represents the situation accurately, because each time the triangle is cut, the perimeter of each existing triangle is increased by one triangle with perimeter equal to half the original perimeter. The new perimeter is then $1\frac{1}{2}$ times the old one. The induction proof follows:

    Induction Step: $P_n = \frac{3}{2}(P_{n-1})$
    $$= \frac{3}{2} \cdot \frac{3^n}{2^{n-1}}$$
    $$= \frac{3^{n+1}}{2^n}$$

    Base Step: The first triangle $(n = 0)$ has perimeter $1 + 1 + 1 = 3$. Substituting $n = 0$ yields $\frac{3^{0+1}}{2^0} = \frac{3}{1} = 3$.

    Thus, by the Principle of Mathematical Induction, the perimeter of the figure is $P_n = \frac{3^{n+1}}{2^n}$ for $n \geq 0$.

    Some students might look at this problem in a different way, as follows. You could calculate the perimeter and then prove that the result of this calculation is equal to $\frac{3^{n+1}}{2^n}$. To calculate the perimeter, note that the perimeter of the *n*th stage of the Sierpinski triangle is the sum of the perimeter of the original triangle and the triangles added at each step. Thus, (perimeter at *n*th stage) $= P_n = 3 + \frac{1}{2}(3) + \frac{1}{4}(3^2) + \frac{1}{8}(3^3) + \dots + \frac{3^n}{2^n}$.

MORE *continued*

You must prove that $P_n = \frac{3^{n+1}}{2^n}$. The recursive formula in this case is $P_n = P_{n-1} + \frac{3^n}{2^n}$. The induction proof follows:

Induction Step:
$$P_n = P_{n-1} + \frac{3^n}{2^n}$$
$$= \frac{3^n}{2^{n-1}} + \frac{3^n}{2^n}$$
$$= \frac{2 \cdot 3^n}{2^n} + \frac{3^n}{2^n}$$
$$= \frac{3 \cdot 3^n}{2^n}$$
$$= \frac{3^{n+1}}{2^n}$$

Base Step: If you look at the case of $n = 0$, you have the first term of the series, $P_0 = 3$. For $n = 0$ in the conjecture you have $P = \frac{3^1}{2^0} = 3$, so the conjecture is true for $n = 0$.

Thus, by the Principle of Mathematical Induction, $P_n = \frac{3^{n+1}}{2^n}$ for $n \geq 0$.

c. As n gets very large, the area approaches 0 and the perimeter approaches infinity. The area goes to 0 because 4^{n+1} grows faster than 3^n. The perimeter approaches infinity because 3^{n+1} grows faster than 2^n. Students might conjecture this simply by substituting a large value of n into the function rules for area and perimeter.

5. You need to prove that $S_n = \frac{n(n+1)}{2}$, $n \geq 1$. By the definition of S_n, you know the recursive pattern is $S_n = S_{n-1} + n$.

Induction Step: Assume $S_{n-1} = \frac{(n-1)(n)}{2}$. Thus:
$$S_n = S_{n-1} + n$$
$$= \frac{n(n-1)}{2} + n$$
$$= \frac{n^2 - n}{2} + \frac{2n}{2}$$
$$= \frac{n^2 + n}{2}$$
$$= \frac{n(n+1)}{2}$$

Base Step: The sum of the first positive integer is $1 = \frac{1(2)}{2}$.

From these two steps, you can conclude that the sum of the first n positive integers is $\frac{n(n+1)}{2}$, for $n \geq 1$.

Organizing

1. $C(n, 2) = \frac{n!}{2!(n-2)!} = \frac{n(n-1)}{2}$ $\qquad S_{n-1} = \frac{n(n-1)}{2}$ $\qquad E_n = \frac{n(n-1)}{2}$

Explanation for why $E_n = C(n, 2)$: The number of edges in a complete graph on n vertices is $C(n, 2)$ because each edge corresponds to choosing two of the n vertices.

Explanation for why $S_{n-1} = E_n$: Connect the first vertex of n vertices to the other $(n-1)$ vertices, yielding $(n-1)$ new edges; connect the second vertex to the remaining $(n-2)$ vertices, yielding $(n-2)$ new edges; continuing this process yields $E_n = (n-1) + (n-2) + \dots + 1 = S_{n-1}$.

MORE *continued*

2. **a.** A table of the number of set elements, subsets, and number of subsets may help students see the pattern.

Number of Elements	Subsets	Number of Subsets
0	∅	1
1	∅, {1}	2
2	∅, {1}, **{2}**, **{1, 2}**	4
3	∅, {1}, {2}, **{3}**, {1, 2}, **{1, 3}**, **{2, 3}**, **{1, 2, 3}**	8
4	∅, {1}, {2}, {3}, **{4}**, {1, 2}, {1, 3}, **{1, 4}**, {2, 3}, **{2, 4}**, **{3, 4}**, {1, 2, 3}, **{1, 2, 4}**, **{1, 3, 4}**, **{2, 3, 4}**, **{1, 2, 3, 4}**	16

From this table, it appears that if n is the number of elements in a set, and S_n is the number of subsets for a set of n elements, then $S_n = 2^n$.

b. First, find the recursive relationship between S_{n-1} and S_n. Looking at the table, note (by looking at the bold subsets) that each time an element is added to the set, the number of subsets doubles (because all the original subsets are still subsets, and the new element can be added to each to make new subsets). Thus, $S_n = 2S_{n-1}$.

Induction Step: To prove the conjecture $S_n = 2^n$, assume that it is true for the $(n-1)$ case, $S_{n-1} = 2^{n-1}$, and use the recursion equation. Thus,

$$S_n = 2S_{n-1}$$
$$= 2(2^{n-1})$$
$$= 2^n$$

Base Step: The empty set has only itself as a subset. Thus, $S_0 = 1 = 2^0$, so the conjecture is true for the initial value $n = 0$.

From these two steps, you can conclude that the number of subsets S_n of a set with n elements is $S_n = 2^n$, for $n \geq 0$.

3. Induction Step: Assume the statement is true for $n - 1$, that is, assume $(n-1)! > 2^{n-1}$. Next, show that the statement is true for n.

$n! = n(n-1)! > n \cdot 2^{(n-1)}$, by the induction hypothesis. But since $n \geq 4$, this becomes $n! > n \cdot 2^{(n-1)} \geq 4 \cdot 2^{(n-1)} > 2 \cdot 2^{(n-1)} = 2^n$. Thus, $n! > 2^n$.

Base Step: $4! = 24 > 16 = 2^4$

These two steps prove the inequality $n! > 2^n$, for $n \geq 4$.

4. Induction Step: Assume that the statement is true for $m = k - 1$ and show that it is true for m. Assuming it is true for $m - 1$ gives $\log x^{m-1} = (m-1)\log x$.

By the rules of exponents and logarithms, you know that

$$\log x^m = \log (x^{m-1} \cdot x) = \log x^{m-1} + \log x$$

Unit 4

MORE *continued*

But the induction hypothesis assumed that $\log x^{m-1} = (m-1)\log x$, so

$$\log x^m = \log x^{m-1} + \log x$$
$$= (m-1)\log x + \log x$$
$$= m \log x$$

Base Step: You also need to show that the statement is true when $m = 0$.

$\log x^0 = \log 1 = 0$ and $0 \log x = 0$

Thus, when $m = 0$, $\log x^m = m \log x$.

These two steps prove that $\log x^m = m \log x$ for all nonnegative integers m.

5. **a.** You are to prove the conjecture $S_n = \frac{1-r^{n+1}}{1-r}$ for $n \geq 0$. The $(n-1)$ case of the conjecture is $S_{n-1} = \frac{1-r^n}{1-r}$. You need a recursive expression that relates S_n and S_{n-1}. Since the last term of the series S_n is r^n and the last term of S_{n-1} is r^{n-1}, the recursive formula is $S_n = S_{n-1} + r^n$.

Induction Step: $S_n = S_{n-1} + r^n$

$$= \frac{1-r^n}{1-r} + r^n$$
$$= \frac{1-r^n}{1-r} + \frac{(1-r)(r^n)}{1-r}$$
$$= \frac{1-r^n+r^n-r^{n+1}}{1-r}$$
$$= \frac{1-r^{n+1}}{1-r}$$

Base Step: To show that the conjecture is true for $n = 0$, notice that the initial term of the series is 1, and that no more terms are added. Substituting $n = 0$, yields $\frac{1-r}{1-r} = 1$, so the conjecture is true for $n = 1$.

The two parts of the induction proof are successfully completed, so the proof is finished.

b. You are trying to prove that $1 + r + r^2 + \ldots + r^{n-1} + r^n = \frac{1-r^{n+1}}{1-r}$. Multiplying $S_n = 1 + r + r^2 + \ldots + r^{n-1} + r^n$ by $(1-r)$ produces

$$(1-r)S_n = (1-r)(1 + r + r^2 + \ldots + r^{n-1} + r^n)$$
$$(1-r)S_n = (1 + r + r^2 + \ldots + r^{n-1} + r^n) - r - r^2 - \ldots - r^n - r^{n+1}$$
$$(1-r)S_n = 1 - r^{n+1}$$
$$S_n = \frac{1-r^{n+1}}{1-r}$$

Reflecting

1. There are two steps to an induction proof—the induction step, where you assume the $(n-1)$ case to show the n case; and the base step, where you show that the statement is true for the starting value(s) of n. The base step is missing in this proof. In fact, if you try to do the base step you find that the statement is false. The statement is not true when $n = 1$ (or when n equals any particular value).

MORE *continued*

2. Sequences can sometimes be described by recursive and/or function formulas. If you know the recursive formula and have a conjecture for the function formula, then this is a situation where you could try to prove the function formula using mathematical induction. The recursive formula gives the recursive pattern that can be used to help prove the function formula.

3. Responses will vary. (Poincaré felt that the principle of mathematical induction was intuitively true and that everyone would agree with it. Students who do not agree may not have fully understood mathematical induction.)

4. A diagonal can be determined by the two vertices that are its endpoints. Thus, you can determine the number of diagonals by counting pairs of appropriate vertices. There are n choices for one vertex-endpoint of a diagonal. The other vertex-endpoint cannot be the same vertex or adjacent to it, so that eliminates 3 vertices. Thus, there are $(n - 3)$ choices for the other vertex-endpoint. But the order of the endpoints doesn't matter, so divide by 2. This yields $\frac{n(n - 3)}{2}$ diagonals. Students will have different opinions about whether this proof is more convincing or easier than the induction proof.

Extending

1. Induction Step: Assume the formula holds for $n - 1$, and notice that $(x + 1)^n = (x + 1)(x + 1)^{n - 1}$. Thus: $(x + 1)^n = (x + 1)(x + 1)^{n - 1} = (x + 1)[C(n - 1, 0)x^{n - 1} + C(n - 1, 1)x^{n - 2} + C(n - 1, 2)x^{n - 3} + \ldots + C(n - 1, k)x^{n - 1 - k} + \ldots + C(n - 1, n - 1)x^0]$.

Apply the distributive property:

$$(x + 1)^n = x[C(n - 1, 0)x^{n - 1} + C(n - 1, 1)x^{n - 2} + C(n - 1, 2)x^{n - 3} + \ldots + C(n - 1, k)x^{n - 1 - k}$$
$$+ \ldots + C(n - 1, n - 1)x^0] + [C(n - 1, 0)x^{n - 1} + C(n - 1, 1)x^{n - 2} +$$
$$C(n - 1, 2)x^{n - 3} + \ldots + C(n - 1, k)x^{n - 1 - k} + \ldots + C(n - 1, n - 1)x^0]$$

$$= C(n - 1, 0)x^n + [C(n - 1, 1)x^{n - 1} + C(n - 1, 0)x^{n - 1}] + [C(n - 1, 2)x^{n - 2} +$$
$$C(n - 1, 1)x^{n - 2}] + \ldots + [C(n - 1, k)x^{n - 1 - k} + C(n - 1, k - 1)x^{n - 1 - k}] + \ldots$$
$$+ [C(n - 1, n - 1)x^1 + C(n - 1, n - 2)x^1] + C(n - 1, n - 1)x^0$$

Now use the identity $C(n, k) = C(n - 1, k) + C(n - 1, k - 1)$ and the facts that $C(n - 1, 0) = C(n, 0) = 1$ and $C(n, n) = C(n - 1, n - 1) = 1$:

$$(x + 1)^n = C(n, 0)x^n + C(n, 1)x^{n - 1} + C(n, 2)x^{n - 2} + \ldots + C(n, k)x^{n - k} + \ldots + C(n, n)x^0$$

Base Step: For $n = 1$, $(x + 1)^1 = x + 1 = C(1, 0)x^1 + C(1, 1)x^0$. (You could also use $n = 0$ as the initial value.)

These two steps prove this special case of the Binomial Theorem.

MORE *continued*

2. You may need to review sigma notation with students before they tackle this task. To prove that $\sum_{k=0}^{n-1} C(n, k) = 2^n$, first look for the recursive relationship between $\sum_{k=0}^{n} C(n, k)$ and $\sum_{k=0}^{n} C(n-1, k)$. Students who see that $\sum_{k=0}^{n} C(n, k)$ represents the sum of the numbers in row n of Pascal's triangle can examine the sums of the first several rows (1, 2, 4, 8, 16, …) and conjecture that the sum of each row is twice the sum of the previous row; that is $\sum_{k=0}^{n} C(n, k) = 2 \sum_{k=0}^{n-1} C(n-1, k)$. This recursive relationship can be proven as follows:

$$\sum_{k=0}^{n} C(n, k) = C(n, 0) + C(n, 1) + C(n, 2) + \ldots + C(n, n-1) + C(n, n)$$

Using an identity from Lesson 2, $C(n, k) = C(n-1, k-1) + C(n-1, k)$, you can write $\sum_{k=0}^{n} C(n, k) = C(n, 0) + [C(n-1, 0) + C(n-1, 1)] + [C(n-1, 1) + C(n-1, 2)] + \ldots + [C(n-1, n-2) + C(n-1, n-1)] + C(n, n)$.

Expanding $\sum_{k=0}^{n-1} C(n-1, k)$ gives $C(n-1, 0) + C(n-1, 1) + \ldots + C(n-1, n-2) + C(n-1, n-1) = 1 + C(n-1, 1) + \ldots + C(n-1, n-2) + 1$. Thus, if you rewrite the second expression for $\sum_{k=0}^{n} C(n, k)$, you will obtain $\sum_{k=0}^{n} C(n, k) = C(n, 0) + C(n-1, 0) + 2[C(n-1, 1) + \ldots + C(n-1, n-2)] + C(n-1, n-1) + C(n, n) = 1 + 1 + 2[C(n-1, 1) + \ldots + C(n-1, n-2)] + 1 + 1 = 2[1 + C(n-1, 1) + \ldots + C(n-1, n-2) + 1]$, or $\sum_{k=0}^{n} C(n, k) = 2 \sum_{k=0}^{n-1} C(n-1, k)$.

Thus, the recursive relationship, as shown above, is $\sum_{k=0}^{n} C(n, k) = 2 \sum_{k=0}^{n-1} C(n-1, k)$.

The induction proof follows:

Induction Step: Now, $\sum_{k=0}^{n} C(n, k) = 2 \sum_{k=0}^{n-1} C(n-1, k)$, but you are assuming the conjecture is true for $n-1$, so $\sum_{k=0}^{n-1} C(n-1, k) = 2^{n-1}$.

Hence, $\sum_{k=0}^{n} C(n, k) = 2(2^{n-1}) = 2^n$.

Base Step: If $n = 0$, the conjecture is true because $C(0, 0) = 1$, and $2^0 = 1$.

Hence, you have completed the two steps of a proof by mathematical induction and can conclude that $\sum_{k=0}^{n} C(n, k) = 2^n$ for $n \geq 0$.

This statement is related to counting subsets of a set as follows: $C(n, k)$ is the number of subsets of k elements chosen from a set with n elements. Thus, the number of subsets of all sizes chosen from a set with n elements is $\sum_{k=0}^{n} C(n, k)$. Another way to count the number of all subsets from a set with n elements is the following: Think of constructing an arbitrary subset by starting with n empty slots, representing each of the n elements of the set. For each slot, you will either fill it with the corresponding set ele-

MORE *continued*

ment, or you will not fill it with that element. Thus, for each slot there are two choices: include the corresponding element of the set or not. Since there are n slots, there are 2^n ways to create a subset. Hence, you now have two expressions that count the number of subsets of a set, and thus they must be equal. That is, $\sum_{k=0}^{n} C(n, k) = 2^n$ for $n \geq 0$.

3. **a.** Induction Step: Assume the conjecture is true for $n - 1$, so
$(1 + x)^{n-1} \geq 1 + (n - 1)x$.
Also notice that $(1 + x)^n = (1 + x)(1 + x)^{n-1}$. Thus:
$$(1 + x)^n = (1 + x)(1 + x)^{n-1} \geq (1 + x)[1 + (n - 1)x]$$
$$= (1 + x)(1 + nx - x)$$
$$= 1 + nx - x + x + nx^2 - x^2$$
$$= 1 + nx + (n - 1)x^2 \geq 1 + nx$$

To get the first inequality in this chain, multiply the $(n - 1)$ case of the Bernoulli inequality by $(1 + x)$, which is positive since $x > -1$. To get the last inequality, note that for $n \geq 1$, $(n - 1) \geq 0$ and $(n - 1)x^2 \geq 0$.

Base Step: When $n = 0$ (and $x > -1$), you have $(1 + x)^0 = 1 \geq 1 = 1 + 0(x)$.

These two steps together prove the Bernoulli inequality.

b. For $x > 0$,
$$(1 + x)^n = C(n, 0)x^0 + C(n, 1)x + \text{other positive terms}$$
$$= 1x^0 + nx + \text{other positive terms}$$
$$> 1 + nx$$

4. **a.** S_1 = sum of the first term = a_1

Using the formula, $S_1 = \frac{1}{2}(1)[2a_1 + (1 - 1)d] = \frac{1}{2} \cdot 2a_1 = a_1$

S_2 = sum of the first two terms = $a_1 + (a_1 + d) = 2a_1 + d$

Using the formula, $S_2 = \frac{1}{2}(2)[2a_1 + (2 - 1)d] = 2a_1 + d$

S_3 = sum of the first three terms = $a_1 + (a_1 + d) + (a_1 + 2d) = 3a_1 + 3d$

Using the formula, $S_3 = \frac{1}{2}(3)[2a_1 + 2d] = 3a_1 + 3d$

b. You need to show that the sum of the first n terms of an arithmetic series, S_n, is equal to $\frac{1}{2}n[2a_1 + (n - 1)d]$, for $n \geq 1$.

Induction Step: It is clear from the definition of S_n as a sum that $S_n = S_{n-1} + [a_1 + (n - 1)d]$. Assume that the statement is true for $n - 1$, that is, you assume that $S_{n-1} = \frac{1}{2}(n - 1)[2a_1 + (n - 2)d]$. Then,

$$S_n = S_{n-1} + [a_1 + (n - 1)d]$$
$$= \frac{1}{2}(n - 1)[2a_1 + (n - 2)d] + [a_1 + (n - 1)d]$$
$$= (n - 1)a_1 + \frac{(n - 1)(n - 2)}{2} d + a_1 + nd - d$$

Unit 4

Assessments 126–128

MORE *continued*

$$= na_1 - a_1 + \frac{1}{2}(n^2 - 3n + 2)d + a_1 + nd - d$$

$$= na_1 + \left(\frac{1}{2}n^2 - \frac{3}{2}n + 1\right)d + nd - d$$

$$= na_1 + \frac{1}{2}n^2 d - \frac{3}{2}nd + nd$$

$$= na_1 + \frac{1}{2}n^2 d - \frac{1}{2}nd$$

$$= \frac{1}{2}n[2a_1 + nd - d]$$

$$= \frac{1}{2}n[2a_1 + (n - 1)d]$$

Base Step: In Part a, you have already shown that the statement is true for $n = 1$.

This completes both parts of the induction proof, so $\frac{1}{2}n[2a_1 + (n - 1)d]$ is the sum of the first n terms of an arithmetic sequence for $n \geq 1$.

c. $S_n = a_1 + (a_1 + d) + (a_1 + 2d) + \ldots + [a_1 + (n - 1)d]$

$\quad = na_1 + [1 + 2 + \ldots + (n - 1)]d$

$\quad = na_1 + \frac{(n - 1)(n)}{2}d \quad$ (Use the result from Modeling Task 5 to determine the sum of the first $(n - 1)$ positive integers.)

$\quad = \frac{1}{2}n[2a_1 + (n - 1)d]$

d. $\frac{n(a_1 + a_n)}{2} = \frac{1}{2}n[a_1 + a_n]$

$\quad = \frac{1}{2}n[a_1 + (a_1 + (n - 1)d)] \quad$ since in an arithmetic sequence

$\quad\quad\quad\quad\quad\quad\quad\quad\quad\quad\quad\quad\quad a_n = a_1 + (n - 1)d$

$\quad = \frac{1}{2}n[2a_1 + (n - 1)d]$

See Assessment Resources 126–131.

Assessments 129–131

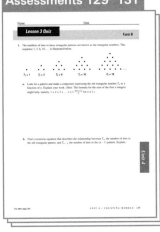

REVIEW AND PRACTICE individual task

▶**PUMP**

Answers

1. (e)
2. (d)
3. (a)
4. (b)
5. (a)

6. (e)
7. (d)
8. (c)
9. (a)
10. (d)

Lesson 4 *Looking Back*

SYNTHESIZE UNIT IDEAS   small-group activity

If your students have not completed Lesson 3, Task 6 should not be assigned.

1. In this task, students review their work on combinations and permutations from Lesson 1, and they complete the "Analyzing Counting Situations" table. This table will be a good summary and review tool.

    a. Students should be sure that they have the correct entries in the table for combinations and permutations.

    b. ■ Some examples might be license plate numbers, telephone numbers, PINs, or zip codes, in which numbers (and/or letters) can be repeated. Since repetition is allowed in all of these examples, they are not examples of combinations or permutations.

    ■ The general formula is n^k.

---

c. Since repetition is allowed, the 3-side-dish choices are not examples of combinations or permutations. See below for the completed table.

Analyzing Counting Situations

	No Repetitions	**Repetitions OK**
Different Orderings Count as Different Possibilities.	**Permutations** $P(n, k) = \frac{n!}{(n-k)!}$ P–VP–T	Part b. n^k 4-digit PIN where each digit is 0–9
Different Orderings Do Not Count as Different Possibilities.	**Combinations** $C(n, k) = \frac{n!}{(n-k)!k!}$ Committees Subsets	Part c. Side Dishes Selections $C(n + k - 1, k)$ (**Note:** The name and formula are not part of this task. See Extending Task 5 in Lesson 1.)

Some students may have found a formula for this type of problem in Extending Task 5 (page 237) of Lesson 1. Depending on the level of your class and time available, you may wish to discuss the derivation of this formula. See the discussion provided in the solution to Extending Task 5.

Unit 4

SYNTHESIZE *continued*

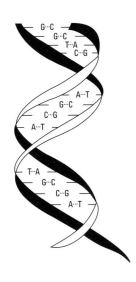

2. For interested students, note that the companion chain, on the other half of the pair, must have a similar structure that matches T with A and G with C, so the companion chain begins CCAG.

    a. One base per segment could only encode 4 amino acids. Two bases per segment could encode $4 \times 4 = 16$ possible amino acids. Three bases could encode $4^3 = 64$ possible amino acids. Therefore, the minimum number of bases needed is 3.

    b. Think of filling five blanks. First choose where the two Ts will go. There are $C(5, 2)$ choices for the two Ts. For each choice of the two Ts, there are 3^3 ways to fill the remaining three blanks. Thus, the number of possible 5-base DNA chains that contain exactly two thymines is $C(5, 2) \times 3^3 = 10 \cdot 27 = 270$.

    c. There are $4^{2.1 \times 10^{10}}$ possible human DNA chains. To estimate this number as a power of 10, consider the following: $4^{2.1 \times 10^{10}} = (4^{10})^{2.1 \times 10^9} > (10^6)^{2.1 \times 10^9} = 10^{12.6 \times 10^9} > 10^{10^{10}} = 10^{10,000,000,000}$. This number is 1 followed by 10 billion zeroes. (This is a huge number, far larger than the number of atoms in the universe. By comparison, the number of people on Earth is less than 1 followed by 10 zeros.)

3. a. **Students should complete at least two of the following five calculations:**

    The number of possible completed tickets is $[C(21, 2)]^3 = 9{,}261{,}000$.

    There is only one possible Match 6 winner.

    Count the number of Match 5 winners as follows: In one color, you must get one number correct and one number wrong. There are 19 incorrect numbers and two correct numbers from which to choose. This accounts for $19 \times 2 = 38$ choices. In the other colors, both numbers must be correct. Thus, there is just one choice in each of them. There are three choices for the color that has the incorrect number. Therefore, the total number of winning Match 5 choices is $38 \times 3 = 114$.

    Count the number of Match 4 winners as follows: There are two cases. In the first case, you choose one correct number in each of two colors and two correct numbers in the third color. Any of the three colors could be the one that has both numbers correct. This yields $(19 \times 2) \times (19 \times 2) \times 1 \times 3 = 4{,}332$ choices. In the second case, you choose two correct numbers in each of two colors and both numbers are incorrect in the 3rd color. Any of the three colors could be the one in which both numbers are incorrect. This yields $1 \times 1 \times C(19, 2) \times 3 = 513$ choices. Therefore, the total number of winning Match 4 choices is $4{,}332 + 513 = 4{,}845$.

    Count the number of Match 3 winners as follows: There are two cases. In the first case, you choose two correct numbers in one color, one correct number in another color, and no correct numbers in the third color. This yields $1 \times (2 \times 19) \times C(19, 2) \times 6 = 38{,}988$ choices. Here you multiply by 6 at the end because there are $3! = 6$ ways to order the three colors according to which has no correct numbers, which has one correct number, and which has two correct numbers. In the second case, you choose

SYNTHESIZE *continued*

one correct number in each of the three colors. This yields $38 \times 38 \times 38 = 54{,}872$. Therefore, the total number of winning Match 3 choices is $38{,}988 + 54{,}872 = 93{,}860$.

Count the number of Match 2 winners as follows: There are two cases. In the first case, you choose two correct numbers in one color and no correct numbers in the other two colors. This yields $1 \times C(19, 2) \times C(19, 2) \times 3 = 87{,}723$ choices. In the second case, you choose one correct number in each of two colors and no correct numbers in the third color. This yields $38 \times 38 \times C(19, 2) \times 3 = 740{,}772$ choices. Therefore, the total number of Match 2 winners is $87{,}723 + 740{,}772 = 828{,}495$.

b. Since all outcomes are equally likely (that is, each set of numbers drawn or each way of filling out a lottery ticket is equally likely), the probability can be computed using the definition given at the beginning of Lesson 2:

$$\frac{\text{number of favorable outcomes}}{\text{total number of possible outcomes}}$$

Thus, the probabilities of Match 6, 5, 4, 3, and 2, respectively are

$$\frac{1}{9{,}261{,}000} \approx 0.0000001,$$

$$\frac{114}{9{,}261{,}000} \approx 0.0000123,$$

$$\frac{4{,}845}{9{,}261{,}000} \approx 0.0005232,$$

$$\frac{93{,}860}{9{,}261{,}000} \approx 0.0101350,$$

$$\frac{828{,}495}{9{,}261{,}000} \approx 0.0894606.$$

c. From Part b, you can see that the probabilities for all the prizes are quite small, especially for the big prizes. Players have only very small chances to win any prize. Thus, this is a very effective way for the state to make money. For the same reasons, it is not an effective way for players to make money.

Some students may use expected value to analyze this situation. The expected value v of the payoff is $\sum P(x) \cdot \text{prize} \approx \$0.44$. Since each play costs \$1, the state makes on average \$0.56 for each ticket sold.

4. ■ $C(n, 3) = \frac{n!}{(n-3)!3!}$

$C(n, n-3) = \frac{n!}{[n-(n-3)]!(n-3)!} = \frac{n!}{3!(n-3)!}$

Thus, $C(n, 3) = C(n, n-3)$.

■ $C(n, 3)$ is the number of ways to choose 3 objects from n objects. But choosing 3 objects to take is equivalent to choosing $(n-3)$ objects to reject, and there are $C(n, n-3)$ ways to choose $(n-3)$ objects to reject. Thus, $C(n, 3) = C(n, n-3)$.

5. a. In terms of Pascal's triangle, this statement says that the sum of the entries in row n of Pascal's triangle is 2^n.

b. For positive integers n, the Binomial Theorem says

$(a + b)^n = C(n, 0)a^n + C(n, 1)a^{n-1}b + C(n, 2)a^{n-2}b^2 + \dots + C(n, k)a^{n-k}b^k + \dots + C(n, n-2)a^2b^{n-2} + C(n, n-1)ab^{n-1} + C(n, n)b^n.$

Unit 4

SYNTHESIZE *continued*

Letting $a = 1$ and $b = 1$ gives
$(1 + 1)^n = C(n, 0) + C(n, 1) + C(n, 2) + \ldots + C(n, k) + \ldots + C(n, n)$ or
$2^n = C(n, 0) + C(n, 1) + C(n, 2) + \ldots + C(n, k) + \ldots + C(n, n)$.

c. You can count the number of subsets of a set in two ways, each corresponding to one side of the identity. Considering combinations, the number of subsets with k elements is $C(n, k)$. Thus, the number of subsets of all sizes is $C(n, 0) + C(n, 1) + C(n, 2) + \ldots + C(n, n)$. Another way to count subsets is to think about constructing an arbitrary subset as follows: Consider n blanks, corresponding to the n elements of the set. To construct a subset, you consider each blank and either include its corresponding element or not. Since there are 2 choices for each blank, there are 2^n different ways to fill the blanks, and therefore there are 2^n different subsets. Thus, you have counted the number of subsets of a set in two ways, and the two results must be equal. Hence, $2^n = C(n, 0) + C(n, 1) + C(n, 2) + \ldots + C(n, n)$.

6. a. Since L_n has length equal to the length of the hypotenuse of an isosceles right triangle with legs of length L_{n-1}, the length of L_n is $\sqrt{2}(L_{n-1})$, so the recursive relationship is $L_n = \sqrt{2}L_{n-1}$. The relationship between n and L_n is $L_n = \left(\sqrt{2}\right)^n$, where $n = 0$ corresponds to the initial segment, $\overline{AB}$. These patterns seem to be true for all integers $n \geq 0$.

b. You must prove that $L_n = \left(\sqrt{2}\right)^n$, for $n \geq 0$. Induction proof:

Induction Step: Assume that $L_{n-1} = \left(\sqrt{2}\right)^{n-1}$. Using this induction hypothesis and the recursive relationship from Part a gives $L_n = \left(\sqrt{2}\right)L_{n-1} = \left(\sqrt{2}\right)\left(\sqrt{2}\right)^{n-1} = \left(\sqrt{2}\right)^n$.

Base Step: $n = 0$ corresponds to segment $\overline{AB}$, which has length of 1, and indeed $\left(\sqrt{2}\right)^0 = 1$.

These two steps complete an induction proof that $L_n = \left(\sqrt{2}\right)^n$, for $n \geq 0$

c. ■ $1 + \sqrt{2} + 2 + 2\sqrt{2} + 4 = 7 + 3\sqrt{2} \approx 11.24$

■ The sequence of segment lengths is a geometric sequence because you get each term of the sequence by multiplying the previous term by a constant, namely, $\sqrt{2}$.

■ In this situation, $r = \sqrt{2}$. Thus, the total length of a spiral with n segments is the sum of n terms: $1 + r + r^2 + \ldots + r^{n-1} = \frac{1-r^n}{1-r}$, where $r = \sqrt{2}$.

The total length of a spiral with 25 segments is $\frac{1-(\sqrt{2})^{25}}{1-\sqrt{2}} \approx 13{,}982.2$ units.

SHARE AND SUMMARIZE full-class discussion

Checkpoint

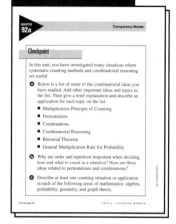

See Teaching Masters 92a and 92b.

ⓐ ■ The Multiplication Principle of Counting says roughly that you count the number of ways each event can happen and then multiply these numbers to get the number of ways all the events can happen together. For example, consider computer configurations. If there are 4 types of monitors, each of which can go with 3 different CPUs, then there are $4 \times 3 = 12$ different monitor-CPU configurations possible.

■ Permutations are arrangements in which order makes a difference and repetitions are not allowed. An example of a problem involving permutations is to find the number of possible first-second-third place outcomes in a contest with 16 contestants.

■ Combinations are arrangements in which order does not make a difference and repetitions are not allowed. For example, how many ways are there to name 3 honorable-mention contestants when there are 16 contestants from which to choose?

■ Combinatorial reasoning involves reasoning about how to form and count combinations. For example, this kind of reasoning was used to show that $C(n, k)$, which is the number of ways of choosing k objects from n objects or the number of ways of choosing k-person committees from n people, is the same as $C(n, n - k)$, which can be thought of as the number of ways of choosing the $(n - k)$ objects or people to reject.

■ The Binomial Theorem tells you how to expand a binomial expression. That is, $(a + b)^n = C(n, 0)a^n + C(n, 1)a^{n-1}b + C(n, 2)a^{n-2}b^2 + \ldots + C(n, k)a^{n-k}b^k + \ldots + C(n, n-1)ab^{n-1} + C(n, n)b^n$.

■ The General Multiplication Rule for Probability is $P(A \text{ and } B) = P(A) \times P(B|A)$. This rule is necessary when events are not independent, such as drawing without replacement.

■ Other topics that students might add to the list include the following:

Pascal's triangle and connections to the binomial coefficients

Systematic lists or tree diagrams used when there are multiple choices, for example, the fleece jackets in Investigation 1 of Lesson 1

Other situations such as choosing side dishes where repetitions are allowed and order doesn't matter

Combination properties such as $C(n, k) = C(n, n - k)$

ⓑ Order and repetition are factors that help determine the method and result of counting. For example, in combinations, repetitions are not allowed and order does not count. In permutations, repetitions are not allowed but order does count. By considering the four configurations of repetition and order, as in Task 1 of this lesson, you get four different types of counting situations that involve picking k objects from n objects.

ⓒ ■ Algebra: the Binomial Theorem

■ Probability: computing probability by counting outcomes

■ Geometry: counting regions, triangles, segments, or points

■ Graph Theory: counting edges or number of colors

Unit 4

Masters 93a–93c

Assessments 132–143

Assessments 144–155

SHARE AND SUMMARIZE *continued*

d The coefficients in the expansion of $(a + b)^n$ are the same as the entries in row n of Pascal's triangle. According to the Binomial Theorem, these coefficients are also the numbers $C(n, k)$. Students also saw that the entries in Pascal's triangle are the numbers $C(n, k)$. (In Extending Task 4 in Lesson 2, some students may have seen why the entries in Pascal's triangle are the numbers $C(n, k)$ by considering the combinatorial identity $C(n, k) = C(n - 1, k - 1) + C(n - 1, k)$.)

e **If your students have not completed Lesson 3, Part e of the Checkpoint should be omitted.**

The Principle of Mathematical Induction is a principle that allows you to prove a statement involving n that is supposed to be true for all integer values of n greater than or equal to some initial value. A proof by mathematical induction involves two steps. In the induction step, you prove that if the $(n - 1)$ case is true, then the n case is true. In the base step, you prove that the statement is true for the initial value of n. After completing these two steps, the Principle of Mathematical Induction asserts that the statement is true for all integer values of n greater than or equal to the initial value of n. Informally, by completing these two steps, you have shown that the statement is true for the first value of n, and therefore it is true for the next value of n, and so on, leading to the conclusion that it is true for all values of n greater than or equal to the initial value.

Proof by induction is likely to be a useful method of proof for situations involving integers where (a) you know the results for an initial value of n, (b) you know a recursive relationship, and (c) you have a good conjecture for a closed-form relationship (which may be a function rule).

APPLY **individual task**

On Your Own

See Teaching Masters 93a–93c.

Responses will vary. Above all, this should be something that is useful to the individual student. You may wish to have students use Teaching Masters 93a–93c, "Counting Models" Unit Summary, to help them organize the information.

See Assessment Resources pages 132–155.

Looking Back, Looking Ahead

▶Reflecting on Mathematical Content

In this unit, students learned concepts and methods for solving counting problems. Counting problems were studied informally in previous courses, but not as an explicit instructional goal. Thus, some of the informal work with counting in previous courses was pulled together and formalized in this unit. Along the way, students also studied the Binomial Theorem and the General Multiplication Rule for probability. In addition, those students who studied Lesson 3 learned how to do proof by mathematical induction.

Counting problems occur in many situations, both within and outside mathematics. In the first lesson, students learned fundamental methods of counting in the context of many real-world applications. For example, they learned about counting trees, the Multiplication Principle of Counting, combinations, and permutations while investigating telephone numbering schemes, DNA structure, lotteries, and committee choices. The second lesson focused on applications of counting throughout mathematics, with emphasis on the General Multiplication Rule for probability, Pascal's triangle, and the Binomial Theorem. Also, students developed the skill of combinatorial reasoning and, for those who studied Lesson 3, proof by mathematical induction.

These new skills in counting and reasoning will be applied in future units. For example, combinations are required in Unit 5, "Binomial Distributions and Statistical Inference," for the binomial probability formula, counting arguments related to binary strings are used in Unit 9, "Informatics," and Pascal's triangle is revisited in Unit 10, "Problem Solving, Algorithms, and Spreadsheets."

Unit 4 Assessment

Binomial Distributions and Statistical Inference

Unit 5

UNIT OVERVIEW In this unit, students study the probability distribution for a binomial situation and its use in tests of significance. Students are also introduced to the design and analysis of experiments.

Students were briefly introduced to the binomial distribution in Course 2, Unit 7, "Patterns in Chance." In Course 3, Unit 2, "Modeling Public Opinion," they studied this distribution extensively by simulation, making box plots to summarize the outcomes of the simulation. These box plots showed the variation that one would expect from repeated sets of binomial trials. In Lesson 1 of this unit, students first use simulation to construct an approximation of a binomial distribution and then develop the binomial probability formula and use it to compute probabilities exactly. The relationship of the binomial probability formula to the binomial theorem is explored in Organizing Task 4.

In Lesson 2, students examine the graphs of many binomial distributions. They see that as the sample size increases, the shape of the distribution becomes more approximately normal. They learn the formulas for the mean and standard deviation of a binomial distribution. A sketch of the proofs of these formulas is found in Extending Task 2. The characteristics of the distribution for the number of successes are compared to those of the distribution for the proportion of successes.

In Lesson 3, the informal ideas about significance testing that have appeared all along in the *Contemporary Mathematics in Context* curriculum are formalized in the context of the significance of a binomial proportion. Students first learn to use the normal distribution to approximate binomial probabilities. Then, in the second investigation, they learn the steps in a formal test of significance, the *z*-test for a proportion.

In Lesson 4, students learn to distinguish between experiments, surveys, and observational studies and the conclusions that can be drawn from each. They learn the characteristics of well-designed experiments. Finally, they learn to use a randomization test to determine if the difference in the results from two treatments is statistically significant and how to use a *z*-test as a substitute for the more computationally-intensive randomization test.

If you would like to learn more about binomial distributions and *z*-tests, the following introductory statistics textbooks are recommended:

Cobb, George, Richard L. Scheaffer, and Ann E. Watkins. *Statistics in Action.* Berkeley, Calif.: Key Curriculum Press, 2002.

Devore, Jay, and Roxy Peck. *Statistics: The Exploration and Analysis of Data.* 4th ed. Pacific Grove, Calif.: Duxbury Press, 2000.

Freedman, David, Robert Pisani, and Roger Purves. *Statistics.* 3rd ed. New York: W.W. Norton, 1997.

Moore, David S., and George P. McCabe, *Introduction to the Practice of Statistics*, 3rd ed. New York: W. H. Freeman, 1999.

Rossman, Allan J., Beth L. Chance, and J. Barr Von Oehsen. *Workshop Statistics: Discovery with Data and the Graphing Calculator*, 2nd ed. Emeryville, CA: Key College Publishing, 2001.

Siegel, Andrew F., and Charles J. Morgan. *Statistics and Data Analysis: An Introduction.* 2nd ed. New York: John Wiley & Sons, 1998.

Yates, Daniel S., David S. Moore, and George P. McCabe. *The Practice of Statistics: TI-83 Graphing Calculator Enhanced.* New York: W.H. Freeman, 1999.

Unit 5 Planning Guide

Lesson Objectives	Assignments	Suggested Pacing	Materials Needed
Lesson 1 *Binomial Situations* • To use simulation to construct empirical binomial distributions and to interpret them • To study informal hypothesis testing: Can this result reasonably be attributed to chance or should you look for another explanation? • To review the concepts of simulation, probability distributions, the Law of Large Numbers, a rare event, the formulas for the mean and standard deviation of a frequency table, and the General Multiplication Rule: $P(A \text{ and } B) = P(A) \cdot P(B \mid A)$ • To develop the binomial probability formula and use it to construct binomial distributions	**MORE** **after page 282** Students can begin Modeling Task 1 or 2, Organizing Task 1 or 2, or Reflecting Task 1 from p. 290. **after page 287** Students can begin Reflecting Task 2 from p. 290. **page 290** **Modeling:** 1 or 2, 3, and 5* **Organizing:** 1, 2, and 4 **Reflecting:** 1 and 2 **Extending:** 1 and choice of one* **PUMP** pages 298–299	**Path A:** 5 days **Path B:** 7 days	• Teaching Resources 94–103 • Assessment Resources 156–161
Lesson 2 *Characteristics of Binomial Distributions* • To understand what happens to the shape, mean, and spread of a binomial distribution of the number of successes as n gets larger but p remains fixed • To understand what happens to the shape, mean, and spread of a distribution of the sample proportion of successes as n gets larger but p remains fixed • To examine the simple formulas for the mean, $\mu = np$, and standard deviation, $\sigma = \sqrt{np(1-p)}$, of a binomial distribution • To understand and use the formulas for the mean and standard deviation of a binomial distribution of the number of successes and the formulas for the mean and standard deviation of the distribution of the sample proportion • To understand that the normal approximation to the binomial is an approximation and has satisfactory accuracy when $np \geq 10$ and $n(1-p) \geq 10$	**MORE** **after page 306** Students can begin Organizing Task 1 or Reflecting Task 4 from p. 311. **after page 307** Students can begin Organizing Task 2 from p. 311. **page 311** **Modeling:** 1 or 2, and 3 or 4* **Organizing:** 1, 2, and 4 **Reflecting:** 1 and 4 **Extending:** 1 and choice of one* **PUMP** pages 316–317	**Path A:** 5 days **Path B:** 7 days	• Teaching Resources 104–109 • Assessment Resources 162–167
Lesson 3 *Chance Variation in a Binomial Situation* • To use the normal approximation to the binomial distribution to estimate binomial probabilities • To perform a *z*-test for a proportion, including stating a null hypothesis, describing the binomial distribution given that the null hypothesis is true, locating the result from the sample on that distribution, and stating a conclusion • To understand the logic of a significance test, including the types of errors that are possible	**MORE** **after page 322** Students can begin Modeling Task 1a or 2a; Organizing Task 1, 2, 3, or 4; Reflecting Task 1; or Extending Task 2 or 3 from p. 326. **page 326** **Modeling:** 1 or 2, and 3 or 4* **Organizing:** 3 and choice of one* **Reflecting:** 1, 3, and 4 **Extending:** 1 and choice of one* **PUMP** pages 330–331	**Path A:** 4 days **Path B:** 5 days	• Teaching Resources 110–114 • Assessment Resources 168–171

Lesson Objectives	Assignments	Suggested Pacing	Materials Needed
Lesson 4 *Experiments: Proving Cause and Effect* • To distinguish between an experiment, a survey, and an observational study • To know the characteristics of a well-designed experiment • To understand the importance of subject and evaluator blinding and the placebo effect • To apply a randomization test to see if the results of an experiment are statistically significant • To perform a *z*-test for the difference of two proportions in an experiment	**MORE** **after page 338** Students can begin Modeling Task 1a or 2a, or Reflecting Task 2 or 3 from p. 344. **page 344** **Modeling:** 1, 3, and 2 or 4* **Organizing:** 1 and 3 **Reflecting:** 2 and 4 **Extending:** 1 and 2 **PUMP** **pages 352–353**	**Path A:** 5 days **Path B:** 7 days	Per Group: • 53 beads (or counters) of one color and 22 beads (or counters) of a different color • Teaching Resources 115–118 • Assessment Resources 172–177
Lesson 5 *Looking Back* • To review and test the major objectives of the unit		**Path A:** 2 days **Path B:** 3 days	• Teaching Resources 119–121 • Assessment Resources 178–197

*When choice is indicated, it is important to leave the choice to the student.
Note: It is best if Organizing tasks are discussed as a whole class after they have been assigned as homework.

Lesson 1 *Binomial Situations*

Think About This Situation

Suppose that in a large judicial district, 30% of the eligible jurors are college graduates.

ⓐ On a particular jury of 12 people, only one is a college graduate. Do you think having only one juror who is a college graduate can reasonably be attributed to chance? What strategies could you use to support your view?

ⓑ If 12 jurors are selected at random from those eligible, what do you think the probability distribution of the number of jurors who are college graduates would look like?

ⓒ How do you think the shape, mean, and spread of the probability distribution of the number of jurors who are college graduates would change if the jury were a grand jury of 24 people rather than a 12-person jury?

LESSON OVERVIEW In this lesson, students will learn to identify binomial situations, as well as situations that can be treated as binomial. Students first create empirical binomial distributions using simulation and then, in Investigation 2, develop the binomial probability formula and use it to create exact binomial distributions. Informal understanding of hypothesis testing is laid in this lesson and formalized in Lesson 3. In addition, students will draw on their previous work in Courses 1 and 2, further developing the concepts of simulation, probability distributions, the Law of Large Numbers, and a rare event.

Lesson Objectives

- To use simulation to construct empirical binomial distributions and to interpret them
- To study informal hypothesis testing: Can this result reasonably be attributed to chance or should you look for another explanation?
- To review the concepts of simulation, probability distributions, the Law of Large Numbers, a rare event, the formulas for the mean and standard deviation of a frequency table, and the General Multiplication Rule: $P(A \text{ and } B) = P(A) \cdot P(B|A)$.
- To develop the binomial probability formula and use it to construct binomial distributions

LAUNCH full-class discussion

Think About This Situation

See Teaching Master 94.

The details of these responses come out in the activities, so the discussion at this time may be brief.

ⓐ Students' thoughts about whether this outcome can reasonably be attributed to chance will vary. To decide if the composition of the jury can reasonably be attributed to chance, the variation in the composition of juries when jurors are picked at random needs to be considered. To do this, students may suggest a simulation. Let the digits 0, 1, and 2 represent a college graduate. The other digits will then represent someone who did not graduate from college. Look at 12 random digits and count the number that are 0, 1, or 2. Repeat this many times and see what proportion of juries have one or no college graduates. Students need to see what proportion of juries have one or no college graduates because they need to see what proportion of the time a jury, as

LAUNCH *continued*

extreme as the one they got or even more extreme, happens by chance alone. (A graph of the probability distribution appears in Part b. Getting one or no college graduates happens more than 5% of the time, so this would not be a rare event. This can reasonably be attributed to chance. Students will discover this in Activity 1.)

b Students may remember that the distribution should be centered at 0.3(12) = 3.6 college graduates. They may have little idea about the spread or the shape at this point unless they remember the binomial distributions from the Extending tasks in Course 2, Unit 7, "Patterns in Chance" or the box plots from Course 3, Unit 2, "Modeling Public Opinion." The standard deviation is approximately 1.59. The shape is mound-like, but skewed right. The distribution below is provided for your information.

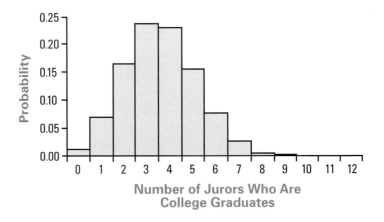

c If the jury were a grand jury of 24 people, the mean number of college graduates would double to 0.3(24) = 7.2. Students should realize that the spread would be larger. The standard deviation is approximately 2.24. The shape of this distribution would be more approximately normal. The distribution appears below for your information.

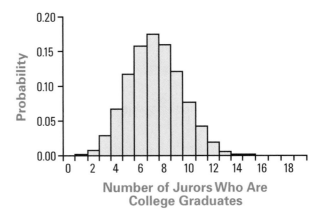

Master 95

Name _____ Date _____

MASTER
95   Activity Master

Distribution of Jurors Selected from a Jury Pool with
30% College Graduates

Number of College Graduates, x	Frequency, f
0	9
1	28
2	90
3	126
4	104
5	76
6	44
7	9
8	4
9	0
10	0
11	0
12	0

Use with page 277.   UNIT 5 • BINOMIAL DISTRIBUTIONS AND STATISTICAL INFERENCE

EXPLORE small-group investigation

INVESTIGATION 1 Constructing Binomial Distributions Using Simulation

The phrase "binomial situation," rather than the more typical "binomial experiment," is used in the text in order to follow the recommendation of many statisticians to reserve the word "experiment" for a situation in which subjects are randomly assigned to two or more treatments in order to compare their effects.

Students may wonder why the third and fourth characteristics of a binomial situation (listed on page 279 of the student text) are both needed. Doesn't a fixed value of p indicate that trials are independent? No, it doesn't. For example, suppose you observe six members of a family next Saturday and count the number who go to a theme park. Suppose further that the family plans to go to the theme park on Saturday if it doesn't rain. The probability of rain is 0.2. Then, there are a fixed number of trials (people), 6. Each person will either go to the theme park (a success) or they won't. The probability of a success on each trial is 0.8. However, the trials aren't independent. If on Saturday you find out that the first member of the family went to the theme park, you know that the others did, too. Students will explore this idea further in Extending Task 1 in the MORE set for this lesson.

Does the fact that the trials are independent indicate a fixed value of p? Again, the answer is no. For example, suppose you are going to spin a penny 10 times (see page 318) and count the number of heads. After three spins, your penny rolls off the table, so you take another penny out of your pocket for the remaining seven spins. In this case, the trials are independent, but the probability of a head on the first three spins won't be exactly equal to the probability of a head on the last seven spins as the two pennies will be balanced a bit differently due to wear and difference in manufacture.

TECHNOLOGY NOTE: If students are using TI-83 calculators, you may wish to discuss the randBin(n,p) feature so that students can use it. The randBin(n,p) function of the calculator is located under the [MATH] PRB menu. This function reports the number of successes in a simulation of a binomial situation with n trials and probability of success p.

The randBin(n,p,N) command takes N random samples each of size n from a population with proportion of successes p and reports the number of successes in each of the N samples.

The simulations described in the following problems use the more common randInt function and simulation techniques learned in earlier courses.

1. See Teaching Master 95.

   a. Student simulations may vary. Here is one simulation using random digits: Let the digits 0, 1, and 2 represent a college graduate. The other digits will then represent a person who did not graduate from college. Look at one random digit and see if it is a 0, 1, or 2.

      The TI-83 calculator command randInt(0,9) will generate one random digit from the set {0, 1, 2, 3, 4, 5, 6, 7, 8, 9}. Repeatedly pressing [ENTER] continues to generate random digits. Alternatively, the command randInt(0,9,12) will generate 12 random digits all at once.

EXPLORE *continued*

b. To simulate selecting 12 jurors, look at 12 random digits. To determine how many are college graduates, count the number of digits that are 0, 1, or 2. Results of students' simulations will vary. Suppose, for example, that a student gets this sequence of 12 random digits:

$$0, 2, 7, 3, 7, 1, 5, 3, 1, 0, 2, 1$$

There are 7 successes, so the frequency listed on the table next to 7 college graduates would be increased to 10.

c. Results of simulations will vary.

d. Estimates will vary somewhat. From the original table without the 10 additional juries, the estimate is $\frac{9 + 28}{490}$, or about 0.076.

e. Estimates will vary somewhat. From the original table without the 10 additional juries, the estimate is $\frac{104 + 76 + 44 + 9 + 4}{490} = \frac{237}{490} \approx 0.48$.

f. The graph below consists of the 490 juries from the table. The addition of 10 juries from the student's simulation won't change the graph much. The distribution is somewhat skewed right. The mean is about 3.6 and the standard deviation about 1.6. Since student responses are estimates, responses will vary, particularly for the standard deviation.

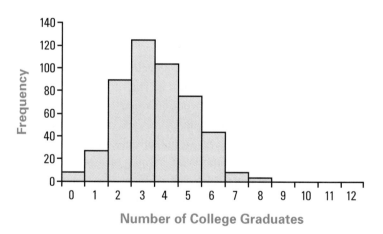

NOTE: In Course 3, Unit 2, "Modeling Public Opinion," definitions for "likely" and "unlikely" events were given. Unlikely events were those in the outer 10% of a probability distribution. Here, a "rare" event is defined as one in the outer 5% of a distribution, which is more standard in statistics textbooks.

EXPLORE *continued*

2. **a.** Estimates will vary somewhat. It probably won't be possible to get exactly 2.5% in each tail. In such cases, have students get as close to 2.5% as they can without going over 2.5%. From the original table without the 10 additional juries, a rare event in the upper tail would be 8 or more college graduates, which has an estimated probability of $0.008 \leq 0.025$. A rare event in the lower tail would be 0 college graduates, which has an estimated probability of $0.02 \leq 0.025$.

    b. There is no evidence here that the jury selection process needs investigating. If the jury selection process is random with respect to selecting college graduates, the probability of getting a jury that qualifies as a rare event is 0.05. For 1,000 such juries, then, you would expect $0.05(1,000) = 50$ of them to be rare events. This lawyer found 52. That's not very different from what would be expected just by chance alone.

    c. Another explanation should be considered. One of the subtle points in statistical inference is that while you expect 5% of juries to be rare events if jurors are selected randomly with respect to whether or not the juror is a college graduate, if you get a "rare" jury on one particular case where juror education matters, you should look for an explanation other than chance. (Be sure that students understand the difference between "an event can be attributed to chance" and "an event reasonably can be attributed to chance." Almost any event *can* be attributed to chance. For example, if a student brought in a coin, started flipping it, and 100 flips later every flip was a head, that event *could* be attributed to chance, but it certainly would not be *reasonable* to do so. In fact, you probably would have challenged the student long before 100 tosses had been completed. Most people will challenge the fairness of the coin or the process after about 5 straight heads. Much of inferential statistics centers around finding cutoff points for when you would say, "Wait a minute! I don't believe that happened just by chance.")

3. **All of the solutions for this activity are based on the original table of 490 values, so your students' answers will vary somewhat based on the results from their simulations.**

NOTE: Technically, binomial distributions must display the number of successes on the x-axis, so distributions such as this one with the proportion of successes on the x-axis aren't called binomial distributions, but rather distributions of sample proportions.

EXPLORE *continued*

a.

Number of College Graduates, x	Proportion of College Graduates, $\hat{p}$	Frequency, f
0	$\frac{0}{12} = 0$	9
1	$\frac{1}{12} \approx 0.08$	28
2	$\frac{2}{12} \approx 0.17$	90
3	$\frac{3}{12} = 0.25$	126
4	$\frac{4}{12} \approx 0.33$	104
5	$\frac{5}{12} \approx 0.42$	76
6	$\frac{6}{12} = 0.50$	44
7	$\frac{7}{12} \approx 0.58$	9
8	$\frac{8}{12} \approx 0.67$	4
9	$\frac{9}{12} = 0.75$	0
10	$\frac{10}{12} \approx 0.83$	0
11	$\frac{11}{12} \approx 0.92$	0
12	$\frac{12}{12} = 1.00$	0

b.

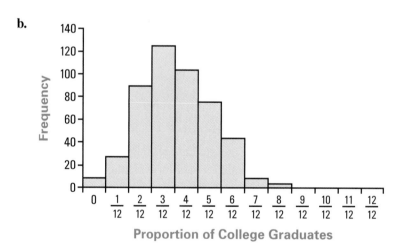

c. For the 12-member jury, about 95% of the distribution falls between 0.08 and 0.58. Dividing the length of this interval by 4, a good estimate of the standard deviation is 0.125. (In fact, it is 0.13).

4. a. The trials are not independent of each other. The probability of a juror being a college graduate depends on which jurors have previously been picked.

b. $\frac{9,000}{30,000} = 0.3$

c. $\frac{8,999}{29,999} \approx 0.2999766659$; $\frac{9,000}{29,999} \approx 0.3000100003$

d. 0.000033

EXPLORE *continued*

e. $\frac{8,989}{29,989} \approx 0.2997432392; \frac{9,000}{29,989} \approx 0.3001100403$

f. 0.000367

g. Parts c and e show that the probabilities don't vary much regardless of who has been previously placed on the jury.

5. a. The trials are not independent of each other. The probability of a juror being a college graduate depends on which jurors have previously been picked.

b. $\frac{15}{50} = 0.3$

c. $\frac{14}{49} \approx 0.2857142857; \frac{15}{49} \approx 0.306122449$

d. 0.020408

e. $\frac{4}{39} \approx 0.1025641026; \frac{15}{39} \approx 0.3846153846$

f. 0.282051

g. Yes, the differences in the probabilities are quite large depending on who has been selected previously.

The lack of independence does not really matter if the population size is large compared to the sample size, but if the population size is small with respect to the sample size, the lack of independence will affect the probabilities much more.

6. a. Yes, this can be treated as a binomial situation. Independence is missing, but that doesn't matter since 20 students is less than 10% of a large student body.

b. Yes, this is a binomial situation since all four characteristics are present.

c. No, this cannot be treated as a binomial situation. Independence is missing and this will matter because the number of students in the classroom is a relatively small population compared to a sample size of 10 students.

d. Yes, this is a binomial situation since all four characteristics are present.

Master 96

SHARE AND SUMMARIZE full-class discussion

Checkpoint

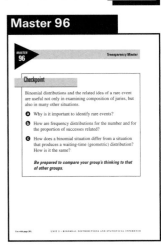

See Teaching Master 96.

ⓐ If something happens that can be classified as a rare event, you should look for a cause other than chance. The result always *could* be due to chance, but in the case of a rare event, chance alone is unlikely to give such a result.

Unit 5

SHARE AND SUMMARIZE *continued*

b The histograms have exactly the same shape but the scale on the horizontal axis differs. (The mean and standard deviation for the proportion of successes can be found by dividing the mean and standard deviation for the number of successes by the number of trials.)

c A binomial situation requires that there be a fixed number of trials, while in a waiting-time situation, trials are repeated until a success is achieved. The two types of situations both require that each trial be classified as a success or failure, that the trials be independent, and that the probability of a success on any one trial be fixed.

CONSTRUCTING A MATH TOOLKIT: Students should write the definition of a rare event. They should explain how to find the proportion of successes and the relationship between the frequency distributions for the number of successes and the proportion of successes. They should also record the four characteristics of binomial situations and the guideline for when a situation can be treated as binomial.

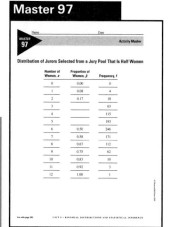
Master 97

APPLY | **individual task**

▶ **On Your Own**

See Teaching Master 97.

a. Yes, this can be treated as a binomial situation since a jury consists of only 12 people from a large population and the other characteristics are present.

b. Responses will vary. One simulation using a coin is described here. Flip a coin 12 times. Let heads represent a woman and tails a man. Count the number of heads.

c. Results will vary. The completed table appears below for the original 998 values.

Number of Women, x	Proportion of Women, $\hat{p}$	Frequency, f
0	$\frac{0}{12} = 0.00$	0
1	$\frac{1}{12} \approx 0.08$	4
2	$\frac{2}{12} \approx 0.17$	18
3	$\frac{3}{12} = 0.25$	63
4	$\frac{4}{12} \approx 0.33$	115
5	$\frac{5}{12} \approx 0.42$	193
6	$\frac{6}{12} = 0.50$	246
7	$\frac{7}{12} \approx 0.58$	171
8	$\frac{8}{12} \approx 0.67$	112
9	$\frac{9}{12} = 0.75$	62
10	$\frac{10}{12} \approx 0.83$	10
11	$\frac{11}{12} \approx 0.92$	3
12	$\frac{12}{12} = 1.00$	1

Unit 5

APPLY *continued*

d.

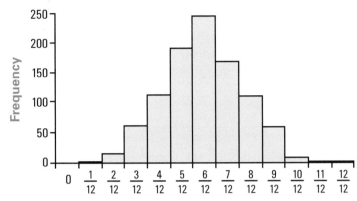

Proportion of Women on the Jury

e. A jury with 2 or fewer women or 10 or more women qualifies as a rare event. (Note that the "or fewer" and "or more" are necessary parts of this answer.) Since 5% of 1,000 is 50, the 25 juries at either end of the frequency distribution are rare events.

f. The shape of this distribution is more symmetrical, the mean is located near 0.5 rather than at 0.3, and the standard deviation or spread is a bit larger.

ASSIGNMENT *pp.*
290–297

Students can now begin Modeling Task 1 or 2, Organizing Task 1 or 2, or Reflecting Task 1 from the MORE set following Investigation 2.

EXPLORE   small-group investigation

INVESTIGATION 2 The Binomial Probability Formula

In this investigation, students develop the binomial probability formula. They then use the formula to construct tables and graphs of binomial distributions. In later activities, students find the probability of a given proportion of successes. They also explore how to use the binomial function capabilities of their calculators.

1. a. $(0.51)^4 \approx 0.068$

This is not a rare event since 0.068 is greater than 0.025.

b. The Multiplication Rule of probability was used. This rule requires that the events be independent. (Note: Independence is theoretically necessary, but a problem in applications, where it can never be proved. So to make computations possible, we often "assume" independence—but only when it is completely reasonable to do so.)

c. $(0.49)^4 \approx 0.058$

EXPLORE *continued*

d.

Number of Boys	Probability
0	0.058
1	0.240 (to be added in Activity 3c)
2	0.375 (to be added in Activity 3b)
3	0.260 (to be added in Activity 3a)
4	0.068

2. a. $0.058 + 0.065 + 0.062 + 0.060 + 0.068 = 0.313$, but the sum should be 1 since these are all the possible outcomes.

 b. When the student computed the probability of getting three boys and one girl, she took only one sequence of births into account: BBBG. There are three others: BBGB, BGBB, and GBBB. Likewise, she did not take into account all the sequences of births for getting two boys and two girls or for getting one boy and three girls.

3. a. BBBG, BBGB, BGBB, GBBB

  - In each case, the probability is the same, $(0.51)^3(0.49)$ or about 0.0650. To find each probability, you multiply the same numbers, but in different orders.

  - The probability is $4(0.51)^3(0.49)$ or about 0.260. Since the four birth sequences in Part a are mutually exclusive (no two of them can happen in the same family), the Addition Rule for mutually exclusive events can be used.

 b. BBGG, BGBG, BGGB, GBBG, GBGB, GGBB

  - In each case, the probability is the same, $(0.51)^2(0.49)^2$ or about 0.062. To find each probability, you multiply the same numbers, but in different orders.

  - $6(0.51)^2(0.49)^2 \approx 0.375$

 c. There are four sequences consisting of one boy and three girls. So the probability is $4(0.51)(0.49)^3 \approx 0.240$.

 d. $0.058 + 0.260 + 0.375 + 0.240 + 0.068 = 1.001 \approx 1$

  Totals will depend on how much precision students used in their tables.

4. a. Finding how many different ways there are to determine the birth order positions of the three boys is the same as evaluating $C(4, 3)$, so the probability will be $C(4, 3)(0.51)^3(0.49)$.

 b. There are $C(4, 2) = 6$ ways to choose both order positions for the two boys, so the probability will be $C(4, 2)(0.51)^2(0.49)^2$.

EXPLORE *continued*

c.   The number of possible birth sequences corresponding to three boys and one girl will be the same as the number of possible birth sequences corresponding to three girls and one boy. So the probability that a family of four children will have one boy and three girls can be expressed as $C(4, 1)(0.51)(0.49)^3$ which is the same as $C(4, 3)(0.51)(0.49)^3$.

5.   **See Teaching Master 98.**

a.   There are a total of 2^5 or 32 sequences.

b.   ■ $C(5, 0) = 1$ sequence

   ■ $C(5, 1) = 5$ sequences

   ■ $C(5, 2) = 10$ sequences

   ■ $C(5, 3) = 10$ sequences

   ■ $C(5, 4) = 5$ sequences

   ■ $C(5, 5) = 1$ sequence

c. $P(5 \text{ outs}) = (0.6)^5 \approx 0.0778$

   $P(4 \text{ outs}) = (0.4)(0.6)^4 \approx 0.0518$

   $P(3 \text{ outs}) = (0.4)^2(0.6)^3 \approx 0.0346$

   $P(2 \text{ outs}) = (0.4)^3(0.6)^2 \approx 0.0230$

   $P(1 \text{ out}) = (0.4)^4(0.6) \approx 0.0154$

   $P(0 \text{ outs}) = (0.4)^5 \approx 0.0102$

d.

Number of Hits	Number of Possible Sequences	Probability of One Particular Sequence	Probability
0	1	$(0.6)^5$	$(0.6)^5 \approx 0.078$
1	5	$(0.4)(0.6)^4$	$5(0.4)(0.6)^4 \approx 0.259$
2	10	$(0.4)^2(0.6)^3$	$10(0.4)^2(0.6)^3 \approx 0.346$
3	10	$(0.4)^3(0.6)^2$	$10(0.4)^3(0.6)^2 \approx 0.230$
4	5	$(0.4)^4(0.6)$	$5(0.4)^4(0.6) \approx 0.077$
5	1	$(0.4)^5$	$(0.4)^5 \approx 0.010$

The "Number of Possible Sequences" column shows symmetry because $C(n, k) = C(n, n - k)$. In the third column, the exponents on 0.6 decrease by 1 as you go down the table, and the exponents on 0.4 increase by 1. Thus, their sum is always 5, the number of trials.

e.   The total number of possible sequences is $1 + 5 + 10 + 10 + 5 + 1 = 32$, and the total probability is 1.

Unit 5

Master 98

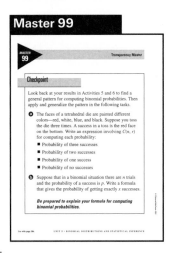

EXPLORE *continued*

6. See Teaching Master 98.

a.

Number of College Graduates	Number of Possible Sequences	Probability of Each Sequence	Probability
0	1	$(0.7)^{12}$	0.013841
1	12	$(0.3)(0.7)^{11}$	0.071184
2	66	$(0.3)^2(0.7)^{10}$	0.167790
3	220	$(0.3)^3(0.7)^9$	0.239700
4	495	$(0.3)^4(0.7)^8$	0.231140
5	792	$(0.3)^5(0.7)^7$	0.158496
6	924	$(0.3)^6(0.7)^6$	0.079248
7	792	$(0.3)^7(0.7)^5$	0.029111
8	495	$(0.3)^8(0.7)^4$	0.007798
9	220	$(0.3)^9(0.7)^3$	0.001485
10	66	$(0.3)^{10}(0.7)^2$	0.000191
11	12	$(0.3)^{11}(0.7)$	0.000015
12	1	$(0.3)^{12}$	0.000001

Master 99

b. $P(4 \text{ or more}) \approx 1 - (0.013841 + 0.071184 + 0.167790 + 0.239700) = 0.507485$. This is a bit different from the probability computed in Investigation 1. They differ because the probability computed here is the theoretical probability and the probability in Investigation 1 was estimated from a simulation.

c. $P(9 \text{ or more}) = 0.001485 + 0.000191 + 0.000015 + 0.000001 = 0.001692$

d. A rare event would be getting no college graduates or getting 8 or more college graduates, since rare events are defined as those in the upper $2\frac{1}{2}\%$ and the lower $2\frac{1}{2}\%$ of the distribution.

SHARE AND SUMMARIZE   full-class discussion

Checkpoint

See Teaching Master 99.

a   ■ $C(3, 3)(0.25)^3$

   ■ $C(3, 2)(0.25)^2(0.75)$

SHARE AND SUMMARIZE *continued*

- $C(3, 1)(0.25)(0.75)^2$
- $C(3, 0)(0.75)^3$
b $C(n, x)(p)^x(1 - p)^{n - x}$

NOTE: You may want to remind students that in other textbooks $C(n, x)$ may be written $\binom{n}{x}$.

CONSTRUCTING A MATH TOOLKIT: Students should record the binomial probability formula, along with what the variables represent. They may also wish to record a sample problem illustrating the use of the binomial probability formula.

APPLY individual task

▶**On Your Own**

a. $C(13, 6)\left(\frac{1}{6}\right)^6\left(\frac{5}{6}\right)^7 \approx 0.0103$

b. $C(36, 23)(0.5)^{23}(0.5)^{13} \approx 0.0336$

c. $C(24, 8)(0.3)^8(0.7)^{16} \approx 0.16$

$C(24, 0)(0.7)^{24} + C(24, 1)(0.3)(0.7)^{23} + C(24, 2)(0.3)^2(0.7)^{22} \approx 0.0119$

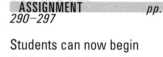

MORE ASSIGNMENT *pp.* 290–297

Students can now begin Reflecting Task 2 from the MORE assignment following Investigation 2.

EXPLORE small-group investigation

7. a. Getting 25% college graduates out of 12 people is the same as getting exactly 3 college graduates. The probability is $C(12, 3)(0.3)^3(0.7)^9 \approx 0.240$.

b. Getting 30% heads out of 50 flips is the same as getting exactly 15 heads. The probability is $C(50, 15)(0.5)^{15}(0.5)^{35} \approx 0.002$.

8. a.

Number of Girls	Probability
0	0.034503
1	0.165747
2	0.318495
3	0.306005
4	0.147002
5	0.028248

b. The distribution is skewed a bit to the right since the probability of a girl is a bit less than 0.5.

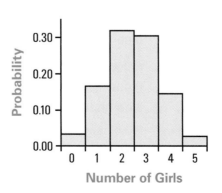

Unit 5

EXPLORE *continued*

c.

Proportion of Girls	Probability
0	0.034503
0.2	0.165747
0.4	0.318495
0.6	0.306005
0.8	0.147002
1	0.028248

d. It is skewed a bit to the right.

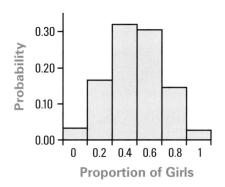

e. The graphs are identical except for the scale on the horizontal axis.

TECHNOLOGY NOTE: Commands given are for the TI-83. The TI-82 and the TI-89 do not have any binomial probability functions. The command **binompdf(n,p,x)** computes the probability of getting exactly x successes in n trials with probability of success p. The command **binompdf(n,p)** computes the probabilities for all x, $0 \le x \le n$. The command **binomcdf(n,p,x)** computes the probability of getting x or fewer successes in n trials of a binomial situation with probability of success p. These commands are found in the **DISTR** (distributions) menu.

9. a. P(4 college graduates) = **binompdf(12,0.3,4)** ≈ 0.2311

P(4 or fewer college graduates) = **binompdf(12,0.3,4)** + **binompdf(12,0.3,3)** + **binompdf(12,0.3,2)** + **binompdf(12,0.3,1)** + **binompdf(12,0.3,0)** ≈ 0.7237.

b. P(2 with own car) = **binompdf(20,0.18,2)** ≈ 0.1730

P(3 or fewer own car) = **binompdf(20,0.18,3)** + **binompdf(20,0.18,2)** + **binompdf(20,0.18,1)** + **binompdf(20,0.18,0)** ≈ 0.5026

P(2 or more own car) = 1 – (**binompdf(20,0.18,0)** + **binompdf(20,0.18,1)**) ≈ 0.8982

EXPLORE *continued*

c. $\mathsf{binomcdf(12,0.3,4)} = 0.7236554696$

- If all decimal places provided by the calculator are considered, this answer is only 0.0000000001 different from the answer for P(4 or fewer college graduates) found in Part a. This difference is probably due to roundoff error.

- The command $\mathsf{binomcdf(n,p,x)}$ computes the probability of getting *x or fewer* successes in *n* trials of a binomial situation with probability of success *p*.

- P(3 or fewer own car) = $\mathsf{binomcdf(20,0.18,3)} \approx 0.5026$
  P(2 or more own car) = $1 - \mathsf{binomcdf(20,0.18,1)} \approx 0.8982$

d. $\mathsf{binomcdf(400,0.5,100)} \approx 1.30 \times 10^{-24}$. The computation involves calculating 101 different probabilities and then finding the sum of those 101 numbers and so would not be practical to compute without the help of a calculator.

e. There will be at least 20% or 20 doubles if there are 80 or fewer non-doubles; or if no more than 19 of the rolls are doubles. This can be computed as
$1 - \mathsf{binomcdf(100,1/6,19)} = \mathsf{binomcdf(100,5/6,80)} = 0.2197$.

f. To create a histogram on the TI-83 calculator, enter the possible numbers of girls in List 1 ($\mathsf{L_1}$). Define $\mathsf{L_2}$ as $\mathsf{binompdf(5,0.49,L_1)}$. Then make a histogram under $\mathsf{STATPLOT}$ with $\mathsf{xList:L_1}$ and $\mathsf{Freq:L_2}$. Before graphing, be sure to set the Xscl to 1 in your window.

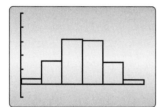

```
WINDOW
  Xmin =0
  Xmax=6
  Xscl =1
  Ymin =-.1
  Ymax=.5
  Yscl =.1
  Xres =1
```

SHARE AND SUMMARIZE   full-class discussion

Checkpoint

See Teaching Master 100.

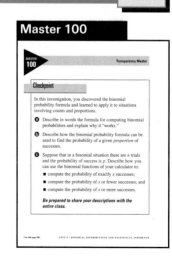

a The formula for computing the probability of *x* successes in *n* trials with the probability of success on each trial being *p* is $C(n, x)(p)^x(1 - p)^{n - x}$. This formula says to first find the number of ways of getting a sequence with *x* successes in it. Then, multiply this number by the probability of each sequence, which is the probability of each success raised to the number of successes multiplied by the probability of each failure raised to the number of failures.

    Here is why this formula works: The only outcomes for each trial are success, with probability *p*, and failure, with probability $1 - p$. So using the multiplication rule for independent events the probability of getting *x* successes and $(n - x)$ failures is $(p)^x(1 - p)^{n - x}$.

SHARE AND SUMMARIZE *continued*

This probability is then multiplied by the number of different ways you can get *x* successes and (*n* − *x*) failures, which is *C*(*n*, *x*).

b Convert the proportion of successes to the number of successes by multiplying it by the number of trials. Then use the formula $C(n, x)(p)^x(1 - p)^{n-x}$ in the usual way.

c Commands given are for the TI-83 calculator.

- binompdf(n,p,x)
- binomcdf(n,p,x)
- 1 − binomcdf(n,p,x − 1)

APPLY individual task

▶On Your Own

a. ■ $C(10, 3)(0.51)^3(0.49)^7 \approx 0.108$; binompdf(10,0.51,3) ≈ 0.108.

■ *P*(fewer than 30% saw the movie) = $C(10, 2)(0.51)^2(0.49)^8 + C(10, 1)(0.51)^1(0.49)^9 + C(10, 0)(0.51)^0(0.49)^{10} \approx 0.048$; binomcdf(10,0.51,2) ≈ 0.048.

b.

Number of Sixes	Probability
0	0.193807
1	0.348852
2	0.279082
3	0.130238
4	0.039071
5	0.007814
6	0.001042
7	0.000089
8	0.000004
9	0.000000

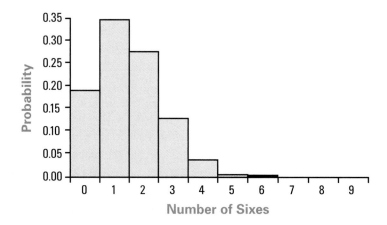

The probability of getting 2 or more sixes is the sum of the probability column from 2 to 9, or about 0.457. Alternatively, it is 1 − binomcdf(9,1/6,1) ≈ 0.457.

Unit 5

MORE independent assignment

NOTE: For this MORE set, you will need to let students know whether they should use the full power of their calculators such as the **binompdf** command or whether they should use the binomial probability formula directly. Most students will need considerable practice with the latter.

Modeling

1. **a.** Student simulations may vary. Here is one simulation: Let the digits 0, 1, 2, and 3 stand for getting a hit. The other digits stand for not getting a hit. Look at 10 random digits and count the number that are 0, 1, 2, or 3.

   b. **See Teaching Master 101.**

   Results will vary. Responses for Parts c–g will be based upon the given table with 998 values.

   c. Since $0.025 \times 1,000 = 25$, find the lower 25 and upper 25 number of hits on the frequency chart. Thus, it is a rare event to get no hits or to get 8 or more hits.

   Alternatively, students may determine the numbers of hits that are two or more standard deviations from the mean. They are remembering that 5% of the values of a normal distribution lie more than two standard deviations from the mean. However, this should be considered a rough estimate as this distribution is only somewhat approximately normal. The results of this method are getting no hits or 8 or more hits is a rare event.

   d. Since getting two hits is not a rare event, it can reasonably be attributed to chance.

   e. Some people believe that in sports people have "slumps" and "streaks," that is, if a player is hitting poorly, they are in a "slump" and will continue to hit poorly for a while, so the probability of a hit is less than the player's usual batting average. However, statisticians have looked at the sequences of hits and outs made by professional baseball players and the sequences of baskets and misses made by professional basketball players. The statisticians do not see streaks and slumps, but rather what looks like a sequence of binomial trials. The streaks of hits and misses aren't any longer than would happen just by chance.

2. **a.** Responses may vary. Using the digits 0 through 9, let the digits 0, 1, and 2 represent a college graduate and the other digits represent a person who is not a college graduate. Generate 24 random digits and then count the number that are 0, 1, or 2. Another method available on a TI-83 is **randBin(24,0.3)**. This command will return the number of successes in the sample. Repeatedly pressing ENTER will generate more samples. (You can generate 100 such samples of size 24 and store the numbers of successes in List 1 with the command **randBin(24,0.3,100) → L₁**.)

   b. **See Teaching Master 102.**

   Results will vary depending on the results of each student's simulation. The answers given here for the remaining part of this task are based upon the original 499 values. Students' answers should be very close to these since one additional trial will not change things very much.

ASSIGNMENT *pp.* 290–297

Modeling: 1 or 2, 3, and 5*
Organizing: 1, 2, and 4
Reflecting: 1 and 2
Extending: 1 and choice of one*

*When choice is indicated, it is important to leave the choice to the student.
NOTE: *It is best if Organizing tasks are discussed as a whole class after they have been assigned as homework.*

Master 101

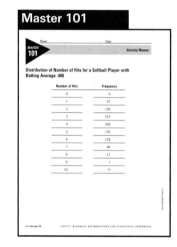

Master 102

Unit 5

MORE *continued*

c.

Frequency

Proportion of College Graduates

For the 12-member jury, about 95% of the distribution falls between 0.08 and 0.58. Dividing the length of this interval by 4, a good estimate of the standard deviation is 0.125. For the grand jury, about 95% of the distribution falls between 0.125 and 0.458, for an estimated standard deviation of 0.0825.

d. A grand jury contains between 20% and 40% college graduates if it has 5, 6, 7, 8, or 9 college graduates. The estimate for the grand jury is $\frac{53 + 86 + 79 + 78 + 62}{499} \approx 0.72$. The estimate for a 12-person jury is $\frac{126 + 104}{490} \approx 0.47$.

e. Reading from the table in Part b, the lower $2\frac{1}{2}\%$ (or the lower $499 \times 0.025 \approx 12$ results) have a proportion of college graduates of 0.08 or less and the upper $2\frac{1}{2}\%$ have proportion 0.54 or more. For the jury of 12, the lower $2\frac{1}{2}\%$ (or the lower $0.025 \times 490 \approx 12$ results) have proportion 0, and the upper $2\frac{1}{2}\%$ have proportion 0.67 or more.

f. This cannot reasonably be attributed to chance since the probability of getting 1 or fewer college graduates is much less than 0.025. Consider another explanation.

3. a. $P(\text{no sixes}) = \left(\frac{5}{6}\right)^5 \approx 0.40188$

b. $P(\text{exactly two sixes}) = C(5, 2)\left(\frac{1}{6}\right)^2\left(\frac{5}{6}\right)^3 \approx 0.16075$ or **binompdf(5,1/6,2)** ≈ 0.16075.

c.

Number of Sixes	Probability
0	0.401878
1	0.401878
2	0.160751
3	0.032150
4	0.003215
5	0.000129

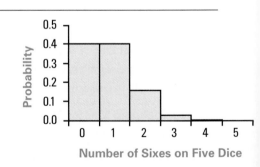

MORE *continued*

d. A good estimate for both mean and standard deviation would be "a little less than 1." (The actual mean is 0.833 and the standard deviation is 0.833. The fact that the mean and standard deviation are equal is a coincidence. This happens when $np = \sqrt{np(1-p)}$. Students will observe this in Activity 1 of Lesson 2, Investigation 2.)

4. **a.** The probability distribution is shown in the following table:

Number of Women	Probability
0	0.0002
1	0.0029
2	0.0161
3	0.0537
4	0.1208
5	0.1934
6	0.2256
7	0.1934
8	0.1208
9	0.0537
10	0.0161
11	0.0029
12	0.0002

NOTE: Dr. Spock was found guilty, but his conviction was overturned on appeal in 1969 based on insufficient evidence of guilt.

This distribution can be constructed quickly using the TI-83 by placing the sequence 0, 1, 2, ..., 12, in L_1. Then place the cursor on top of L_2 and enter **binompdf(12,0.5,L₁)**. Alternatively, you can type **binompdf(12,0.5)** $\rightarrow L_2$ in the home screen.

b. A jury consisting of fewer than 3 or more than 9 women would be a rare event since the probability of each of these events is less than 0.025.

c. The probability of getting no women on the jury is 0.0002. This makes having no women an extremely rare event.

5. **a.** $C(5, 0)(0.25)^0(0.75)^5 =$ **binompdf(5,0.25,0)** ≈ 0.2373

b. $C(5, 2)(0.25)^2(0.75)^3 =$ **binompdf(5,0.25,2)** ≈ 0.2637

c. The probability that at least one child will not carry the defective gene is the same as the probability that no more than four of the children do have the defective gene. Each child has a 75% chance of inheriting the defective gene. P(no more than 4 with defective gene) $= 1 - C(5, 5)(0.75)^5(0.25)^0 \approx 0.7627$ or **binomcdf(5,0.75,4)** ≈ 0.7627.

MORE *continued*

Organizing

1. **a.** This can be thought of as a binomial situation where there are two equally likely possibilities, left and right, for the ball at each nail. In this case, there are eight trials of going left or right that occur with each ball. The direction the ball takes at each nail is independent of what happened before. Thus, all four characteristics of a binomial situation are satisfied.

   b. Yes, it is typical. The columns, going from left to right, correspond to the number of "rights," 0 to 8, in the eight trials. The number of sequences with four rights is $C(8, 4)$ and this number is greater than $C(8, r)$ for any other possible r. Also, $C(8, 3) = C(8, 5)$ so about the same number of balls would be expected to collect in the third column and the fifth column. Similarly,

   $$C(8, 2) = C(8, 6), C(8, 1) = C(8, 7), \text{ and } C(8, 0) = C(8, 8).$$

   c. The number labels on the channels represent the number of possible routes a ball could take to get to that column. This pattern is the eighth line in Pascal's triangle.

   d. ■ There is only one route that a ball could take to get to Column 0. There are a total of $2^8 = 256$ different routes. The probability of a ball falling into Column 0 is $\frac{1}{256} \approx 0.0039$.

   ■ There are $C(8, 5) = 56$ different routes a ball could take to Column 5. The probability of a ball falling into Column 5 is $\frac{56}{256} \approx 0.21875$.

2. Technically, this is not a binomial situation because the probability of getting a household that recycles changes slightly with each trial, depending on which households have previously been selected. This task shows students that when the population is large compared to the sample (at least 10 times as large), the probabilities don't change much at all and so the situation can be considered binomial.

   a. $\frac{1,465,241}{2,000,000} \cdot \frac{1,465,240}{1,999,999} \cdot \frac{1,465,239}{1,999,998} \cdots \frac{1,465,230}{1,999,989} \approx 0.023908017$

   b. $\left(\frac{1,465,241}{2,000,000}\right)^{12} \approx 0.0239083058$

   c. The difference is about 2.9×10^{-7}. It makes very little difference.

3. **a.** $\frac{k}{N} \cdot \frac{k-1}{N-1}$

   $\frac{k}{N} \cdot \frac{k-1}{N-1} \cdot \frac{k-2}{N-2} \cdots \frac{k-11}{N-11}$

   b. $\left(\frac{k}{N}\right)^2$

   $\left(\frac{k}{N}\right)^{12}$

4. **a.** $p^5 + 5p^4q + 10p^3q^2 + 10p^2q^3 + 5pq^4 + q^5$

   b. $p + q = 1$

   c. $(p + q)^5 = 1^5 = 1$

MORE *continued*

d. The fourth term of the expansion is the probability of getting exactly 2 successes in a binomial situation with 5 trials and probability of success *p*. Similarly, the other terms represent the probabilities of the other possible numbers of successes. This proves that the sum of the probabilities in a binomial situation with 5 trials is always 1, as it should be.

5. $\displaystyle\sum_{x=0}^{8} C(8, x) \cdot (0.5)^x (1 - 0.5)^{8-x} = \sum_{x=0}^{8} C(8, x) \cdot (0.5)^8$

$$= \sum_{x=0}^{8} C(8, x) \cdot \frac{1}{256}$$

$$= \frac{1}{256} \sum_{x=0}^{8} C(8, x)$$

$$= \frac{1}{256}(256)$$

$$= 1$$

The reason for the next-to-last step is that the sum, $\displaystyle\sum_{x=0}^{8} C(8, x)$, is the sum of the eighth row of Pascal's triangle. Thus, the sum is equal to 2^8 or 256. row of Pascal's triangle. Thus, the sum is equal to 2^8 or 256.

Reflecting

1. a. There are six possible outcomes and no classification as to what constitutes a success or a failure.

b. The trials aren't independent. The probabilities of getting a male and of getting a female change depending on what has happened on previous trials.

c. The probability it will last 200 hours won't be the same for each battery, but will depend on how fresh it is and its location in the calculator. Also, the trials probably aren't independent; if one battery has gone dead, it may strain the others and so increase the probability that the others will also.

d. The number of trials isn't fixed. This is a waiting-time (geometric) situation, not a binomial one.

e. There are many possible outcomes and no classification as to what constitutes a success or a failure.

2. Students could have thought in terms of permutations. Thinking in terms of permutations, the problem would be to find all possible (ordered) sequences of four Cs and eight Ns, where C represents "a college graduate" and N represents "not a college graduate." There are 12! = 479,001,600 sequences, but since the four Cs and eight Ns are indistinguishable, 12! must be divided by 4!8! = (24)(40,320) = 967,680 to get 495. But it is simpler to look at this in an "unordered" way by thinking of the 12 possible positions in the sequence and asking how many ways the 4 positions in which to place a "success" can be chosen. The answer to that question is simply C(12, 4) = 495.

Unit 5

MORE *continued*

3. **a.** $C(1,000, 500)(0.26)^{500}(0.74)^{500}$

   b. An overflow error message is obtained when using a TI-82 or TI-83 calculator to compute this probability. The TI-89, TI-92, and computer software such as Mathematica® will produce the exact value $C(1,000, 500)$, which is approximately 2.70×10^{299}.

4. **a.** One example is HHTHTTTHHT. The probability of this particular sequence is $(0.5)^{10} \approx 0.00098$.

   b. One example is HHTHHHHHHH. The probability of this particular sequence is $(0.5)^{10} \approx 0.00098$.

   c. When flipping a coin ten times, you are more likely to get 5 heads and 5 tails than 9 heads and 1 tail. The difference is due to the expression $C(n, x)$ in the binomial probability formula. For Part a, there are $C(10, 5) = 252$ ways to get a sequence of 5 heads and 5 tails. Thus, the probability of 5 heads and 5 tails is $252(0.00098) \approx 0.246$. In Part b, there are only 10 ways to get only 1 tail, so the probability is approximately $10(0.00098) = 0.0098$.

Extending

1. **a.** If you take a sample of size 20 from a population that has 30% successes, 90% of the time you get a number of successes that falls within the box; that is, between 3 and 9 successes. Ten percent of the time you get more than 9 or fewer than 3 successes.

   b. Since this can be rather tedious, students might want to construct the distribution using statistical software or their calculators. On the TI-83, the DISTR command binompdf(20,0.3) $\rightarrow$ L$_2$ will put the probabilities in List 2. Alternatively define L$_2$ as binompdf(20,0.3).

Number of Successes	Probability	Number of Successes	Probability
0	0.0008	11	0.01201
1	0.00684	12	0.00386
2	0.0278	13	0.00102
3	0.0716	14	0.00022
4	0.13042	15	0.000037
5	0.17886	16	0.000005
6	0.19164	17	0.000001
7	0.16426	18	0.000000
8	0.1144	19	0.000000
9	0.06537	20	0.000000
10	0.03082		

MORE *continued*

c. Since this is a 90% box, 5% (or less) should be below the box and 5% (or less) should be above the box. Thus, the box should extend from 3 successes to 9 successes, leaving 0.035 below the box, and 0.048 above the box.

d. This box is the same as the one in the chart.

2. a. 0.4 or 40%

b. $\mu = 0.4$, $\sigma \approx 0.490$

c. ■ Sixteen 1s and four 0s

■ $\mu = \frac{16}{20} = 0.8$

$\sigma = \sqrt{\frac{(1-0.8)^2 \cdot 16 + (0-0.8)^2 \cdot 4}{20}} = 0.4$

d. $\mu = \frac{1(k) + 0(N-k)}{N} = \frac{k}{N} = p$, the proportion of successes

$\sigma = \sqrt{\frac{(1-\mu)^2(k) + (0-\mu)^2(N-k)}{N}}$

$= \sqrt{\frac{(1-p)^2(k) + (0-p)^2(N-k)}{N}}$

$= \sqrt{\frac{(1-p)^2(k)}{N} + \frac{(p)^2(N-k)}{N}}$

$= \sqrt{(1-p)^2(p) + (p)^2(1-p)}$

$= \sqrt{p(1-p)[(1-p) + p]}$

$= \sqrt{p(1-p)}$

e. In each case, this formula gives the same value of σ:

$\sqrt{(0.6)(0.4)} = \sqrt{0.24} \approx 0.490$ and $\sqrt{(0.8)(0.2)} = 0.4$.

3. a. This is the same binomial probability formula that students have been using, except for a difference in notation. Since the sampling is done with replacement, the situation is binomial. The probability of a success is $\frac{S}{N}$, and the probability of a failure is $\frac{F}{N}$. Note that $s + f = n$, where s is the number of successes in the sample of size n, and f is the number of failures.

b. This formula represents the number of ways of getting exactly s successes and f failures divided by the number of ways to choose n outcomes from N; that is, it is of the form

$$\frac{\text{number of successful outcomes}}{\text{number of possible outcomes}}$$

The numerator uses the Multiplication Principle of Counting, finding the number of successful outcomes by multiplying the number of ways to pick s successes from S successes by the number of ways to pick f failures from F failures.

MORE *continued*

c. With replacement:

$$C(8, 6)(0.6)^6(0.4)^2 \approx 0.209$$

Without replacement:

$$\frac{C(15, 6) \cdot C(10, 2)}{C(25, 8)} \approx 0.208$$

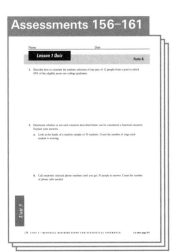

4. a. q^5, $5pq^4$, $10p^2q^3$, $10p^3q^2$, $5p^4q$, p^5

b. This tree diagram gives the binomial probabilities. For example, if the number of trials is 4, go to the fourth row. Then, count over to the number of successes needed and substitute the values of p and q to get the probability of that number of successes.

   Notice that the numerical coefficient in each circle is the number of different paths down to that circle. Students should recognize this pattern as Pascal's triangle. The p's and q's along each of these paths show the different sequences that give the particular power of p and q in the circle.

See Teaching Masters 103a–103e for Maintenance tasks that students can work on after Lesson 1.

See Assessment Resources 156–161.

REVIEW AND PRACTICE   individual task

▶PUMP

Answers

1.	(b)	6.	(c)
2.	(e)	7.	(d)
3.	(a)	8.	(c)
4.	(b)	9.	(e)
5.	(e)	10.	(d)

Lesson 2 *Characteristics of Binomial Distributions*

LESSON OVERVIEW In this lesson, students examine a variety of binomial distributions where either the number of successes is fixed or the probability of success is fixed. Students then extend this understanding to distributions for the sample proportion. In Investigation 2, students examine and apply the simple formulas for the mean and standard deviation of a binomial probability distribution.

Before beginning this lesson, you may want to review the 68%-95%-99.7% rule from Course 3, Unit 5 "Patterns in Variation." (In a normal distribution, 68% of the values lie within one standard deviation from the mean, 95% of the values lie within two standard deviations from the mean, and 99.7% of the values lie within three standard deviations from the mean.)

Lesson Objectives

- To understand what happens to the shape, mean, and spread of a binomial distribution of the number of successes as n gets larger but p remains fixed
- To understand what happens to the shape, mean, and spread of a distribution of the sample proportion of successes as n gets larger but p remains fixed
- To examine the simple formulas for the mean, $\mu = np$, and standard deviation, $\sigma = \sqrt{np(1-p)}$, of a binomial distribution
- To understand and use the formulas for the mean and standard deviation of a binomial distribution of the number of successes and the formulas for the mean and standard deviation of the distribution of the sample proportion
- To understand that the normal approximation to the binomial is an approximation and has satisfactory accuracy when $np \geq 10$ and $n(1-p) \geq 10$

Unit 5

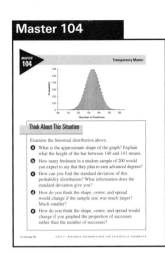

Master 104

Think About This Situation

See Teaching Master 104.

ⓐ The shape of the graph is approximately normal. The height of the bar between 140 and 141 gives the probability of getting exactly 140 freshmen who say they plan to get an advanced degree out of a random sample of 200 freshmen.

ⓑ You would expect that two-thirds of 200 or about 133 freshmen would say they expect to earn an advanced degree.

ⓒ Students could compute the probability for each value of x and then use the formula $\sigma = \sqrt{\sum (x - \mu)^2 \cdot p(x)}$ to find the standard deviation. This would be a tremendous amount of work. Students may estimate the standard deviation by observing that about 95% of the values will be within two standard deviations of the mean. A reasonable estimate is 6 to 8. Since this distribution is approximately normal, if the standard deviation were known, the z-scores could be found for various numbers of freshmen and then a table of the normal distribution used to estimate the corresponding probabilities.

ⓓ If the sample size were increased, then the shape would become even more approximately normal, the center would increase, and the spread would increase. If the sample size were made smaller, the shape would be skewed to the left and the center and spread would decrease. At this time, students may not realize the distribution based on a smaller sample size will be skewed, but should realize that it will be less normal-looking.

ⓔ Students will likely suggest that the shape is the same based on their work in Lesson 1. They will learn that if they were graphing the proportion of successes $\hat{p}$ rather than the number of successes x, then the center would be at $\frac{2}{3}$ and the spread would also be divided by 200.

INVESTIGATION 1 ▶ The Shapes of Binomial Distributions

In this investigation, students examine the shape, mean, and spread for two binomial distributions as the sample size increases. Then they consider the changes in binomial distributions for a situation with sample size of 40 as the probability of success increases from 0.10 to 0.90. Students also use the conditions $np \geq 10$ and $n(1 - p) \geq 10$ to decide whether a binomial distribution can be considered approximately normal. Students then examine what happens to the shape, mean, and spread of a distribution of the sample proportion as the sample size or probability of success changes.

Note that in the graphs in Activity 1, all the distributions appear to have the same height because the vertical axes were rescaled. For example, you may want to show students that the distribution for $n = 100$ is much shorter than the distribution for $n = 10$. This indicates that the probability of the mean is much smaller for $n = 100$ than $n = 10$.

EXPLORE *continued*

1. **a.** $C(10, 2)(0.2)^2(0.8)^8 \approx 0.3020$

NOTE: The tallest bar in a binomial distribution is always the one closest to the mean for $\mu = np$.

   b. There are more bars as the sample size increases since there is a greater number of possible successes. For a sample size of n, there should be $(n + 1)$ bars representing $0, 1, 2, \ldots, n$ successes out of n trials. Only 7 bars show on the graph for $n = 10$ (for $0, 1, 2, 3, 4, 5, 6$) because the others are so short they don't show up. For example, for $n = 10$, the bar above $x = 7$ would be only 0.00079 high.

   c. As the sample size increases, the shape of the graph more closely resembles a normal distribution.

   d. As the sample size increases, the mean number of successes increases. (As students will learn later, it increases proportionally with n.)

   e. As the sample size increases, the standard deviation of the number of successes increases. $\left(\text{As students will learn later, it increases proportionally with } \sqrt{n}.\right)$

2. **a.** The histograms become more smooth and approximately normal in shape as n increases.

   b. The mean increases.

   c. The standard deviation also increases.

3. **a.** All are slightly skewed except the one for $p = 50\%$. At first they are skewed right, this skewness decreases until $p = 50\%$, and then the left skew increases. The graph for $p = 50\%$ is most nearly normal.

   b. The mean increases.

   c. The standard deviation increases from $p = 10\%$ to $p = 50\%$ and then decreases.

   d. The graphs for p and for $1 - p$ are identical under a reflection across a vertical line through $x = 20$. The graph for $p = 50\%$ is symmetrical about the same line, which goes through its center.

   e. This set of graphs is very similar to the 90% box plot chart from Course 3, Unit 2, "Modeling Public Opinion," except that the chart has box plots that summarize these distributions. The box plots identify the middle 90% of each distribution. Students may notice that the spread of the distribution increases up to $p = 0.50$ and then decreases. (You may wish to come back to the box plots when you discuss spread of binomial distributions in the Checkpoint.)

EXPLORE *continued*

4. **a.** ■ More

   ■ Less

   b. There are two exceptions:

   If $p = 0.5$, the distribution is symmetric for all values of n.

   If $p = 0$ or $p = 1$, there is only one bar on the histogram, so you wouldn't discuss skewness.

NOTE: Students need the $np \geq 10$ and $n(1 - p) \geq 10$ rule so that they can know when it is appropriate to use a normal distribution to approximate probabilities for binomial distributions.

5. **a.** The value $n(1 - p)$ is the expected number of failures.

   b. Here $p = 0.2$. Only $n = 50$ and $n = 100$, since in both cases np and $n(1 - p)$ are 10 or larger. This agrees with the visual impression from the graphs. These two histograms appear more nearly symmetrical than the others.

   c. Here $p = 0.5$. All except for $n = 10$ give values of np and $n(1 - p)$ of 10 or larger, and thus can be considered approximately normal. This agrees with the visual impression.

   d. $p = 30\%$, 40%, 50%, 60%, and 70% give values of np and $n(1 - p)$ of 10 or larger, and so those distributions can be considered approximately normal. These are also the histograms that look approximately normal.

6. **a.** The distribution will be similar to that for $p = 20\%$ in the set of graphs in Activity 3. It is slightly skewed to the right.

   b. It is centered at $0.2(35) = 7$. The standard deviation is 2.37. Any estimate between 2 and 4 would be good.

   c. The following instructions are for the TI-83 calculator:

   Place the numbers 0 through 35 in List 1 using the command

   seq(A,A,0,35) → L$_1$.

   Place the binomial probabilities in List 2 using the command

   binompdf(35,0.2) → L$_2$.

   Then, make a histogram under STAT PLOT with xList: L$_1$ and Freq: L$_2$.

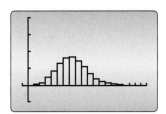 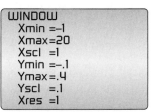

   The mean and standard deviation can be found using STAT CALC 1-Var Stats L$_1$, L$_2$.

SHARE AND SUMMARIZE full-class discussion

Checkpoint

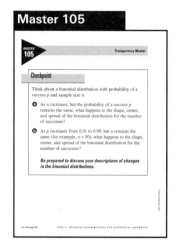

See Teaching Master 105.

a The shape becomes more approximately normal and less skewed; the center and spread both increase.

b The shape becomes less skewed right until $p = 0.5$, when it is symmetrical, then becomes increasingly skewed left; the center increases; the spread increases until $p = 0.5$, then decreases. (You may wish to refer back to the set of graphs in Activity 3 to help students cement this concept.)

APPLY individual task

▶On Your Own

a. The one with sample size 50 will be more symmetrical and look more like a normal distribution. It will have a larger mean (15 rather than 7.5) and a larger standard deviation. Also, it will have 51 bars rather than 26.

b. The shapes are identical under reflection across the line $x = 12.5$. The spreads are the same but the means are 7.5 and 17.5, respectively.

MORE

ASSIGNMENT *pp. 311–315*

Students can now begin Organizing Task 1 or Reflecting Task 4 from the MORE assignment following Investigation 2.

EXPLORE small-group investigation

7. Divide by the sample size (or number of trials) n.

8. a. As sample size increases, the mean of the distribution stays at 0.2.

   b. As sample size increases, the standard deviation of the distribution decreases. If you want a more precise estimate of p, it makes sense to have a larger sample size.

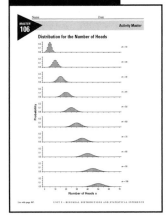

Master 106

Master 107

EXPLORE *continued*

9. **See Teaching Master 106.**

To get the new graphs, the students should divide each number of successes on the *x*-axis by the sample size for that graph. The graphs for *n* = 40 and *n* = 100 are shown below.

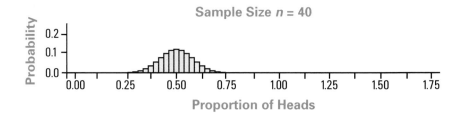

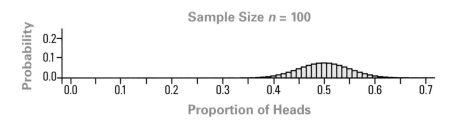

a. As the sample size increases, the mean of the distribution stays at 0.5.

b. As the sample size increases, the standard deviation of the distribution decreases.

SHARE AND SUMMARIZE   full-class discussion

Checkpoint

See Teaching Master 107.

ⓐ The shape becomes more approximately normal; the center remains the same, and spread decreases.

ⓑ Students can refer to the graphs in Activity 3 to think about this question. The shapes are identical under a reflection across the line $x = 0.5$. The spread is identical. However, one is centered at p and the other at $1 - p$. (See Organizing Task 2 for extended analysis of this reflection.)

ⓒ The main difference is that as n increases, the standard deviation of the number of successes increases, while the standard deviation of the proportion of successes decreases. This should make sense intuitively. With larger sample sizes, you are more confident that the value of $\hat{p}$ is closer to the value of p.

CONSTRUCTING A MATH TOOLKIT: Students should write a summary of Investigation 1 which describes what happens to shapes, centers, and spreads for number of, as well as proportion of, successes when either *n* or *p* are fixed. Sample sketches may be helpful.

Unit 5

APPLY individual task

▶On Your Own

a. The distribution with sample size 50 is more approximately normal and has a smaller standard deviation. (The mean for both is 0.3.)

b. The shapes are identical under reflection across the line $x = 0.5$. The spreads are the same, but the centers are at 0.3 and 0.7, respectively. The distribution with $p = 0.3$ is skewed right and the distribution with $p = 0.7$ is skewed left.

c. The answers to Part a differ in that the mean of the proportion is the same regardless of sample size, but the mean of the number of successes depends on sample size. Also, the standard deviation of the proportion decreases as n increases, while the standard deviation of the number of successes increases as n increases. The answers to both Part b questions are essentially the same.

ASSIGNMENT *pp. 311–315*

Students can now begin Organizing Task 2 from the MORE assignment following Investigation 2.

EXPLORE small-group investigation

INVESTIGATION ▶2 Simple Formulas for the Mean and the Standard Deviation

In this investigation, students examine and apply the simple formulas for the mean ($\mu = np$) and standard deviation $\left(\sigma = \sqrt{np(1-p)}\right)$ of the number of successes in a binomial situation and then compare these formulas to the corresponding formulas for the proportion of successes $\left(\mu = p \text{ and } \sigma = \sqrt{\frac{p(1-p)}{n}}\right)$.

1. a. $P(3 \text{ successes}) = C(4, 3)(0.2)^3(0.8)^1 = 0.0256$

NOTE: Reflecting Task 2 asks students to find the condition that produces equal means and standard deviations.

b. $\mu = \sum x \cdot p(x)$

$= 0(0.4096) + 1(0.4096) + 2(0.1536) + 3(0.0256) + 4(0.0016)$

$= 0.8$

$\sigma = \sqrt{\sum(x - \mu)^2 \cdot p(x)}$

$= \sqrt{(0 - 0.8)^2(0.4096) + (1 - 0.8)^2(0.4096) + (2 - 0.8)^2(0.1536) + (3 - 0.8)^2(0.0256) + (4 - 0.8)^2(0.0016)}$

$= \sqrt{0.64}$

$= 0.8$

c. This value is the same as that computed in Part b.

2. a. $\sigma = \sqrt{4(0.2)(1 - 0.2)} = 0.8$

You may wish to mention to students that when a complicated process like that in Activity 1 Part b gives such a simple answer, a good mathematician will suspect there may be a simpler way to get that answer, as there was here.

Unit 5

Master 108

Name _____ Date _____

MASTER
108
Activity Master

Using Formulas for the Mean and the Standard Deviation of a
Binomial Distribution

2b.
Sample Size *n*	Mean *μ*	Standard Deviation *σ*
5		
10		
25		
50		
100		

3.
Probability of a Success *p*	Mean *μ = np*	Variance *σ²*
0.1	0.9	0.81
0.2	1.8	1.44
0.3	2.7	1.89
0.4	3.6	2.16
0.5	4.5	2.25
0.6		
0.7		
0.8		
0.9		

Use with page 309.   UNIT 5 · BINOMIAL DISTRIBUTIONS AND STATISTICAL INFERENCE

EXPLORE *continued*

b. See Teaching Master 108.

Sample Size *n*	Mean *μ*	Standard Deviation *σ*
5	1	0.894
10	2	1.265
25	5	2.000
50	10	2.828
100	20	4.000

c. The mean is 0.2 times the sample size, so each time the sample size is doubled, the mean is doubled. As the sample size increases by a factor of 2, the standard deviation increases by a factor of $\sqrt{2} \approx 1.4$.

d. The mean varies directly as the sample size *n*. The standard deviation varies directly as the square root of the sample size. To see this clearly, students may need to look at what happens to the standard deviation when the sample size quadruples.

3. a. See Teaching Master 108.

Probability of a Success *p*	Mean *μ = np*	Variance *σ²*
0.1	0.9	0.81
0.2	1.8	1.44
0.3	2.7	1.89
0.4	3.6	2.16
0.5	4.5	2.25
0.6	5.4	2.16
0.7	6.3	1.89
0.8	7.2	1.44
0.9	8.1	0.81

b. As the probability of a success increases, the mean increases. As the probability of a success increases, the variance increases up to *p* = 0.5, then decreases, taking the same values as before.

c. The points (p, σ^2) lie on the graph of a parabola.

d. To find the equation of the parabola, students might reason from how they filled in the table, use quadratic regression, use finite differences, or use a matrix equation.

e. The equation is $\sigma^2 = 9p(1 - p)$ or $y = 9x(1 - x) = -9x^2 + 9x$.

4. a. The shape is approximately normal since $np = 1{,}000(0.26) = 260 \geq 10$ and $n(1 - p) = 1{,}000(1 - 0.26) = 740 \geq 10$. The mean is $\mu = np = 1{,}000(0.26) = 260$. The standard deviation is $\sigma = \sqrt{np(1-p)} = \sqrt{1{,}000(0.26)(0.74)} \approx 13.87$.

b. More than $260 + 2(13.87) \approx 287$ or less than $260 - 2(13.87) \approx 232$.

EXPLORE *continued*

Master 109

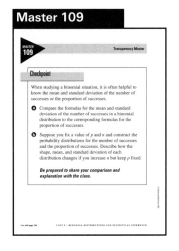

5. **a.** Divide by n to get $\mu = p$.

   b. In the long run, the average value of $\hat{p}$ should be p.

   c. Divide by n to get $\sigma = \dfrac{\sqrt{np(1-p)}}{n} = \sqrt{\dfrac{np(1-p)}{n^2}} = \sqrt{\dfrac{p(1-p)}{n}}$.

   d. The formula for the standard deviation of the proportion has an n (representing the sample size) in the denominator of the fraction inside the square root sign. As n increases, the number under the square root sign will decrease, so the standard deviation will decrease.

   e. The Law of Large Numbers indicates that with a large sample size, the value of $\hat{p}$ tends to be closer to p, thus the standard deviation of $\hat{p}$ will be smaller.

SHARE AND SUMMARIZE full-class discussion

Checkpoint

See Teaching Master 109.

ⓐ Since the proportion of successes is just the number of successes divided by n, the formulas for the mean differ only by a factor of n with the mean of the number of successes equal to n times the mean of the proportion of successes.

   The formulas for the standard deviation also differ by a factor of n, with the standard deviation of the number of successes equal to n times the standard deviation of the proportion of successes.

ⓑ As the sample size increases, the mean of the distribution of the number of successes increases, while the mean of the distribution of the proportion of successes stays constant. This is due to the fact that the formula for the mean number of successes is $\mu = np$, so μ increases as n increases, whereas the mean for a probability distribution of the proportion of successes is always p.

   The standard deviation of the distribution of the number of successes increases, while the standard deviation of the distribution of the proportion of successes decreases. This can be seen in the formulas for the standard deviation $\sigma = \sqrt{np(1-p)}$ and $\sigma = \sqrt{\dfrac{p(1-p)}{n}}$. The first of these increases as n increases, and the second decreases as n increases. In both cases, the shape becomes more approximately normal.

CONSTRUCTING A MATH TOOLKIT: Students should record the simplified formulas for the mean and standard deviation of the number and proportion of successes in a binomial distribution. They may wish to supply appropriate examples.

APPLY individual task

On Your Own

a.

Number of Successes x	Probability $p(x)$
0	0.166
1	0.408
2	0.334
3	0.091

APPLY *continued*

b. $\mu = np = 3(0.45) = 1.35$

   $\mu = \sum x \cdot p(x) = 0(0.166) + 1(0.408) + 2(0.334) + 3(0.091) = 1.349$

c.   Using the formula $\sigma = \sqrt{np(1-p)}$, $\sqrt{3(0.45)(0.55)} \approx 0.862$. Using the formula $\sigma = \sqrt{\sum(x - \mu)^2 \cdot p(x)}$ and the probability distribution table above,

   $\sigma = \sqrt{(0 - 1.35)^2(0.166) + (1 - 1.35)^2(0.408) + (2 - 1.35)^2(0.334) + (3 - 1.35)^2(0.091)} \approx 0.861$.

d. $\mu = p = 0.45$, $\sigma = \sqrt{\dfrac{(0.45)(0.55)}{3}} \approx 0.287$, or alternatively $\sigma = \dfrac{0.862}{3} \approx 0.287$ as developed in Part a of the Checkpoint.

MORE

ASSIGNMENT   *pp. 311–315*

Modeling: 1 or 2, and 3 or 4*
Organizing: 1, 2, and 4
Reflecting: 1 and 4
Extending: 1 and choice
   of one*

*When choice is indicated, it is important to leave the choice to the student.
NOTE: It is best if Organizing tasks are discussed as a whole class after they have been assigned as homework.

MORE   **independent assignment**

Modeling

1. a.   Yes, the distribution will be approximately normal since $np = 1{,}500(0.10) = 150$ and $n(1 - p) = 1{,}500(0.90) = 1{,}350$ are both at least 10.

   b.   The mean is $np = 1{,}500(0.1) = 150$ and the standard deviation is $\sigma = \sqrt{1{,}500(0.10)(0.90)} \approx 11.62$.

   c.

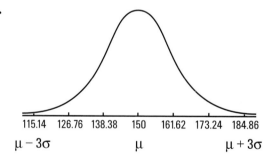

| 115.14 | 126.76 | 138.38 | 150 | 161.62 | 173.24 | 184.86 |

$\mu - 3\sigma$ μ $\mu + 3\sigma$

   d.   No, 130 falls between one and two standard deviations below the mean, so that wouldn't put it in the outer 5% of the distribution.

2. a.   Yes, the distribution of the number of children will be approximately normal since $np = 200(0.2) = 40$ and $n(1 - p) = 200(0.8) = 160$ are both at least 10.

   b.   The mean is $np = 40$ and the standard deviation is $\sigma = \sqrt{200(0.2)(0.8)} \approx 5.66$.

   c.

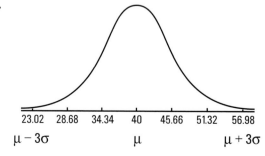

| 23.02 | 28.68 | 34.34 | 40 | 45.66 | 51.32 | 56.98 |

$\mu - 3\sigma$ μ $\mu + 3\sigma$

MORE *continued*

   d. To be two standard deviations above average, the sample would have to have about 40 + 2(5.66) = 51.32 or 52 children.

   e. To be two standard deviations below the mean, the sample would have to have about 40 − 2(5.66) = 28.68 or 28 children.

   f. The probability of being more than two standard deviations above or below the mean is about 5%. The probability of being more than one standard deviation away from the mean is about 32%. (This is true for all approximately normal distributions.)

   g. A rare event would be 52 or more children or 28 or fewer children in the sample.

   h. You shouldn't expect to get exactly 40 children. Getting 45 children could easily happen just by chance. In fact, being 5 or more children away from 40 happens more than 32% of the time if you take random samples of 200 people.

3. If you take a random sample of 500 adults (aged 25 years and above) from a population with 84% who completed high school, you would expect to get 420 who report having completed high school. Although that is the mean, you probably wouldn't get exactly 420. The number you might get may vary around 420 with a standard deviation of about $\sqrt{500(0.84)(0.16)} \approx 8.2$. In this sample, there are 425 such adults. This is less than one standard deviation from the mean and so is not a rare event.

4. There are about 17,440 women students at this university. If you take a random sample of 29,066 people from a population with 49% women, you would get, on the average, 14,242 women. The standard deviation of the number of women is $\sqrt{29,066(0.49)(0.51)} \approx 85.23$. The number of women at this university is about 37.5 standard deviations above average: $\frac{17,440 - 14,242}{85.23} \approx 37.5$. This cannot reasonably be attributed to chance since the probability of getting at least 17,440 women in a random sample of 29,066 young adults is almost 0. The university should look for some other explanation.

Organizing

1. **a.** i

   b. iv

   c. iii

   d. ii

MORE *continued*

2. The graphs show that the probability of getting *x* successes when the probability of a success is *p* is the same as the probability of getting $(n - x)$ successes when the probability of a success is $1 - p$. The formulas for these two probabilities are

$$P(x \text{ successes}) = C(n, x)(p)^x(1-p)^{n-x} \text{ and } P(n - x \text{ successes}) = C(n, n-x)(1-p)^{n-x}(p)^x.$$

These two probabilities are equal because $C(n, x) = \dfrac{n!}{x!(n-x)!} = \dfrac{n!}{(n-x)!x!} = C(n, n-x)$.

3. Getting doubles exactly 25% of the time is the same as getting exactly 8 doubles:

$$P(8 \text{ successes}) = C(32, 8)\left(\frac{1}{6}\right)^8\left(\frac{5}{6}\right)^{24} \approx 0.079$$

4. a.

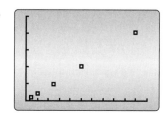

- The pattern indicates a linear relationship.
- The relationship between *n* and μ is linear and $\mu = 0.2n$.
- This relationship can be deduced from the formula $\mu = np$.

b.

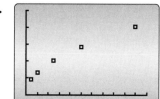

- The pattern indicates a curve that increases at a decreasing rate. One family of functions with this property is the square root function family.
- The relationship between *n* and σ is a square root function since $\sigma = \sqrt{np(1-p)} = \sqrt{n(0.2)(1-0.2)} = 0.4\sqrt{n}$.

Reflecting

1. Students have not proved either of these formulas. They have worked with numerical examples to show that they hold in certain cases. (A proof is outlined in Extending Task 2 of this MORE set.)

Unit 5

MORE *continued*

2. Students can determine when the mean and the standard deviation of a binomial distribution will be equal by examining the equation $\mu = np = \sqrt{np(1-p)} = \sigma$. This equation will be true when $np = 1 - p$, that is, when the mean of the distribution is equal to the probability of a failure.

3. **a.** To find the mean from the probability distribution table, multiply x times $p(x)$ 101 times and then add these 101 numbers for 100 additions. This is 201 operations.

b. To use the formula $\sigma^2 = \sum (x - \mu)^2 \cdot p(x)$, given the table and the value of μ, do 101 subtractions to find the values of $x - \mu$, 101 multiplications to do the squaring, 101 multiplications to get the values of $(x - \mu)^2 \cdot p(x)$, and 100 additions to get the sum. That is 201 addition/subtractions and 202 multiplications.

4. A normal distribution is continuous and smooth. The binomial distribution, on the other hand, is discrete—it is made up of individual bars. While the binomial distribution begins to look smoother as n increases (and hence the number of bars increases), no matter how many bars there are, they are still bars and not a smooth curve. Therefore, a binomial distribution can never be exactly normal.

Extending

1. **a.**

Number of Minutes	Probability
4	$\frac{1}{3}$
9	$\frac{1}{3}$
17	$\frac{1}{3}$

The mean of the probability distribution is $\frac{1}{3}(4 + 9 + 17) = 10$. The variance is $\frac{(4-10)^2 + (9-10)^2 + (17-10)^2}{3} = 28\frac{2}{3}$.

b.

Number of Minutes	Probability
4	$\frac{1}{3}$
6	$\frac{1}{3}$
11	$\frac{1}{3}$

The mean of the probability distribution is $\frac{1}{3}(4 + 6 + 11) = 7$. The variance is $\frac{(4-7)^2 + (6-7)^2 + (11-7)^2}{3} = 8\frac{2}{3}$.

Unit 5

MORE *continued*

c.

Number of Minutes	Probability
8	$\frac{1}{9}$
10	$\frac{1}{9}$
13	$\frac{1}{9}$
15	$\frac{2}{9}$
20	$\frac{1}{9}$
21	$\frac{1}{9}$
23	$\frac{1}{9}$
28	$\frac{1}{9}$

The mean of the probability distribution is

$\frac{1}{9}(8 + 10 + 13 + 20 + 21 + 23 + 28) + \frac{2}{9}(15) = 17$. The variance is

$$\frac{(8-17)^2 + (10-17)^2 + (13-17)^2 + 2(15-17)^2 + (20-17)^2 + (21-17)^2 + (23-17)^2 + (28-17)^2}{9} = 37\frac{1}{3}.$$

d. In the case of independent drives, you can add the individual means and variances to find the mean and variance of the total travel time.

e. Adding the standard deviation of the morning times, 5.3541, to the standard deviation of the evening times, 2.9439, does not give the standard deviation of the total, 6.1101. You can use the individual standard deviations to find the standard deviation of total travel time, but you first must convert them both to variances by squaring, add the two variances, and then take the square root to get the standard deviation of the sum.

f.

Number of Minutes	Probability
8	$\frac{1}{3}$
15	$\frac{1}{3}$
28	$\frac{1}{3}$

The mean is $\frac{1}{3}(8 + 15 + 28) = 17$. The variance is $\frac{(8-17)^2 + (15-17)^2 + (28-17)^2}{3} = 68\frac{2}{3}$.

g. You can find the mean by adding, but adding does not work for the variance unless the morning and afternoon times are independent.

2. The theorem mentioned in this task is, in fact, quite general. Suppose you have any two distributions with respective means μ_1 and μ_2 and respective variances σ_1 and σ_2. Take one value at random from the first distribution and one value at random from the second distribution. Add them. Now consider the distribution of all possible sums. The mean of this distribution is $\mu_1 + \mu_2$ and the variance is $\sigma_1 + \sigma_2$. This task uses only the special case where the two distributions are the same. This special case is equivalent to the fact that if you take a simple random sample of size n from a distribution with mean μ and standard deviation σ, then the sampling distribution of the sample mean has mean μ and standard deviation $\frac{\sigma}{\sqrt{n}}$. (For a more complete, but introductory, explanation of these theorems, see David S. Moore and George P. McCabe, *Introduction to the Practice of Statistics, 3rd Ed.* New York: W. H. Freeman, 1999, pages 328–334, 370–382, and 395.)

   Students may have seen the idea of this theorem in Extending Task 1 above or in Extending Task 4 (about boxes of raisins) in Course 3, Unit 5, "Patterns in Variation," page 361.

   a. The mean is p. The variance is $(0 - p)^2(1 - p) + (1 - p)^2 p = p^2(1 - p) + (1 - p)^2 p = p(1 - p)[p + (1 - p)] = p(1 - p)$.

   b. In Extending Task 2 in the MORE set of Lesson 1, students learned to code the results of a binomial trial. This is a "coded" binomial trial where a success is coded as a 1 and a failure as a 0.

   c. $x_1 + x_2$ represents the number of successes in two trials. The mean is $2p$ and the variance is $2p(1 - p)$.

   d. The mean is np and the variance is $np(1 - p)$.

   e. These are the "short-cut" formulas for the mean and variance of a binomial distribution with n trials and probability of success p.

3. a. The standard deviation should be 0 because there is no variation in the distribution. The binomial distribution has only one bar, at n, the number of trials. Every trial is a success. The probability distribution table looks like this:

Number of Successes	Probability
0	0
1	0
$\vdots$	$\vdots$
n	1

   By the formulas, the mean of the distribution is $n \cdot 1 = n$ and the standard deviation is $\sqrt{n \cdot 1 \cdot 0} = 0$. These are the same values that are expected.

Assessments 162–164

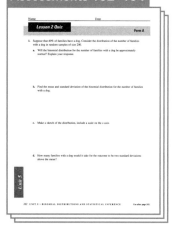

MORE *continued*

b. The standard deviation should be 0 because the distribution has only one bar, at 0. No trial is a success. The probability distribution table looks like this:

Number of Successes	Probability
0	1
1	0
⋮	⋮
n	0

By the formulas, the mean of the distribution is $n \cdot 0 = 0$ and the standard deviation is $\sqrt{n \cdot 1 \cdot 0} = 0$. These are the same values that are expected.

c. The standard deviation should be the same since the distributions are the same shape but reflections of each other. The formula gives this result also:

$$\sigma = \sqrt{np(1-p)} = \sqrt{n(1-p)[1-(1-p)]} = \sqrt{n(1-p)(p)}.$$

d. From looking at the graphs in Activity 3 of Investigation 1, the standard deviation is the largest when $p = 0.5$. From the formula, the largest value of $p(1-p)$ occurs when $p = 0.5$. This can be proved by considering the graph of $y = p(1-p) = p - p^2 = -p^2 + p$. This is a parabola that opens down. The maximum occurs at the vertex when $p = -\dfrac{b}{2a} = \dfrac{1}{2}$.

See Assessment Resources pages 162–167.

Assessments 165–167

REVIEW AND PRACTICE individual task

 PUMP

Answers

1. (c)	**6.** (e)
2. (d)	**7.** (d)
3. (b)	**8.** (e)
4. (c)	**9.** (a)
5. (a)	**10.** (a)

Lesson 3 *Chance Variation in a Binomial Situation*

In this lesson, students will formalize some of the techniques that they have been using to determine if an event can reasonably be attributed to chance. In the first investigation, they use a normal approximation to a binomial distribution to estimate binomial probabilities. The normal approximation can be used when the binomial distribution is approximately normal. In situations where cumulative probability is needed, it is often much more feasible to estimate probabilities using the normal approximation than to compute them exactly from the binomial distribution. The second investigation introduces students to significance testing. In particular, they will test if a sample proportion is significantly different from a population proportion.

Lesson Objectives

- To use the normal approximation to the binomial distribution to estimate binomial probabilities
- To perform a *z*-test for a proportion, including stating a null hypothesis, describing the binomial distribution given that the null hypothesis is true, locating the result from the sample on that distribution, and stating a conclusion
- To understand the logic of a significance test, including the types of errors that are possible

If you would like to liven up the "Think About This Situation," you can use data collected by your students. You will need 900 spins of a penny. Get pennies from the 1960s or early 1970s if you can. If you have 30 students, ask each student to spin 30 times and count the number of heads. Have students do this at home as it is best to do it on a large table or on the floor and may take a few minutes. There are far fewer than 50% heads if you spin a penny. How many fewer depends on the year of the penny. If you flip a penny in the usual way, the percentage of heads is about 50%.

In this lesson, students will use the rule that if you take a random sample and observe a result that is more than two standard deviations from a hypothesized standard, you should reject that standard as being the true state of affairs. The first use of this rule in jury selection cases was *Castaneda* v. *Partida,* which came out of southern Texas in 1977. The plaintiff argued successfully that Hispanics were underrepresented on juries. The importance of the case lies in one of the key statements in the Supreme Court decision: "As a general rule for such large samples, if the difference between the expected value and the observed number is greater than two or three standard deviations, then the hypothesis that the jury drawing was random would be suspect to a social scientist." (The person responsible for the argument was a statistician.)

Unit 5

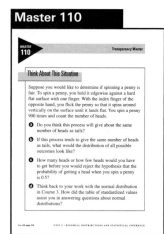

Master 110

LAUNCH   full-class discussion

Think About This Situation

See Teaching Master 110.

ⓐ Responses will vary. Most students will probably think that spinning a penny will give about the same number of heads as tails. In fact, there will be far fewer than 50% heads when spinning a penny.

ⓑ This would be a binomial situation with $n = 900$ and $p = 0.5$. Thus, the distribution has mean 450 and standard deviation 15 and is approximately normal in shape since $np \geq 10$ and $n(1 - p) \geq 10$.

ⓒ If the number of heads is more than two standard deviations from the mean, that casts doubt on whether the proportion is actually 0.5. Those numbers would be more than 480 or fewer than 420. If students use **binomcdf** to find the rare events, they will classify 480 or more or 420 or fewer heads as rare events.

ⓓ When a value is standardized, the distribution undergoes a translation and size change so that it can be compared to the standard normal distribution. That way, only one table is needed for comparisons of distributions that are approximately normal. The table tells the probability of getting a particular standardized value or one that is smaller.

EXPLORE   small-group investigation

INVESTIGATION 1 ▸ Using the Normal Distribution to Approximate Binomial Probabilities

If your students have a TI-83 or other calculator with advanced statistical capabilities, they will have several ways to do the problems in this lesson. For example, suppose you flip a fair coin 900 times. What is the probability of getting 415 or fewer heads?

Method I   Using exact binomial probabilities:
binomcdf(900,0.5,415) = 0.0106982085.

Method II   Using the normal approximation with $\mu = 450$ and
$\sigma = 15$: normalcdf(–999999,415,450,15) = 0.0098153068.

Method III Using the z-score with the normal approximation from
the calculator: $z = \frac{415 - 450}{15} \approx$ **–2.33333**,

normalcdf(–999999,–2.33333) = 0.0098153943.

Method IV   Using the z-score with the normal approximation from the table on
page 320: proportion below $z = -2.3$ is 0.0107.

EXPLORE *continued*

In general, Method I is the most accurate, then II, then III (because it involves more rounding than II), then IV (because the *z*-score is rounded to tenths). It is important that students understand that Method I is exact (subject to rounding in the calculator) while the others are approximations to this probability.

Which method(s) you encourage/allow depends on the goals you have for your students. The mathematical ideas of Method III and Method IV are important if your students plan to study more statistics.

1. **a.** Yes, it is a binomial distribution, as long as the spins are independent. The number of trials is $n = 900$ and the probability of a success is $p = 0.5$.

    b. The mean is $np = 450$.
    The standard deviation is $\sigma = \sqrt{np(1 - p)} = \sqrt{900(0.5)(0.5)} = 15$.

    c. The shape is approximately normal since $np = 450 \geq 10$ and $n(1 - p) = 450 \geq 10$.

    d. binompdf(900,0.5,415) ≈ 0.00175.

    Students may use the binomial probability formula to find the probability. If they try this, they may find that their calculator cannot compute this value. $C(900, 415)$ gives an overflow error.

    e. This can be done on a TI-83 using the command binomcdf(900,0.5,415), which gives 0.0107. (The calculator may use the binomial probability formula 416 times to compute the probability of getting exactly 0, 1, 2, 3, …, 413, 414, and 415 successes. Then the calculator adds these probabilities.)

    f. The TI-83 is unable to compute exact binomial probabilities for $n > 999$.
    The TI-83+ is unable to compute exact binomial probabilities for $n > 999{,}999$.

2. **See Teaching Master 111 for Activities 2–5.**

    Technology Note:
    If students have a TI-83, they can find probabilities without first computing a *z*-score. For example, the answer to Part a can be found using the command normalcdf (–999999,11.5,12,2). These values will generally be more exact than those found by using the table. The form of the TI-83 command is normalcdf(lower limit,upper limit,mean,standard deviation). If students compute *z*-scores and then use the calculator rather than the standardized tables, the command is normalcdf(lower limit,z-score) or normalcdf(z-score,upper limit).

Master 111

    a. ■ First, the *z*-score is $z = \frac{11.5 - 12}{2} = -0.25$. Looking up this value in the table, you find the probability lies between 0.3821 and 0.4207. The calculator gives a probability of 0.401294. These answers agree with each other. The calculator generally gives more precise answers than does the table. You may wish to have a short discussion of why –999999 is used in the calculator command.

    ■ The value of *z* is 1.5, so, using the table, the probability is about $1 - 0.9332 = 0.0668$.
    normalcdf(1.5,999999) = normalcdf(15,999999,12,2) ≈ 0.066807.

EXPLORE *continued*

b. The value of z is about 0.87, so the probability is **normalcdf(0.87,999999)** ≈ 0.1922 or **normalcdf(463,999999,450,15)** ≈ 0.19306.

c. The values of z are -2.1 and 2.1, so, using the table, the probability is about $0.9821 - 0.0179 = 0.9642$. The TI-83 commands are **normalcdf(-2.1,2.1)** or **normalcdf(39.5,60.5,50,5)** ≈ 0.96427.

3. a. This binomial distribution is closely approximated by a normal distribution with mean 450 and standard deviation 15. The value of z is about -2.3, so, using the table, the probability is about 0.0107. Students can get this probability directly from the calculator: **normalcdf(-999999,-2.3)** ≈ 0.0107.

b. The answers should be approximately the same but may not be exactly equal because the normal distribution is being used to approximate a binomial situation. The choice of technology method also affects the accuracy of the answer.

c. The mean of the distribution is $9{,}000(0.5) = 4{,}500$ and the standard deviation is $\sqrt{9{,}000(0.5)(1 - 0.5)} \approx 47.4342$.

$$z \approx \frac{4{,}450 - 4{,}500}{47.4342} = -1.054$$

Using the table, the probability is approximately 0.1357. **normalcdf(-999999,-1.054)** or **normalcdf(-999999,4450,4500,47.4342)** ≈ 0.1459.

4. a. Using the formulas for a binomial distribution, $\mu = (0.20)(250) = 50$ and $\sigma = \sqrt{250(0.2)(0.8)} \approx 6.3246$.

b. The probability may be approximated using a normal distribution, since $np = 250(0.2) = 50 \geq 10$ and $n(1 - p) = 250(0.8) = 200 \geq 10$. The value of z is about -1.58, and the probability from the table is 0.9452 and from the calculator is about **normalcdf(40,999999,50,6.3246)** ≈ 0.9431.

c. A rare event would be any number more than 2 (or 1.96 for better accuracy) standard deviations from the mean. This is any number less than about $50 - 2(6.3246) = 37.3508$ or greater than about $50 + 2(6.3246) = 62.6492$. Since you can't have a fractional number of children, rare events would be getting 37 or fewer children or 63 or more children.

d. $\mu = p = 0.20$

$$\sigma = \sqrt{\frac{(0.2)(0.8)}{(250)}} \approx 0.0253 \text{ or } \frac{6.3246}{250} \approx 0.0253$$

e. The value of z is $\frac{0.15 - 0.20}{0.0253} \approx -1.98$. The probability is about 0.0228. **normalcdf(-999999,-1.98)** ≈ 0.02385

f. A rare event would be any proportion more than 2 (or 1.96 for better accuracy) standard deviations from the mean. This is any proportion less than about $0.20 - 2(0.0253) = 0.1494$ or greater than $0.20 + 2(0.0253) = 0.2506$.

g. The answers in Part f can be obtained by dividing the answers in Part c by 250, the sample size. The two sets of answers convey the same information but one gives the number of successes and the other the proportion of successes.

EXPLORE *continued*

5. **a.** To get the exact probability, you would have to add up the areas of the flat-topped bars of the binomial distribution. The normal approximation is a smooth curve that fits closely, but not exactly over the binomial distribution. Thus, finding the area under the normal curve isn't exactly the same as finding the areas of the bars. See the sketch in Part d.

b. $P(3 \text{ or fewer heads}) = C(10, 3)(0.5)^3(1 - 0.5)^7 + C(10, 2)(0.5)^2(1 - 0.5)^8 + C(10, 1)(0.5)^1(1 - 0.5)^9 + C(10, 0)(0.5)^0(1 - 0.5)^{10} \approx 0.1719$. Students may use binomcdf(10,0.5,3) to check their calculations.

c. Here, $\sigma = \sqrt{10(0.5)(0.5)} \approx 1.581$, so $z = \frac{3 - 5}{1.581} \approx -1.27$. The probability is about normalcdf(–999999,–1.27) ≈ 0.1020, or normalcdf(–999999,3,5,1.581) ≈ 0.1029.

d. This isn't a very close approximation. You wouldn't expect it to be because the binomial distribution is approximately normal only when $np \geq 10$ and $n(1 - p) \geq 10$. In this case, each value is only 5. Following is the graph of the binomial distribution. A smooth curve cannot do a very good job of approximating it.

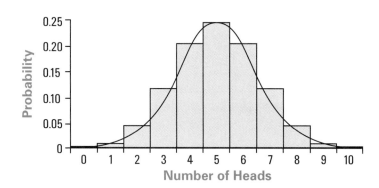

SHARE AND SUMMARIZE   **full-class discussion**

Checkpoint

See Teaching Master 112.

ⓐ One method is to use the binomial probability formula 46 times to compute the probability of getting 55, 56, 57, …, 99, and 100 heads and then add these probabilities, or use the calculator command 1 – binomcdf(100,0.5,54) ≈ 0.1841. A second method is to use the normal approximation to the binomial distribution. Here, you find the area under the normal curve with mean 50 and standard deviation 5 that lies above 55. The first method is exact; the second is an approximation to it. On your calculator, the second method is normalcdf(55,999999,50,5) ≈ 0.1587. Students may also mention simulation as an approximate method.

ⓑ The approximation is reasonably good when $np \geq 10$ and $n(1 - p) \geq 10$.

CONSTRUCTING A MATH TOOLKIT: Students should describe when and how to use the normal approximation to a binomial distribution to find the probability of an event occurring.

Unit 5

APPLY individual task

▶ On Your Own

Note that in Parts a, b, and c, the text refers to the number of times you get doubles. In Parts d and e, it refers to the proportion of times you get doubles.

a. $\mu = \frac{1}{6}(600) = 100$ and $\sigma = \sqrt{600\left(\frac{1}{6}\right)\left(\frac{5}{6}\right)} \approx 9.1287$. The shape is approximately normal since $np = 100$ and $n(1-p) = 500$ are both at least 10.

b. The value of z is about -0.55, so the probability is about
normalcdf(–999999,–0.55) ≈ 0.2912.

c. A rare event would be fewer than $100 - 2(9.1287) \approx 81.74$ doubles or more than $100 + 2(9.1287) \approx 118.26$, that is, rolling 81 or fewer or 119 or more doubles would be a rare event.

d. $\mu = \frac{1}{6}$ and $\sigma = \sqrt{\frac{\left(\frac{1}{6}\right)\left(\frac{5}{6}\right)}{600}} \approx 0.01521$ or $\frac{9.1287}{600} \approx 0.01521$. The shape is approximately normal since $np = 100$ and $n(1-p) = 500$ are both at least 10.

e. The value of z is $\frac{\left(0.2 - \frac{1}{6}\right)}{0.01521} \approx 2.19$, so the probability is about normalcdf(–999999,2.19) $\approx$ 0.9857.

MORE

ASSIGNMENT *pp. 326–329*

Students can now begin Modeling Task 1 Part a or Task 2 Part a; Organizing Task 1, 2, 3, or 4; Reflecting Task 1; or Extending Task 2 or 3 from the MORE following Investigation 2.

EXPLORE small-group investigation

INVESTIGATION ▶ 2 A Test of Significance

Each of the *z*-tests in this investigation can be done two ways, using the number of successes or the proportion of successes. If students use the number of successes in the sample, the approximating normal distribution has mean and standard deviation

$$\mu = np$$
$$\sigma = \sqrt{np(1-p)}$$

If students use the sample proportion $\hat{p}$, the approximating normal distribution has mean and standard deviation

$$\mu = p$$
$$\sigma = \sqrt{\frac{p(1-p)}{n}}$$

Most students will feel more comfortable with the number of successes, but they should practice using both sets of formulas.

1. a. 0.5

EXPLORE *continued*

b. As was found in Activity 1 of Investigation 1, the distribution is approximately normal, with mean 450 and standard deviation 15. A sketch displaying two standard deviations from the mean helps visualize the distribution.

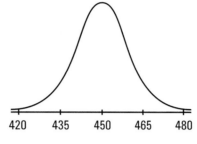

c. 415

420   435   450   465   480

d. As was found in Activity 3 Part a of Investigation 1, the probability of getting 415 or fewer heads is approximately 0.01.

e. The result of 415 heads is in the outer 5% of the distribution, so it is unlikely to occur if the process is fair. Thus, this result cannot reasonably be attributed to chance variation. It is doubtful that spinning a penny is a fair process; it appears to give fewer heads than tails.

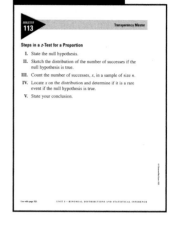

2. **See Teaching Master 113.**

   I. In Part a, you assumed that the probability of heads for a spun penny is 0.5.

   II. In Part b, you described and sketched the distribution of the number of heads for 900 spins if the probability was 0.5.

   III. In Part c, you considered a sample that had 415 heads.

   IV. In Part d, you found the probability of getting 415 or fewer to be approximately 0.01.

   V. In Part e, you reasoned that since 415 heads is unlikely to happen if the probability of getting a head is 0.5, the probability of getting a head isn't 0.5.

3. **a.** The probability that a nickel will come up heads when it is spun is 0.5.

   b. Half of all senior class presidents in the high schools in the United States are boys.

   c. Twenty-six percent of the people who attend action movies are under the age of 18.

   d. The probability that a roll of this pair of dice gives a sum of 7 or a sum of 3 is $\frac{8}{36}$.

4. **I.** The null hypothesis is that 30% of the people who are on juries in this judicial district are college graduates.

   II. If the null hypothesis is true and you examine 1,200 jurors selected at random, the distribution of the number of college graduates would be approximately normal in shape with mean $(1,200)0.3 = 360$ and standard deviation $\sqrt{1,200(0.3)(0.7)} \approx 15.8745$.

   III. The number of college graduates in the sample is 300.

Unit 5

EXPLORE *continued*

IV. If the null hypothesis is true, the number from the sample would have a *z*-score of $\frac{300 - 360}{15.87} \approx -3.78$. This is more than three standard deviations from the mean and thus a rare event. The probability of getting 300 or fewer jurors who are college graduates is **normalcdf(–999999,–3.78)** ≈ 0.00008.

V. If the null hypothesis is true, this is an extremely rare event. Thus, you should doubt that the null hypothesis is in fact true. Reject the null hypothesis and conclude that you should look for some reason other than chance variation why there are so few jurors who are college graduates.

5. **I.** The null hypothesis is that the probability that this penny will land heads up when flipped is 0.5.

II. If the null hypothesis is true, the distribution of the number of heads would be approximately normal with mean $800(0.5) = 400$ and standard deviation $\sqrt{800(0.5)(0.5)} \approx 14.1421$.

III. The number of successes in the sample is 417.

IV. If the null hypothesis is true, the number from the sample would have a *z*-score of $\frac{417 - 400}{14.14} \approx 1.20$. This is less than two standard deviations from the mean and thus would not be considered a rare event. The probability of getting 417 or more heads is **normalcdf(1.20,999999)** ≈ 0.1151.

V. If the null hypothesis is true, the result from the sample is about what you would expect from chance variation alone. There is no evidence to doubt the null hypothesis, so it should not be rejected.

6. **I.** The null hypothesis is that the proportion of babies born from mothers who had suffered a traumatic event is 0.512, the same as in the population at large.

II. If the null hypothesis is true, the distribution of the number of boys in all possible random samples of 3,072 births is approximately normal with mean $3,072(0.512) = 1,572.864$ and standard deviation $\sqrt{3,072(0.512)(1 - 0.512)} \approx 27.7048$.

III. The number of boys was $(0.49)(3,072) = 1,505.28 \approx 1,505$.

IV. If the null hypothesis is true, the *z*-score for 1,505 successes is $z = \frac{1,505 - 1,572.9}{27.7} \approx -2.45$.

V. If the null hypothesis is true, it would be unlikely to get only 1,505 boys. Since this is a rare event, there is reason to doubt the null hypothesis and you should reject it.

7. **a.** The two correct decisions are identified in the chart below.

		Defendant is actually	
		Innocent	Guilty
Decision of	Innocent	Correct	
the jury	Guilty		Correct

b. In the American judicial system, a defendant is considered innocent until proven guilty, so the worst case is to find an innocent defendant guilty.

Unit 5

EXPLORE *continued*

c. The two correct decisions and two errors are shown in the chart below.

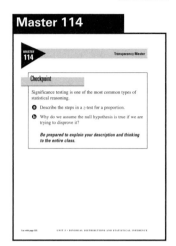

| | | Null hypothesis is actually | |
		True	False
Decision based on the sample	Do Not Reject Null Hypothesis	Correct	Type II Error
	Reject Null Hypothesis	Type I Error	Correct

d. A null hypothesis that is actually true is rejected when a rare event occurs in the sample. For example, suppose you are flipping a coin that is actually fair. If you get only 30 heads out of 100 flips, you would reject the null hypothesis. This is a very, very unlikely result to obtain with a fair coin, but it could happen, and the wrong decision in rejecting the hypothesis that the coin is fair would be made. A true null hypothesis may also be rejected because there may have been some flaw in the study such as not selecting a sample at random or not asking the question clearly.

SHARE AND SUMMARIZE full-class discussion

Checkpoint

See Teaching Master 114.

ⓐ Students should describe the five steps given in this investigation in their own words.

ⓑ In a significance test, there is a statement that is suspected to be false. The statement is assumed to be true and then it is shown that this assumption leads to an event that is so unlikely if the null hypothesis is true that you don't believe it could happen by chance variation. This casts doubt on the null hypothesis, so it is rejected. This does not prove that the null hypothesis is false, rather it shows that if it is true, a situation that is unlikely to happen has occurred.

(The logic of significance testing is similar to that of proof by contradiction. In proof by contradiction, you want to show that a statement is true. You assume that it is actually false and then show that this assumption leads to a contradiction. This then proves that the original statement must have been true. Euclid's proof that there are infinitely many prime numbers is an example of this type of reasoning.)

CONSTRUCTING A MATH TOOLKIT: Students should record the steps in a *z*-test for a proportion.

APPLY individual task

▶ On Your Own

a. The distribution of the number of students would be approximately normal with mean $750(0.45) = 337.5$ and standard deviation $\sqrt{750(0.45)(0.55)} \approx 13.6244$.

b. **I.** The null hypothesis is the proportion of students who wear a shirt or jacket with a logo or other advertisement on it is 0.45.

II. If the null hypothesis is correct, the distribution of the number of successes from all possible random samples of 750 students is approximately normal with mean 337.5 and standard deviation of about 13.6244.

III. The number of successes in the sample is 359.

IV. If the null hypothesis is true, the z-score for this result is $\frac{359 - 337.5}{13.6244} \approx 1.58$. The probability of getting a random sample with 359 or more students wearing such a shirt, if the null hypothesis is true, is **normalcdf(1.58,999999)** ≈ 0.0571.

V. This is not a rare event if the null hypothesis is true. There is no reason to doubt that the null hypothesis is true, so it should not be rejected.

Since you have not rejected the null hypothesis and it might be false, you may have made a Type II error.

MORE

ASSIGNMENT *pp. 326–329*

Modeling: 1 or 2, and 3 or 4*
Organizing: 3 and choice of one*
Reflecting: 1, 3, and 4
Extending: 1 and choice of one*

When choice is indicated, it is important to leave the choice to the student.
NOTE: *It is best if Organizing tasks are discussed as a whole class after they have been assigned as homework.*

MORE independent assignment

Modeling

1. a. This distribution is approximately normal with mean $1,000(0.10) = 100$ and standard deviation $\sqrt{1,000(0.10)(0.90)} \approx 9.4868$.

b. **I.** The null hypothesis is that the proportion of people between the ages of 18 and 24 in your city is 0.10.

II. Assume the null hypothesis is true. Then the distribution of the number of successes in all possible random samples of size 1,000 is approximately normal with mean 100 and standard deviation about 9.4868.

III. The number of successes in the sample is 117.

IV. If the null hypothesis is true, the z-score for 117 successes is $\frac{117 - 100}{9.4868} \approx 1.79$ and the probability of getting 117 or more people this age is **normalcdf(1.79,999999)** ≈ 0.0367.

V. If the null hypothesis is true, the result from the sample is not a rare event since it isn't in the outer 2.5% of one of the tails of the binomial distribution. Thus, there is no reason to doubt the null hypothesis, so it should not be rejected.

MORE *continued*

c. Numbers of people this age that are more than two standard deviations from the mean are rare events, that is, 81 or fewer or 119 or more.

2. a. The distribution is approximately normal with mean proportion 0.68 and standard deviation $\sqrt{\frac{(0.68)(0.32)}{500}} \approx 0.02086$.

 b. **I.** The null hypothesis is that the proportion of children in your city who live with both parents is 0.68.

 II. If the null hypothesis is true, the distribution of the number of successes in all possible random samples of size 500 is approximately normal with mean $\mu = 500(0.68) = 340$ and $\sigma = \sqrt{500(0.68)(0.32)} \approx 10.43$.

 III. The number of children in the sample who live with both parents is 214.

 IV. If the null hypothesis is true, the z-score for 214 successes is $\frac{214 - 340}{10.4307} \approx -12.08$, and the probability of getting a number this extreme or even more extreme is almost 0.

 V. If the null hypothesis is true, there is almost no chance of getting only 214 children who live with both parents in a random sample of size 500. Since this is such a sample, the null hypothesis should be rejected.

 c. Proportions that are more than two standard deviations from the mean proportion are those that are less than 0.6383 or more than 0.7217.

3. **I.** The null hypothesis is that 75% of the voters approve of the job the President is doing.

 II. If the null hypothesis is true and you consider all possible random samples of 1,200 voters, the distribution of the number who approve is approximately normal, with mean of $0.75(1,200) = 900$ and standard deviation of $\sqrt{1,200(0.75)(0.25)} = 15$.

 III. The number of successes in the sample is $0.73(1,200) = 876$.

 IV. If the null hypothesis is true, the number of successes in the sample would have a z-score of $\frac{876 - 900}{15} \approx -1.6$. A poll would get 876 or fewer people saying they approve of the job the President is doing about 0.0548 of the time.

 V. This is not a rare event if the null hypothesis is true. There is no evidence that the Press Secretary's statement is false. There is no need to retract the statement.

 Since you have not rejected the null hypothesis and it might be false, you may have made a Type II error.

4. **I.** The null hypothesis is that the proportion of babies born by cesarean section in the United States in 2002 is 22%.

 II. If the null hypothesis is true, the distribution of the number of successes in all possible random samples of 1,200 births is approximately normal with mean $1,200(0.22) = 264$ and standard deviation $\sqrt{1,200(0.22)(0.78)} \approx 14.35$.

MORE *continued*

III. The number of babies delivered by cesarean section in the sample is 246.

IV. If the null hypothesis is true, the z-score for 246 successes is $\frac{246 - 264}{14.35} \approx -1.25$, and the probability of getting 246 or fewer babies born by cesarean section is 0.1056.

V. If the null hypothesis is true, there is a 10.56% chance of getting 246 or fewer babies born by cesarean section in a sample of 1,200 babies. Since this is not a rare event, there is no reason to doubt the null hypothesis and it should not be rejected.

Since you have not rejected the null hypothesis and it might be false, you may have made a Type II error.

Organizing

1. If you have the number of successes in the sample x, use the normal distribution with mean $(200)(0.25) = 50$ and standard deviation $\sqrt{200(0.25)(0.75)} \approx 6.1237$. If you have the proportion $\hat{p}$ of successes in the sample, use the normal distribution with mean 0.25 and standard deviation

$$\sqrt{\frac{(0.25)(1 - 0.25)}{200}} \approx 0.0306.$$

2. With n trials and probability of success p and using the normal approximation to the binomial, the outer 5% of the binomial distribution are numbers of successes more than about 2 standard deviations from the mean. This is a number of successes larger than

$$np + 2\sqrt{np(1 - p)}$$

or smaller than

$$np - 2\sqrt{np(1 - p)}$$

In terms of the proportion of successes, the outer 5% are proportions larger than

$$p + 2\sqrt{\frac{p(1 - p)}{n}}$$

or smaller than

$$p - 2\sqrt{\frac{p(1 - p)}{n}}$$

3. **a.** When the process is under control, the mean number of broken chips is $150(0.08) = 12$, with a standard deviation of $\sqrt{150(0.08)(0.92)} \approx 3.3226$. The mean of the control chart should be at 12 and the lines dividing the zones occur at 2.0322, 5.3548, 8.6774, 12, 15.3226, 18.6452, and 21.9678.

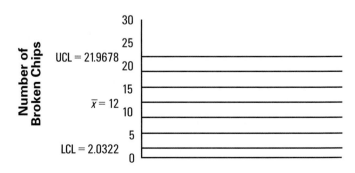

MORE *continued*

b. Three standard deviations below the mean is 2.0322 and three standard deviations above the mean is 21.9678, so the process should be stopped if the number of broken chips is either 2 or fewer, or 22 or more. (If there are 22 broken chips or more, the process is stopped to see what has gone wrong. If there are 2 broken chips or fewer, the process is examined to see what has gone right!)

4. Responses will vary. Continuous distributions that students have seen include people's weights, heights, hand spans, and political opinions, and weights of milk cartons. In each case, the value can be any real number within a certain range. Discrete distributions that students have seen include the geometric distribution (number of children born before a boy, number of times dice rolled before doubles occurs, and so on), the number of people in a family, and the number of games played in the World Series.

Reflecting

1. No, the approximation is better with larger sample sizes and with values of p closer to 0.5. Here "better" means that a normal curve fits more closely over the top of the binomial distribution.

2. A hypothesis is a conjecture that you want to test to see if it is true or false. The word "null" means "nothing." This is a good choice because the "null hypothesis" is a conjecture that nothing unusual is going on or that the usual situation continues.

3. No, it is not the same thing. For example, suppose you do a significance test that the probability a flipped penny lands heads is 0.5. From the result of the sample, you are unable to reject this null hypothesis. That means the result from the sample is close enough to 0.5 that you believe it reasonably could have resulted from a fair process. Saying that it is reasonable to assume that the probability is 0.5 isn't the same thing as saying that the probability is exactly 0.5 (which undoubtedly isn't exactly true for any individual penny).

4. Make the situation even more extreme. Suppose you are handed a coin and you flip it 10,000 times and get no heads at all. Would any reasonable person believe the coin was fair? Certainly not. However, it could have happened with a fair coin. Unfortunately, in a binomial situation any given event is always possible, so in statistical reasoning you must rely on your judgment of what is reasonably likely to occur.

Unit 5

MORE *continued*

Extending

NOTE: The probability given on the TI-83 is the probability of getting a z-score of –2.333 or smaller or a z-score of 2.333 or higher. So you would reject the null hypothesis if p is less than 0.05.

1. a. 1-PropZTest   is the name of the test. You are using a z-score to test a hypothesis about a single proportion.

prop ≠ .5   is the statement of your conclusion if you reject the null hypothesis.

$z = -2.333333333$ is the z-score from the formula $z = \dfrac{415 - 900(0.5)}{\sqrt{900(0.5)(1-0.5)}}$.

$p = .0196306137$ is the probability of getting a z-score as extreme as -2.333333333 if the null hypothesis is true. Since this is less than 0.05, you should reject the null hypothesis.

$\hat{p} = .4611111111$ is the proportion of successes in the sample, $\dfrac{415}{900}$.

$n = 900$ is the sample size.

b.

```
1-PropZTest
 prop ≠ .08
 z=3.616588191
 p=2.9858358ᴇ-4
 p̂=.1053333333
 n=1500
```

The z-score identifies the result from the sample as a rare event if the null hypothesis that 8% of people are left-handed is true. Thus, you should reject the null hypothesis. If only 8% of people are left-handed, getting 158 left-handed people in a random sample of 1,500 people would be very unusual.

2. Since the mean of the binomial distribution is $100(0.40) = 40$ and the standard deviation is $\sqrt{100(0.4)(0.6)} \approx 4.9$, graph the equation $y = \dfrac{1}{4.92\sqrt{\pi}}\, e^{-\left(\frac{x-40}{4.9}\right)^2}$.

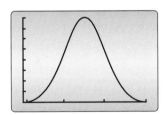

When thinking about the window, use the fact that the graph will be centered at 40 and that the middle 99.7% of values will be from approximately $40 - 3(4.9) = 25.3$ to approximately $40 + 3(4.9) = 54.7$. To set the vertical window, you could use a table of values or otherwise evaluate the value of the function when $x = 40$.

MORE *continued*

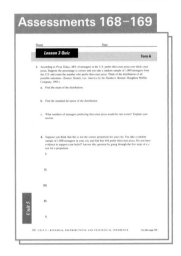

3. a. To answer this question, determine the probability of getting 10% or more defective in a sample of size 200 from a population with 15% defective. The mean of the binomial distribution for the number of defectives in samples of size 200 from this population is $200(0.15) = 30$ and the standard deviation is $\sqrt{200(0.15)(0.85)} \approx 5.0497$. Thus, the probability of getting a z-value of $\frac{20 - 30}{5.0497} = -1.98$ or greater needs to be determined. This probability is **normalcdf(–1.98,999999)** = 0.9761. The company is very likely to reject the shipment (as it should).

b. This problem requires finding the probability of getting 10% or more defective in a sample of size 200 from a population with 8% defective. The mean of the binomial distribution for the number of defectives in samples of size 200 from this population is $200(0.08) = 16$ with a standard deviation of about $\sqrt{200(0.08)(0.92)} = 3.8367$. Thus, the probability of getting a z-value of $\frac{20 - 16}{3.8367} = 1.04$ or greater is needed. This probability of rejecting the shipment if it actually contains 8% rubber bands that break is **normalcdf(1.04,999999)** = 0.1492 or about 15%.

See Assessment Resources pages 168–171.

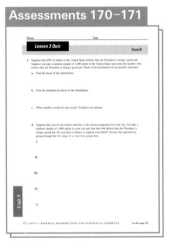

REVIEW AND PRACTICE individual task

▶**PUMP**

Answers

1. (a)	6. (c)
2. (d)	7. (e)
3. (a)	8. (d)
4. (c)	9. (b)
5. (e)	10. (c)

Unit 5

Master 115

Think About This Situation

Joseph Lister (1827–1912), surgeon at the Glasgow Royal Infirmary, was one of the first to believe in the theory of Louis Pasteur (1822–1895) that germs cause infection. In an early medical experiment, Lister disinfected the operating room with carbolic acid before 40 operations. He did not disinfect the operating room before another 35 operations. Of the 40 operations in which carbolic acid was used, 34 patients lived. Of the 35 operations in which carbolic acid was not used, 19 patients lived.

a Why did Joseph Lister need to have one group of patients for whom he didn't disinfect the operating room?

b Does the study above provide convincing evidence that disinfecting operating rooms with carbolic acid results in fewer deaths than not disinfecting? Explain your thinking.

c How is the Lister experiment similar to, and different from, experiments you have conducted in your science classes?

Use with page 332.   UNIT 5 • BINOMIAL DISTRIBUTIONS AND STATISTICAL INFERENCE

Lesson **4** *Experiments: Proving Cause and Effect*

LESSON OVERVIEW   If you want to prove that one thing *causes* another, the only way to do it is with a controlled randomized experiment. In this lesson, students will learn how to design a good experiment and how to use significance tests to determine if one treatment is more effective than another.

Lesson Objectives

- To distinguish between an experiment, a survey, and an observational study
- To know the characteristics of a well-designed experiment
- To understand the importance of subject and evaluator blinding and the placebo effect
- To apply a randomization test to see if the results of an experiment are statistically significant
- To perform a *z*-test for the difference of two proportions in an experiment

SHARE AND SUMMARIZE   full-class discussion

Think About This Situation

See Teaching Master 115.

a Otherwise, he could not demonstrate that using carbolic acid caused a reduction in the death rate.

b Most students will believe that the difference in success rates (85% vs. 54%) is statistically significant. Students will see in Investigation 2 that their intuition is correct. It is almost impossible to get a difference of 85% − 54% = 31% in success rates just by chance. Thus, you should look for an explanation other than chance variation. Perhaps carbolic acid is that explanation. However, first you need to know whether the people who got carbolic acid were selected randomly from the 75 patients. If, for example, Lister did the 35 operations without carbolic acid, noted his low success rate, and then started using carbolic acid, you wouldn't know if his higher success rate in the later operations was due to the carbolic acid or his additional experience as a surgeon.

NOTE: Lister gave a speech in 1876 in Philadelphia about the importance of antiseptics which was heard by Missouri physician Joseph Lawrence, who went back to his laboratory and developed an antibacterial liquid which he called Listerine®.

Unit 5

SHARE AND SUMMARIZE *continued*

(At the time of Lister's experiment, about half of operations ended in the death of the patient several days later from infection. Some types of operations are less dangerous than others so, it would be best to do a study like this with one particular type of surgery. In fact, Lister's operations were all of the same type—amputations. You can be fairly certain that Lister did not conduct his experiment in a way that would be acceptable today either scientifically or ethically.)

c Responses will vary based upon students' experiences in science classes.

The information in the student text about Joseph Lister comes from the following source: Richard J. Larsen and Donna Fox Stroup. *Statistics in the Real World: A Book of Examples.* **New York: Macmillan, 1976, pp. 205–207. Further information can be found in the following book:** *The Conquest of Disease* **Charles-Edward A. Winslow. Madison: University of Wisconsin Press, 1980.**

EXPLORE small-group investigation

INVESTIGATION 1 Characteristics of Experiments

In this investigation, students will learn the differences between an observational study, a survey, and a true experiment. They will learn how to design a good experiment and develop an understanding of the importance of subject and evaluator blinding, the placebo effect, and lurking variables.

1. **a.** The cause is microwave zapping and the effect is sprouting.

   b. Carlos doesn't know the rate of sprouting of mung bean seeds that aren't zapped. That rate could be even higher than 80%.

   c. The "nicest-looking" mung bean seeds may have been the healthiest and so more likely to sprout with or without the zapping. In fact, the zapping may have made them *less* likely to sprout and Mia wouldn't know that.

   d. Joann doesn't know if it was the zapping that caused the one seed to sprout or whether that particular seed was healthier.

   e. Take as large a quantity of mung bean seeds as practical. Randomly divide them into two groups, preferably by using a random digit table. Zap the ones in one group and don't zap the ones in the second group. Plant them, again randomly deciding which seed gets planted where (but keeping track of which got zapped and which didn't), treat them all alike with respect to watering, quality of soil, amount of light, amount of fertilizer, temperature, and so on, and then count the number in each group that sprouted.

NOTE: A statistician would probably use blocking to determine where the plants were placed. This means that the good spots and the bad spots should be balanced among the two groups of seeds.

Unit 5

EXPLORE *continued*

2. **a.** Comparison or control group

   b. Random assignment

   c. Replication

3. **a.** This was an experiment if operating rooms treated or not treated with carbolic acid were randomly assigned to the subjects. Otherwise, it was an observational study.

   b. This was a sample survey if the people were randomly selected from the larger populations of people with and without lung cancer. Otherwise, it was an observational study.

   c. Gallup polls are sample surveys.

4. **Your students may not be familiar with polio. Here is some background information you may wish to share with them, or you may want to encourage them to research this topic on the Internet. (Sources: *World Book Encyclopedia*, various Web sites.)**

   Polio (or poliomyelitis) is an acute viral infection that can invade the nervous system and cause paralysis. Before a vaccine was developed, most victims were children, although adults were affected as well. Two famous people who contracted polio and suffered paralysis that prevented them from walking again without assistance are President Franklin D. Roosevelt (1882–1945) and the violinist Itzhak Perlman (1945–). A great success story of modern medicine is the eradication of this much-feared disease as the result of childhood vaccination. The first effective vaccine was developed by Jonas Salk (1914–1995). An oral vaccine developed by Albert Sabin (1906–1993) was approved soon afterward.

   a. This difficulty meant that replication on a large number of children was necessary. If a small group was used, there might not have been any polio cases even in the placebo group. (This is explored further in Modeling Task 3.)

   b. If the vaccine was expected to be 100% effective, the researchers would not have needed a control group. They would need only to give the vaccine to a very large number of children. If there were no cases of polio in that group, they would be sure the vaccine worked. (This assumes that polio can be diagnosed with certainty.) However, since this wasn't the case and the vaccine was expected to reduce the incidence of polio but not eliminate it, a control group was needed.

   c. Like most infectious diseases, the incidence of polio varied widely from year to year. This made it impossible to use the unvaccinated children from the previous year as controls. Thus, the researchers had to have a control group among the children that same year, randomly assigning the children to the two treatments.

EXPLORE *continued*

d. This difficulty explains why random assignment was necessary. Without random assignment, the children more likely to get polio would have been in the vaccine group and the children less likely to get polio would have been in the placebo group. The worst thing that might have happened would have been for the affluent children to be given the vaccine and still have higher rates of polio than the less affluent children who did not receive the vaccine, even though the vaccine was effective in reducing the rate of polio in each group. (This is explored further in Extending Task 1.)

NOTE: Even before the availability of a polio vaccine, polio was virtually unknown in countries with poor hygiene. In these countries, it is thought that the virus was common, in fact so common that virtually everyone got it as an infant while still having some protection from the mother's immunity. Thus, everyone established his or her own immunity by getting the disease in a very mild form.

5. a. A doctor would be less likely to diagnose polio in a borderline case if he or she knew the child had been vaccinated and more likely to diagnose polio if the child had not been vaccinated. (This is reasonable because if the vaccine had not been expected to work, such a large experiment couldn't have been carried out!) However, this bias would invalidate the experiment. It would result in a smaller proportion of diagnosed polio cases in the vaccinated group than there should have been and a higher proportion of cases in the placebo group, making the vaccine look better than it was.

NOTE: In the Salk experiment, only a code number identified each vial as the vaccine or the placebo, so no one close to the child or the doctor knew which children received the vaccine and which received the placebo.

b. This experiment may have been subject blind if the patients weren't told about the experiment and couldn't smell the carbolic acid. Presumably, the surgeon would have to know as his or her hands would have been washed with carbolic acid. It wasn't necessary for this experiment to be evaluator blind since the only decision to be made was whether or not the person died.

6. a. The Salk experiment controlled for the placebo effect by randomly assigning the vaccine or the placebo to the children and not letting them know which they received. Since the children didn't know whether they received the vaccine or not, any placebo effect from receiving special medical treatment should have been spread evenly over both groups.

b. The placebo effect was probably not a consideration since the patients probably didn't know which treatment they received.

Unit 5

EXPLORE *continued*

7. **a.** One lurking variable might be whether or not the older person is health conscious and follows a healthy lifestyle. Such a person would be more likely to take vitamins. He or she also would be more likely to do other things, such as exercise, that might result in higher cognitive performance.

   Another lurking variable might be access of the older person to medical care. An older person who has access to medical care may have been prescribed vitamins. He or she may also be more likely to be treated for medical conditions that might impair cognitive performance.

   To determine if vitamin B supplements cause higher cognitive performance, you would have to randomly divide a group of older people into a group that receives vitamin B supplements and a group that receives a placebo. After a suitable length of time, you would test each subject's cognitive performance.

   b. Younger, inexperienced drivers tend to drive smaller cars than older people and younger drivers tend to be in more accidents. The article says that "there is some truth there, but not enough to explain small cars' out-of-proportion deaths."

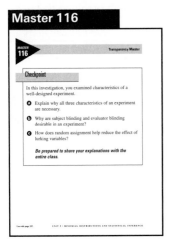

Master 116

c. The journal indicates that extra income and social support may be responsible for the association between working mothers and good health. An alternative explanation for this finding is that women who aren't already in good health would be unable to be a "Supermom," that is, it's the good health that causes the activity, rather than the activity causing the good health.

SHARE AND SUMMARIZE   full-class discussion

Checkpoint

See Teaching Master 116.

ⓐ Replication is necessary so that you have enough subjects to determine whether a difference can reasonably be attributed to chance or whether you should attribute it to the treatment. A small or moderate difference, even if real, won't be statistically significant if the number of subjects is small. A control or comparison group is needed so that you know if the treatment in which you are interested works better than another and so that you can eliminate the placebo effect as the cause of any improvement. Random assignment is needed as it is the best way to "average out" any characteristics of the subjects (lurking variables) that might affect the results and obscure the effect of the treatments.

ⓑ If people expect something to work, it is more likely to work (the placebo effect). Thus, if you want to separate people's expectations from the actual effect of the treatment, if possible, you should not let them know which treatment they are getting or evaluating.

c As indicated in Part a, random assignment helps to distribute any characteristics of the subjects (lurking variables) that might affect the results.

APPLY individual task

▶**On Your Own**

a. This is an observational study, since students weren't assigned randomly to the type of exam. This study isn't subject blind since the first period students, especially, may have noticed that their exam was different from the usual type. It isn't evaluator blind since the teacher graded the problems herself. One lurking variable might be period of the day. Perhaps first-period students are more (or less) alert. Perhaps one particular group of students must enroll in that class during first (or second) period to avoid conflict with band practice. A final lurking variable may be that students who had the harder questions first simply ran out of time and were unable to complete as many questions.

b. The teacher should do two things: First, she should distribute the two types of exams randomly in both periods. Second, she should have the exams graded by someone who doesn't know what she is trying to prove.

MORE

ASSIGNMENT *pp. 344–351*

Students can now begin Modeling Task 1 Part a or Task 2 Part a, or Reflecting Task 2 or 3 from the MORE assignment following Investigation 2. (Reflecting Task 3 is not part of the suggested assignment, but is a good problem for your students to do if there is time.)

EXPLORE small-group investigation

INVESTIGATION 2 ▸ Do Two Treatments Give Different Results?

In this investigation, students will learn how to perform significance tests to determine if one treatment is more effective than another. The randomization test developed in Activity 1 of this investigation is due to R. A. Fisher, perhaps the greatest statistician of all time. Fisher first described it in his 1935 book *The Design of Experiments* in the context of an agricultural experiment. (The 8th edition of this book was published in 1966 by Macmillan.) The advantage of the randomization test is that no assumptions of normality or minimum sample sizes are needed—only that treatments are assigned randomly to subjects. The far more well-known *z*-test (summarized between Activity 3 and Activity 4) can be considered an approximation to the randomization test. Such an approximation was necessary until recently because computers weren't powerful enough to do randomization tests.

1. a. Supposing that treatment with carbolic acid makes no difference at all, the same people who lived would have lived whether or not Lister disinfected the operating room using carbolic acid before their operation. There were a total of $34 + 19 = 53$ who would have lived if he had used carbolic acid before all operations and 53 who would have lived if he hadn't used carbolic acid before any of the operations.

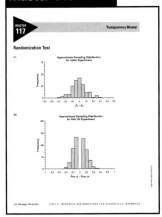

Master 117

EXPLORE *continued*

b. Each group of students should have a bag containing 53 red beads (or counters) and 22 blue beads (or counters) that are exactly the same size as the red ones.

    Results will vary. For example, suppose 35 of the first 40 beads are red and 18 of the remaining 35 beads are red. Then $\hat{p}_c - \hat{p}_n = \frac{35}{40} - \frac{18}{35} \approx 0.361$.

c. **See Teaching Master 117.**
Divide the work up among the groups in your class.

d. For Lister's experiment, $\hat{p}_c - \hat{p}_n = \frac{34}{40} - \frac{19}{35} \approx 0.307$.

e. Lister's result would be an extremely rare event. Note that only one difference this large occurred in the distribution in Part c. Students should conclude that the difference in the proportions is probably not due to the chance assignment of treatments to patients, but rather to the use of carbolic acid.

f. A Type I error may have been made since it's possible that the differences were in fact just due to chance variation and not to the use of carbolic acid. (Additional studies have shown that this is not a Type I error since the efficacy of disinfecting an operating room has been well established.) This is not a Type II error since a Type II error occurs when a null hypothesis is not rejected when it is false.

2. a. The distribution is approximately normal.

b. The mean is close to 0. Theoretically, the mean difference, $\hat{p}_c - \hat{p}_n$, should be exactly 0. This is because this simulation assumes that the use or non-use of carbolic acid makes no difference.

c. The two sample sizes are 40 and 35. The proportion of all patients who survived is $p = \frac{34 + 19}{40 + 35} = \frac{53}{75} \approx 0.707$. Thus, the standard deviation is

$$\sigma = \sqrt{p(1-p)\left(\frac{1}{n_1} + \frac{1}{n_2}\right)}$$
$$= \sqrt{0.707(1-0.707)\left(\frac{1}{40} + \frac{1}{35}\right)}$$
$$\approx 0.105$$

d. Since the distribution is approximately normal, rare events are those more than two standard deviations from the mean of 0. That is, rare events are values smaller than $0 - 2(0.105) = -0.210$ and larger than $0 + 2(0.105) = 0.210$.

EXPLORE *continued*

e. You should look for some other explanation. A difference as large as 0.307 is unlikely to occur if the treatment makes no difference. Here is the logic: The null hypothesis is that carbolic acid makes no difference. Any difference that Lister got in the proportion of patients who survived is simply due to the way treatments were assigned. It is assumed that he did that assignment randomly. Repeating the process of randomly assigning treatments to patients 200 times produced only one occurrence where $\hat{p}_c - \hat{p}_n$ was as large as Lister's difference. (Alternatively, students can use the fact that this distribution is approximately normal and see that a difference of 0.307 is a rare event if the null hypothesis is true.) Thus, it does not seem that his difference is due to the fact that, just by luck, more patients who were going to survive anyway happened to end up in the treatment group that got carbolic acid. It is reasonable to believe that carbolic acid caused a larger proportion of patients to survive.

3. The second conclusion is the best one to draw. The first statement makes an inference to the larger population of patients and you can't be sure that the patients in the study were representative of all patients.

4. a. The null hypothesis is that the difference in the proportion of patients who relapsed was due to the fact that fewer patients who were going to relapse anyway happened to be assigned to the fish oil treatment, not to any beneficial effect of fish oil.

   b. No, there are only 2 relapses in the fish oil treatment group, and the rule for using the *z*-test for the difference of two proportions says at least 5 are needed in every category.

   c. To perform the test, place 13 red beads (representing patients who relapsed) and 22 blue beads (representing patients who didn't relapse) in a bag. Draw out 15 to represent the patients who got fish oil. Compute $\hat{p}_1$, the proportion of beads that are red (relapsed). The remaining 20 beads in the bag will represent the patients who got olive oil. Compute $\hat{p}_2$, the proportion that are red (relapsed). Compute $\hat{p}_1 - \hat{p}_2$. Repeat this at least several hundred times.

   Again, observe that this distribution reflects the possibilities if it makes no difference whatsoever if the patient received fish oil or olive oil. Some will relapse anyway, and they are just as likely to be assigned to either group.

   The actual value of $\hat{p}_1 - \hat{p}_2$ is $\frac{2}{15} - \frac{11}{20} \approx -0.417$. Determine if -0.417 is a rare event if it is true that the treatment makes no difference.

   d. **See Teaching Master 117.**

   Results will vary for the one trial. The actual value from the experiment of $\hat{p}_1 - \hat{p}_2$ is -0.417. A difference this large or larger happened fewer than 10 times out of 500, so you have two choices: either a rare event occurred or the null hypothesis isn't true. You conclude that the null hypothesis should be rejected. The fish oil appears to cause fewer relapses.

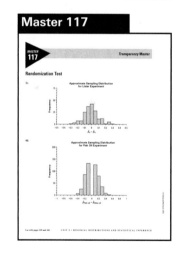

Master 117

Unit 5

EXPLORE *continued*

e. Let x be the number in the fish oil group who relapse. Then, to get a difference $\hat{p}_1 - \hat{p}_2$ near 0, you need

$$\frac{x}{15} - \frac{13-x}{20} \approx 0$$

$$x \approx 5.57$$

Since x must be an integer, try $x = 5$ and $x = 6$:

$$\frac{5}{15} - \frac{8}{20} = -0.067$$

$$\frac{6}{15} - \frac{7}{20} = 0.05$$

Thus, there can be no value of $\hat{p}_1 - \hat{p}_2$ in the interval $(-0.067, 0.05)$, leaving a hole in the histogram between -0.05 and 0.05.

NOTE: The results of this preliminary study were so encouraging that it was halted early and the National Institutes of Health began a three-year study of the treatment.

NOTE: You may want to remind students occasionally that if a result is *statistically* significant, this is not the same thing as saying the difference in the two proportions is of any *practical* significance.

5. You can use the z-test for the difference between two proportions since the number of successes and number of failures in each group is 5 or more. If the null hypothesis is true, the distribution of the difference of proportions in the two treatment groups has mean 0 and standard deviation $\sqrt{(0.572)(0.428)\left(\frac{2}{250}\right)} \approx 0.0443$. Since the difference of $\frac{156}{250} - \frac{130}{250} = 0.624 - 0.52 = 0.104$, has a z-score of 2.350, the difference cannot reasonably be attributed to chance variation.

6. a. Sample survey

You conclude that the proportion of all blueberry eaters who have stained teeth is not equal to the proportion of those who don't eat blueberries who have stained teeth. Specifically, blueberry eaters are more likely to have stained teeth. Blueberry eating and stained teeth are associated, but you don't know the reason. You cannot conclude that eating blueberries *causes* stained teeth since perhaps blueberry eaters also tend to eat more raspberries and it's the raspberries that cause stained teeth.

b. Experiment

You can conclude that, in this group of subjects, eating blueberries caused a greater proportion of teeth to be stained.

c. Observational study

All you can conclude is that among this dentist's patients, a larger proportion of blueberry eaters had stained teeth than did those who don't eat blueberries.

SHARE AND SUMMARIZE full-class discussion

Checkpoint

See Teaching Master 118.

a The null hypothesis is that the treatments are equally effective; any difference in results was just due to the fact that subjects who were "successes" happened to be randomly assigned more often to one group than another. Count the total number of successes in both groups. Get this number of red beads. Count the total number of failures in both groups. Get this number of blue beads. Mix the red and blue beads in a bag. Draw out the same number of beads as there were subjects in the first treatment group. Let $\hat{p}_1$ be the proportion of red beads in this sample. The beads remaining in the bag represent the subjects who were in the second treatment group. Let $\hat{p}_2$ be the proportion of red beads in this sample. Compute $\hat{p}_1 - \hat{p}_2$.

Repeat this procedure until you have at least several hundred values of $\hat{p}_1 - \hat{p}_2$. Display these values on a histogram. Determine if the actual difference from the sample would be a rare event. If so, reject the null hypothesis and decide that the treatment caused an increase in the proportion of successful results. If not, do not reject the null hypothesis and conclude that the difference between the two treatments is no greater than you would expect if the treatments had exactly the same results.

b Students should state the four steps that can be found in the box between Activities 3 and 4 in their own words.

c This is another way of saying that you reject the null hypothesis. Specifically, it means that the difference in the percentage of "successes" in the two groups cannot reasonably be attributed to chance variation; that is, if it makes no difference which treatment a subject receives, it would be unlikely to get a difference in the percentage of "successes" between the two groups that is as large as that from the experiment.

APPLY individual task

On Your Own

a. The null hypothesis is that the difference in the proportions of children who got polio is due to chance variation; that is, the vaccine has no effect. The difference in the proportions is about $0.00041 - 0.00081 = -0.0004$. If the null hypothesis is true, the sampling distribution for the difference $\hat{p}_1 - \hat{p}_2$ is approximately normal with mean 0 and standard deviation about 0.000078. The difference between the treatment groups, $\hat{p}_1 - \hat{p}_2 = -0.0004$, is more than five standard deviations from the mean. Thus, reject the null hypothesis and conclude that the difference in the proportions of children who got polio was caused by the vaccine.

APPLY *continued*

b. A Type I error could have been made since there is some possibility that the null hypothesis is actually true. However, in hindsight it is clear that the vaccine does work and thus no error occurred in rejecting the null hypothesis. This is not a Type II error since a Type II error occurs when a null hypothesis is not rejected when it is false.

MORE

ASSIGNMENT *pp. 344–351*

Modeling: 1, 3, and 2 or 4*
Organizing: 1 and 3
Reflecting: 2 and 4
Extending: 1 and 2

*When choice is indicated, it is important to leave the choice to the student.
NOTE: *It is best if Organizing tasks are discussed as a whole class after they have been assigned as homework.*

MORE independent assignment

Modeling

1. **a.** A well-designed experiment should have had the following characteristics: The 480 cuttings should have been divided into the long and short groups randomly. Then the plants should have been planted in a random fashion so that if some locations were more advantageous than others, not all plants of one length would end up there. (Actually, some sort of blocking would be best.) In addition, the person who was cutting the plants and the person who determined if they were dead should have been told as little as possible about the purpose of the experiment.

   b. The null hypothesis is that the difference between the proportion of the cuttings that were cut long and died, $\frac{84}{240}$, and the proportion of those cut short and died, $\frac{133}{240}$, is not due to how the cuttings were cut. Instead, it is due to the fact that the experimenter just by chance got more of the ones that were going to die anyway in the group that was cut short. To perform the test, place 217 red beads (representing cuttings that die) and 263 blue beads (representing cuttings that survive) in a bag. Draw out 240 to represent the cuttings that will be cut long. Compute $\hat{p}_1$, the proportion of beads that are red (died). The remaining 240 beads in the bag will represent the cuttings that will be cut short. Compute $\hat{p}_2$, the proportion that are red (died). Compute $\hat{p}_1 - \hat{p}_2$. Repeat this at least several hundred times, placing the results in a histogram.

   Again, observe that this distribution reflects the possibilities if it makes no difference whatsoever if the cuttings are cut short or long. Some will die anyway, and they are just as likely to be assigned to one group as the other.

   The actual value of $\hat{p}_1 - \hat{p}_2$ is $\frac{84}{240} - \frac{133}{240} \approx -0.204$. Look at the histogram and determine if 0.204 is a rare event if it is true that the treatment makes no difference. If it is, the null hypothesis should be rejected.

MORE *continued*

c. The distribution of the difference of proportions has mean 0 and standard deviation $\sqrt{\frac{217}{480}\left(1 - \frac{217}{480}\right)\left(\frac{2}{240}\right)} \approx 0.0454$. The difference of $\frac{84}{240} - \frac{133}{240} \approx -0.204$ is about 4.5 standard deviations below 0. The difference is statistically significant. The conclusion is that the difference in the proportion that lived and the proportion that died must be due to the length of the root cuttings rather than due to the random assignment of treatments to cuttings. It was best to make them long.

d. This experiment probably could not have been evaluator blind because the person who evaluated whether the cutting was alive or dead was most likely able to see if it was long or short.

2. a. This must have been an observational study. It certainly was not an experiment as the conditions being compared were male and female, which were not assigned randomly to subjects. It is unlikely to have been a sample survey as the men and women weren't selected at random.

b. The standard deviation of the difference of proportions is $\sqrt{\frac{670}{2,623}\left(1 - \frac{670}{2,623}\right)\left(\frac{1}{1,320} + \frac{1}{1,303}\right)} \approx 0.017$. The difference of $\frac{370}{1,320} - \frac{300}{1,303} \approx 0.050$ is 2.94 standard deviations above the mean of 0. It cannot reasonably be attributed to chance variation.

c. One possibility is that women are more likely to be carrying babies or objects such as purses and diaper bags, which would make it more difficult for them to help. Another possible lurking variable is the gender of the researcher. People may be more (or less) likely to help someone of their own gender.

d. The association given in this table cannot reasonably be attributed to chance variation. Thus, another explanation should be considered. One explanation is that men are more helpful than women. However, since this is not an experiment, there are several lurking variables that might provide the explanation instead.

3. a. $0.0005(40,000) = 20$ children in the placebo group would be expected to get polio. Half of 20 or 10 children in the vaccine group would be expected to get polio.

b. The standard deviation of the difference in proportions is $\sqrt{\frac{30}{80,000}\left(1 - \frac{30}{80,000}\right)\left(\frac{2}{40,000}\right)} \approx 0.000137$. In this situation, the difference of $\frac{20}{40,000} - \frac{10}{40,000} = 0.00025$ is only about 1.82 standard deviations above the mean of 0.

Therefore, you should not reject the null hypothesis that the difference in the rates of polio is due to the fact that children less likely to get polio happened to be selected for the group that got the vaccine.

MORE *continued*

c. The null hypothesis is actually false because the vaccine works. This situation would have resulted in a Type II error. This is not a Type I error because a Type I error is rejecting a null hypothesis that is actually true.

d. 50; 25

e. The standard deviation of the difference in proportions is
$$\sqrt{\frac{75}{200,000}\left(1 - \frac{75}{200,000}\right)\left(\frac{2}{100,000}\right)} \approx 0.000061.$$ The difference in the actual proportions is $\frac{50}{100,000} - \frac{25}{100,000} = 0.00025$. This time the z-score is about 4.10, so the null hypothesis should be rejected. The difference in the proportions who got polio can not reasonably be attributed to the fact that the children who received the vaccine were less likely to get polio.

f. The null hypothesis is actually false. Neither type of error was made, as the conclusion was correct.

g. With relatively small sample sizes, there is more variation in the values of $\hat{p}_1$ and $\hat{p}_2$. This means there is larger variation in the value of $\hat{p}_1 - \hat{p}_2$, even if the null hypothesis is true. Thus, it takes a larger difference before you can trust that the variation you observe isn't just due to the small sample sizes.

4. a. All but dizziness and indigestion have 5 or more people in both the "success" (got the side effect) group and the "failure" group, and thus meet the criteria for performing a z-test of the difference of two proportions.

b. Assuming any difference is due to chance variation, the sampling distribution of $\hat{p}_1 - \hat{p}_2$ is approximately normal with mean 0 and standard deviation about 0.008. The difference of 2.5% − 1.5% = 1% can reasonably be attributed to chance variation rather than a difference of treatments. (The z-score is about 1.3.)

Organizing

1. a. When the number of subjects is quadrupled, the standard deviation is cut in half. Let the quadrupled sample sizes be represented by $4n_1$ and $4n_2$. Then the standard deviation is
$$\sqrt{p(1-p)\left(\frac{1}{4n_1} + \frac{1}{4n_2}\right)} = \sqrt{p(1-p)\frac{1}{4}\left(\frac{1}{n_1} + \frac{1}{n_2}\right)} = \frac{1}{2}\sqrt{p(1-p)\left(\frac{1}{n_1} + \frac{1}{n_2}\right)}$$

MORE *continued*

b. As p moves away from 0.5, the standard deviation becomes smaller. The only part of the formula that changes is $p(1 - p)$. Consider the function $y = p(1 - p) = p - p^2$ or $-p^2 + p$. Its graph is a parabola that opens down. Thus, the maximum value occurs at the vertex, which is at $x = -\frac{b}{2a} = -\frac{1}{2(-1)} = 0.5$.

2. $\sqrt{p - (1 - p)\left(\frac{1}{n_1} + \frac{1}{n_2}\right)} = \sqrt{p(1 - p)\left(\frac{1}{n} + \frac{1}{n}\right)} = \sqrt{p(1 - p)\left(\frac{2}{n}\right)} = \sqrt{\frac{2p(1 - p)}{n}}$

3. You are more likely to reject a false null hypothesis with large sample sizes. All else being equal, the standard deviation is smaller when the sample sizes are larger. This may be easiest to see by rewriting the standard deviation as follows:

$$\sqrt{p(1 - p)\left(\frac{1}{n_1} + \frac{1}{n_2}\right)} = \sqrt{\frac{p(1 - p)}{n_1} + \frac{p(1 - p)}{n_2}}$$

The sample sizes are in the denominators of the fractions, so as they increase, the values of the fractions decrease. Thus, their sum decreases and so does the square root of the sum. A smaller standard deviation results in a larger value of z, so the null hypothesis is more likely to be rejected.

4. a. $\frac{p(1 - p)}{n_1}$

b. $\frac{p(1 - p)}{n_2}$

c. The variance of the difference $\hat{p}_1 - \hat{p}_2$ is the sum of the variances:

$$\frac{p(1 - p)}{n_1} + \frac{p(1 - p)}{n_2} = p(1 - p)\left(\frac{1}{n_1} + \frac{1}{n_2}\right).$$

Finally, the standard deviation is the square root of the variance:

$$\sqrt{p(1 - p)\left(\frac{1}{n_1} + \frac{1}{n_2}\right)}$$

NOTE: Students may recall this from Course 3, Unit 5, page 361 or from Extending Tasks 1 or 2 of Lesson 2 (pages 346–347) of this unit.

Reflecting

1. a. Available subjects (presumably who were at the beginning of a cold) were randomly placed in groups who took the cold medicine and those who took a placebo. Neither the patients nor the doctors who evaluated the length of their colds knew which type of medicine the patient took.

b. No, what looks like a difference in two proportions, the 38%, is not the difference in two proportions, but rather the percentage decrease in the length of a cold. For example, if a cold normally lasts an average of 10 days and it lasted an average of 6.2 days with the cold medicine, that would be a 38% decrease. This is actually a situation about the difference of two means, not two proportions.

2. a. In an experiment, treatments are randomly assigned to available subjects. In a survey, people are randomly selected from a larger population.

b. In a survey, you can generalize to the larger population. In an experiment, you can only say that the treatment was effective or not for that group.

Unit 5

MORE *continued*

3. a. Since most experts are completely convinced that airbags reduce serious injuries, it would be unethical to ask people to participate in such an experiment.

b. Take as large a group of people as practical and divide them randomly into two groups. One group will get cars with airbags and the other, identical cars without airbags. After a certain period, accident records would be checked for the two groups and rates of serious injuries compared.

4. a. Experiment

b. Observational study

c. Sample survey

Extending

1. a. The difference of proportions from the data is approximately 0.000196. The standard deviation of the distribution of the difference of proportions is

$$\sqrt{\frac{142}{345,603}\left(1 - \frac{142}{345,603}\right)\left(\frac{1}{221,998} + \frac{1}{123,605}\right)} \approx 0.0000719.$$ The *z*-score is approximately 2.66, so you can (barely) reject the hypothesis that the vaccine is not effective.

b. In Activity 4 of Investigation 1 of this lesson, students read that, the more affluent parents were the most worried about polio since their children were more likely to get it. Thus, they would tend to be the ones more likely to give permission for their children to receive this (uncertain) vaccine. If the other children were left as the controls, that group would be expected to have fewer cases of polio, even with no Salk vaccine. If their rate was quite a bit less, it might make it appear that the vaccine isn't very effective. And that's what happened; although the difference in the percentages in Part a was statistically significant, the difference wasn't all that large (0.03% compared to 0.05%).

c. It was not possible for the study to be subject blind or evaluator blind since everyone would know whether the child was in second grade or not and thus whether he or she got the vaccine.

d. The standard deviation is approximately 0.0000936 and $z \approx 2.53$. Thus, this result is statistically significant. This establishes that children whose parents chose not to have them receive the vaccine were in the lower risk group for polio. More children in that group were already immune to polio.

MORE *continued*

2. **a.** The number of "successes" in one case is only 4, which is less than 5. This means you cannot use the normal approximation for the sampling distribution of $\hat{p}_1 - \hat{p}_2$.

    b. The null hypothesis is that the promised treatment doesn't affect a person's decision whether to wait together or wait alone. That is, any difference in results was just due to the fact that subjects who would choose to wait together, no matter what treatment they expected to receive, happened to be randomly assigned more often to the painful group.

    There were 16 people who chose to wait together. Get this number of red beads. Get 14 blue beads to represent those who chose to wait alone. Mix the red and blue beads in a bag. Draw out the same number of beads as there were subjects in the painful treatment group, 17. Let $\hat{p}_1$ be the proportion of red beads in this sample. The beads remaining in the bag represent the people who were in the painless treatment group. Let $\hat{p}_2$ be the proportion of red beads in this group. Compute $\hat{p}_1 - \hat{p}_2$.

    Repeat this procedure until you have at least several hundred values of $\hat{p}_1 - \hat{p}_2$. Display these values on a histogram. Determine if the actual difference from the sample, $\frac{12}{17} - \frac{4}{13} \approx 0.398$, would be a rare event. If so, reject the null hypothesis and decide that the treatment caused an increase in the proportion of those who chose to wait together. If not, do not reject the null hypothesis. The difference between the two treatments is no greater than would be expected if people didn't choose to wait together or wait alone based on which treatment they got.

    Here, for your information, is a sample histogram from 500 trials of this randomization test.

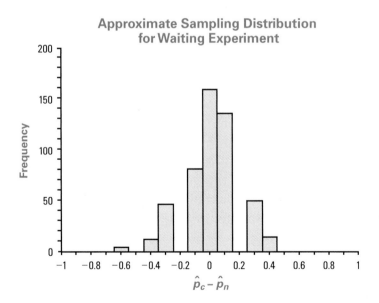

Approximate Sampling Distribution for Waiting Experiment

    c. $\frac{C(16, 4)C(14, 9)}{C(30, 13)} = \frac{(1,820)(2,002)}{119,759,850} \approx 0.0304$, or, equivalently

    $\frac{C(13, 4)C(17, 12)}{C(30, 16)} = \frac{(715)(6,188)}{145,422,675} \approx 0.0304$

MORE *continued*

d. $\dfrac{C(16, 4)C(14, 9)}{C(30, 13)} + \dfrac{C(16, 3)C(14, 10)}{C(30, 13)} + \dfrac{C(16, 2)C(14, 11)}{C(30, 13)} + \dfrac{C(16, 1)C(14, 12)}{C(30, 13)} + \dfrac{C(16, 0)C(14, 13)}{C(30, 13)}$,

or, equivalently $\dfrac{C(13, 4)C(17, 12)}{C(30, 16)} + \dfrac{C(13, 3)C(17, 13)}{C(30, 16)} + \dfrac{C(13, 2)C(17, 14)}{C(30, 16)} +$

$\dfrac{C(13, 1)C(17, 15)}{C(30, 16)} + \dfrac{C(13, 0)C(17, 16)}{C(30, 16)} \approx 0.035$

e. The actual difference in proportions for this experiment was 0.398. Since this outcome would be a rare event (probability about 0.035) if people were picking which group to wait in without regard to their treatment, you can conclude that the larger number who chose to wait together if promised painful shocks cannot reasonably be attributed to chance. Apparently, people prefer to wait together when faced with the prospect of pain.

3. a. Reasonably likely numbers of guesses are those in the interval

$20 \pm 2\sqrt{40(0.5)(1 - 0.5)} \approx 20 \pm 6.2$, or between 13.8 and 26.2 slides, or 14 through 26.

b. $\dfrac{C(3, 1)C(50, 29)}{C(53, 30)}$ or, equivalently, $\dfrac{C(30, 1)C(23, 2)}{C(53, 3)} = \dfrac{(30)(253)}{23{,}426} \approx 0.324$

c. $\dfrac{C(3, 1)C(50, 29)}{C(53, 30)} + \dfrac{C(3, 0)C(50, 30)}{C(53, 30)}$, or, equivalently, $\dfrac{C(30, 1)C(23, 2)}{C(53, 3)} + \dfrac{C(30, 0)C(23, 3)}{C(53, 3)} \approx 0.399$

d. The difference in the proportions, which after all is only because of one child, can easily be attributed to chance variation. There is no evidence that color slides make any difference. However, the investigator should have tried a harder task (or recorded the exact number of slides identified). There was almost no variation in the results because almost all children scored better than chance level.

e. The randomization test and Fisher's exact test can be used only if the subjects were randomly assigned to treatments. Note that that isn't the case here as entire classrooms were used for the two treatments. There is no mention of random assignment at all. (There is an alternative to random assignment of children to the two treatments. That would be to randomly determine for each child whether they saw the color or black and white slides first. With this type of randomization, interference is possible.)

MORE *continued*

4. a. This is an observational study. There is no control group or randomization. A group of children with a history of asthma was observed after exercise.

   b. No. Not only aren't these independent samples, there is really only one proportion $\frac{9}{32}$. If those are the "successes," then $1 - \frac{9}{32} = \frac{23}{32}$ represents the "failures" from the same group. However, you could use the z-test for a proportion from Lesson 3 to test, for example, whether the proportion with a fall several hours later was less than some proportion you hypothesize, such as 50%.

5. The difference is not statistically significant, since $|z| < 2$.

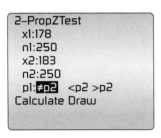

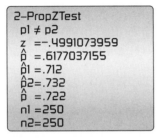

See Assessment Resources pages 172–177.

REVIEW AND PRACTICE **individual task**

PUMP

Answers

1. (c)	6. (c)
2. (e)	7. (b)
3. (c)	8. (c)
4. (a)	9. (a)
5. (b)	10. (d)

Lesson **5** *Looking Back*

SYNTHESIZE UNIT IDEAS   small-group activity

1. **a.** It can be treated as a binomial situation because there are a fixed number of trials (80), each trial can be classified a success (takes public transportation) or a failure (does not), there is a fixed but unknown probability of a success, and the size of the sample, 80, is small in relation to the number of working adults in Houston.

   b.   ■ $C(80, 10)(0.065)^{10}(0.935)^{70} \approx 0.0201$

   ■ binompdf(80,0.065,10) ≈ 0.0201

   c.   ■ $C(80, 0)(0.935)^{80} + C(80, 1)(0.065)(0.935)^{79} + C(80, 2)(0.065)^2(0.935)^{78} \approx 0.1009$

   ■ binomcdf(80,0.065,2) ≈ 0.1009

   d. binomcdf(80,0.065,1) ≈ 0.030

   Since the probability of having one or zero successes out of this sample of 80 people is not less than 0.025, it is not a rare event.

Master 119

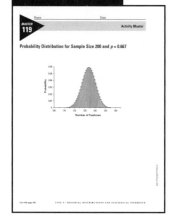

2. **See Teaching Master 119.**

   a. The mean of the distribution is $\left(\frac{2}{3}\right)(200) \approx 133.3$ and the standard deviation is $\sqrt{200\left(\frac{2}{3}\right)\left(\frac{1}{3}\right)} \approx 6.667$.

   b. The mean is $\frac{2}{3}$ and the standard deviation is 0.033.

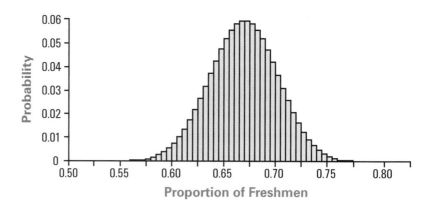

Unit 5

SYNTHESIZE *continued*

   c. As the sample size increases, the mean number of students increases and the standard deviation increases.

   d. As the sample size increases, the mean of the sample proportion stays the same and the standard deviation decreases.

3. a. Using the binomial probability function of the calculator, binomcdf(185,0.3,40) ≈ 0.00679.

Using the normal approximation, you have $\mu = 185(0.3) = 55.5$ and $\sigma = \sqrt{185(0.3)(0.7)} \approx 6.2330$. So, $z = \frac{40 - 55.5}{6.2330} \approx -2.49$. The probability is normalcdf(−999999,−2.49) ≈ 0.0064.

   b.   **I.** The null hypothesis is that the proportion of caramel candies that are brown is 0.30.

        II. If the null hypothesis is true, the distribution is approximately normal with a mean number of 55.5 and a standard deviation of about 6.2330.

       III. The number from the sample is 40.

       IV. If the null hypothesis is true, the result from this sample proportion has a z-score of $\frac{40 - 55.5}{6.2330} \approx -2.49$. The probability of getting 40 brown candies or fewer is 0.0064.

        V. This is definitely a rare event if the null hypothesis is true. Thus, you doubt the null hypothesis, so you should reject it.

4. a. An experiment, but to be sure it would need to be clear that treatments were randomly assigned to subjects.

   b. No, it could not have been subject blind as the subjects knew what treatment they got. It could have been evaluator blind if the patients did not mention their behavior to the evaluator.

   c. The standard deviation of the distribution of the difference of the proportions is $\sqrt{\frac{124}{183}\left(1 - \frac{124}{183}\right)\left(\frac{1}{91} + \frac{1}{92}\right)} \approx 0.069103$. The difference of the actual proportions is approximately $\frac{64}{91} - \frac{60}{92} \approx 0.0511$. Thus, $z \approx 0.739$, and the difference in the two proportions can reasonably be attributed to chance variation. Thus, the headline accurately reflects the results of the study even though a larger percentage of those with the bed-rest treatment felt better after two weeks.

   d. The article does not say whether the people who had bed rest were also given painkillers. Also, if doctors used anything like the phrase "get on with their lives," that would suggest to the subjects that that is the right thing to do.

SHARE AND SUMMARIZE full-class discussion

Checkpoint

See Teaching Masters 120a and 120b.

a The characteristics of a binomial situation are

- There are a fixed number of individual trials, n.

- Each trial is classified as a "success" or a "failure."

- Each trial is independent of the others. (Recall that trials are independent if the result of one trial does not change the probability of a success on any other trial.)

- On each trial, the probability of a success is a fixed (but possibly unknown) value p and the probability of a failure is $1 - p$.

b To find the probability of getting a fixed number of successes x in a series of binomial trials, you first find the probability of getting one particular sequence. Since you need x successes and $(n - x)$ failures, the probability is $(p)^x(1 - p)^{n - x}$. Multiply the probability of a particular sequence by the number of possible sequences with x successes and $(n - x)$ failures to get

$$C(n, x)(p)^x(1 - p)^{n - x}$$

c In each case, if n is the number of trials, and p is the probability of a success, and if np and $n(1 - p)$ are both at least 10, the shape is approximately normal. If p is less than 0.5, the distribution is skewed right (more so as p gets close to 0 but less so as n increases). If p is 0.5, the distribution is symmetric. If p is greater than 0.5, the distribution is skewed left (more so as p gets close to 1 but less so as n increases). The mean of the number of successes is $\mu = np$ and the standard deviation is $\sigma = \sqrt{np(1 - p)}$. The mean of the proportion of successes is $\mu = p$ and the standard deviation is $\sigma = \sqrt{\frac{p(1 - p)}{n}}$.

d ■ To use the binomial probability formula you must evaluate $\sum_{k = 0}^{x} C(n, k)(p)^k(1 - p)^{n - k}$. That is, you must add the probabilities for getting each number of successes less than or equal to x.

■ Find the value of `binomcdf(n,p,x)`.

■ As long as $np \geq 10$ and $n(1 - p) \geq 10$, you can approximate the binomial distribution with a normal distribution. A normal curve with mean np and standard deviation $\sqrt{np(1 - p)}$ fits very closely over the top of the bars of the binomial distribution of the number of successes. (Or, equivalently, a normal curve with mean p and standard deviation $\sqrt{\frac{p(1 - p)}{n}}$ fits very closely over the top of the bars of the distribution of the proportion of successes.) Thus, by finding areas under this normal curve, you get a close approximation to the areas of the bars.

You use this approximation so you don't have to use the binomial probability formula to find the area of each bar in the binomial distribution. Using the normal probability functions of the calculator, you can evaluate `normalcdf(-999999,x,np,`$\sqrt{(np(1-p))}$`)`. Alternatively, you can find the z-value associated with x, $z = \frac{x - np}{\sqrt{np(1 - p)}}$, and use the table of probabilities on page 320 or the calculator command `normalcdf(-999999,z)`.

SHARE AND SUMMARIZE *continued*

e A null hypothesis is a statement about the proportion of successes hypothesized to be in a population. If you reject a null hypothesis, it means the following sequence of logic occurred:

■ You assumed the null hypothesis is true.

■ You took a random sample from the population in question or assigned treatments randomly to subjects.

■ You found that the result from your sample was unlikely to occur if the null hypothesis is true.

■ You therefore had reason to doubt the truth of the null hypothesis and so rejected it. Thus, if you reject a null hypothesis, it means one of two things. Either the null hypothesis is false or the null hypothesis is true and a rare event occurred. In the latter case, you have made a Type I error. In the former case, you made a correct decision.

f The main difference is how randomization is used to define the two groups you are comparing. In a survey, people are selected randomly from a larger population or populations and so inferences can be made about that population or populations. In an experiment, available subjects are randomly assigned to treatments and so inferences can be made about whether one treatment causes a different effect than another treatment. In an observational study, there is no randomization, and so, "what you see is all you get" (to quote George Cobb).

g The null hypothesis is that the treatments are equally effective; any difference in results was just due to the fact that subjects who were "successes" happened to be randomly assigned more often to one group than another. Count the total number of successes in both groups. Get this number of red beads. Count the total number of failures in both groups. Get this number of blue beads. Mix the red and blue beads in a bag. Draw out the same number of beads as there were subjects in the first treatment group. Let $\hat{p}_1$ be the proportion of red beads in this sample. The beads remaining in the bag represent the people who were in the second treatment group. Let $\hat{p}_2$ be the proportion of red beads in this sample. Compute $\hat{p}_1 - \hat{p}_2$.

Repeat this procedure until you have at least several hundred values of $\hat{p}_1 - \hat{p}_2$. Display these values in a histogram. Determine if the actual difference from the sample would be a rare event. If so, reject the null hypothesis and decide that the treatment caused an increase in the proportion of successful results. If not, do not reject the null hypothesis. The difference between the two treatments is no greater than you would expect if the treatments had exactly the same results.

▶ **On Your Own**

See Teaching Masters 121a–121e.

Responses will vary. Above all, this should be something that is useful to the individual student. You may wish to have students use Teaching Masters 121a–121e, "Binomial Distributions and Statistical Inference" Unit Summary, to help them organize the information.

See Assessment Resources pages 178–197.

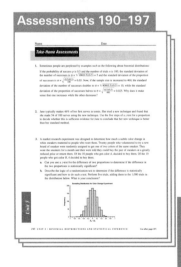

Masters 121a–121e

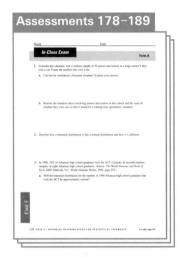

Assessments 178–189

Assessments 190–197

Unit 5

LESSON 5 · LOOKING BACK   **T411**

Looking Back, Looking Ahead

▶Reflecting on Mathematical Content

Throughout the *Contemporary Mathematics in Context* curriculum, students have been developing the ability to analyze data intelligently, to recognize and measure variation, and to understand the patterns that underlie probabilistic situations. In this unit, students have connected their previous study of probability distributions and data analysis in developing a formal understanding of binomial distributions and hypothesis testing. This unit completes the story of probability and statistics that students learn in this curriculum.

Students have learned the basics about statistical inference: confidence intervals in Course 3, Unit 2, "Modeling Public Opinion" and hypothesis testing in this unit. Sample proportions have been used to illustrate the basics of statistical inference. Although there has been little work with means, the ideas in this unit about proportions generalize quite directly to the case of means.

Students who have finished this unit by the end of the first semester of their senior year have sufficient time to prepare for the Advanced Placement Examination in Statistics. The additional major topics that students would have to study are confidence intervals and hypothesis tests for means. In addition, students should review correlation and regression from a slightly more advanced point of view, including inference for slope.

Unit 5 Assessment

Index of Mathematical Topics

multiplicative identity
of, *T451*
multiplicative inverses
of, *T451*
operations of, and
geometric
transformations,
T586–T589, T597
polar coordinates of,
T586–T587
product of, and its
conjugate, *T451*
product of two, *T451*
quotient of two, *T451*
relationship between
complex roots of
polynomial functions
and, *T450–T451*
relationship between
position vectors and,
T585–T586
solving equations
involving, *T459–T460*
subtraction of, *T450–T451*
triangle inequality for,
T585–T586
trigonometric form of,
T586–T587
Complex roots of real
numbers, *T591–T594*
Component analysis,
T116–T120
Components of a vector,
T112–T113
Composition of functions,
T194–T196
$g(f(x))$, T194–T195
noncommutativity of,
T195–T196
Computer Algebra System
(CAS), T294
using, to solve equations,
T578–T611
Conditional probability,
T300–T301
Cone
cross sections, *T622–T625*
double, *T632, T661–T663,
T668–T669, T680–T681*
surface of revolution,
T666–T668
Confidentiality, *T715–T716*
Conic graph paper
in drawing ellipses, *T643*
in drawing hyperbolas,
T643–T644
Conic sections
identifying, from
equations, *T634–T635,
T640–T641, T684–T685*
in terms of intersection
of a plane and a
double cone, *T632*
writing equation from
graph, *T647–T648,
T684–T685*
Conics, *T632*
Conjugate, *T451*
Constant of proportionality,
T254–T256
Continuous distribution,
T387
Contour diagrams,
T622–T623, T648–T649

interpreting, *T624–T625*
Contour lines, *T620*
Contour maps, *T620*
interpreting, *T626–T627,
T647–T648, T683*
making, *T626–T627,
T683–T684*
relationship between
relief maps and, *T630*
Control charts, T385–T387
Coordinate planes,
T628–T629, T645
equations of, and planes
parallel to them, *T653*
Coordinates and vectors,
T122–T127, T130–T134
Correlation coefficient
indicating whether or
not a linear model
is appropriate,
T253–T254
interpreting, T244–T245
Cosecant (csc) function,
T539–T542
domain, range, and
period of, *T539–T542*
graph of, *T539–T542*
Cosine (cos) function
circular function,
T537–T538
derivative of, T41,
T560–T561
Cosine(s)
double angle identity,
T555–T556
finding exact values,
T551–T552
Law of, T116–T118
right triangle ratios,
T111–T112
sum and difference
identities for,
T547–T553, T559–T560
Cotangent (cot) function,
T539–T542
domain, range, and
period of, *T539–T542*
graph of, *T539–T542*
Counterexample, T308
Counting
methods of, T269–T287
Multiplication Principle
of, T272, T290–T292
organized lists in, T271
throughout mathematics,
T289–T305
tree diagrams in, T271
when repetitions are
allowed, T273–T276,
T286–T287
Cross sections, *T622–T623,
T629–T632, T656–T665*
Cryptography, *T715–T716*
Cryptosystems, *T716*
fixed-shift letter-
substitution,
T716–T717
hybrid, *T725*
public-key, *T723–T727*
ROT13, *T716*
symmetric-key,
T716–T719
Cube roots of unity, *T591*
Cycle graph, T301–T302

Cylinder, cross sections of,
T631
Cylindrical surfaces,
T666–T669
elliptic, *T669–T671*
logarithmic, *T669–T671*
parabolic, *T668–T669*

D

Damped oscillations, *T488*
Data
linearizing, T230–T258
transforming to
determine appropriate
model, T230–T258
Deceleration, T8–T9,
T11–T12
Decibel scale, T214
Degree, measure, T155
Degree of polynomial, *T419*
DeMoivre, Abraham,
T589–T590
DeMoivre's Theorem,
T589–T591
proof of, using algebraic
reasoning, *T602–T604*
proof of using Principle
of Mathematical
Induction, *T591*
Derivative, T34–T35
decreasing, T44
dy/dx, T55
estimate using
difference quotient,
T37–T38
estimating by slope of
graph, T30–T33,
T44–T46
exponential function,
T39–T43
function f', T35–T36
functions, T34–T39
of $f(x) = \ln x$, T520–T522
graphs from function
graphs, T43–T47
increasing, T44
linear function, T37–T39
negative, T44
positive, T44
power function, T39–T43
quadratic function,
T37–T39
rules for linear and
second degree power
functions, T55
sums of functions and,
T57–T59
trigonometric function,
T39–T43
zero, T44
Determinant of a 2×2
matrix, *T729–T730, T732*
Difference identities
for cosine and sine
functions, *T547–T553,
T559–T560*
for tangent functions,
T555–T556
using, *T551–T552*
Difference quotient, T37–T38
Differentiation, T54–T55,
T81–T83

Digital signatures, *T725*
characteristics of, *T727*
Dihedral group, *T743*
Directed line segments,
T104–T105
Direction (heading),
T104–T105
Direction of vector,
T123–T124
Discrete distribution, T387
Disjoint set, *T700–T702*
Distributive Property of
multiplication
over addition, *T452–T453*
scalar multiplication
over vector addition,
T109–T111, T131–T133
over subtraction,
T452–T453
Dot product, T136–T138
Double cone
equation of, *T668–T669,
T680–T681*
plane intersections of,
T632, T648–T649
Doubling time for investments
(Rule of 72), *T759–T762*

E

Edge coloring, T301–T302
e, T518–T519
defined as infinite series,
T532–T533
Electronic information,
accuracy in transmission
of, *T734*
Ellipses, *T632*
drawing with conic
graph paper, *T643*
equations for, *T634–T638,
T661*
foci of, *T636–T637*
geometry of, *T637–T638*
horizontal axis of,
T634–T635
locus-of-points
definition of,
T636–T637
major axis of, *T634–T635*
minor axis of, *T634–T635*
sketching, using standard
form of equation of,
T634–T635
standard form of
equation of,
T634–T635
symmetry of, *T637–T638,
T661*
vertical axis of,
T634–T635
Ellipsoid, *T661, T680–T681*
equation for, *T661*
Elliptical orbits, T160–T162,
T170–T171
Elliptical paraboloid,
T680–T681
Elliptical paths, parametric
equations for, T160–T162,
T170–T171
Elliptic cylindrical surface,
T669–T671

Empty set, T280–T281,
T700–T702
Equal sets, *T693–T694*
Equations, substitution of
variable to help solve,
T461, T515–T516
Equivalent mod *n*,
T719–T720, T728–T729
Erdös, Paul, T289
Error function, *T461*
Errors, correcting and
detecting, *T734–T738*
Euclidean algorithm for
finding multiplicative
inverse in Z_n, *T732*
Euler, Leonhard, *T601–T602*
Euler's formula, *T601–T602*
Euler's Theorem, *T724*
Even function, *T556–T558*
Experiments, characteristics
of, T391–T395
clinical trial, T402
comparison group, T392
control group, T392
double-blind, T392–T393
evaluator-blind,
T392–T393
random assignment, T392
replication, T391
subject-blind, T392–T393
subjects, T391
treatment, T391
Exponential equations
solving, *T512–T516,
T610–T611, T778–T780*
logarithms in,
T210–T213
substitution of variable
to help in, *T515–T516*
Exponential functions,
T24–T25, *T508–T512,
T822–T824*
derivative of, T39–T43,
T532–T533
domain and range of,
T509–T511
doubling time for,
T514–T515
e and the derivative of,
T532–T533
estimating instantaneous
rates of change of,
T24–T25
growth rates and,
T509–T511, T789–T790
inverses for, T201–T207
linearizing data and,
T233–T234
log transformations and,
T238–T242
recursive formula for,
T509–T511
rewriting in equivalent
forms, *T509–T511,
T527–T528*
Exponential regression
equations and
technology method,
T239–T240
Exponents
properties of, T207–T208,
T511
relationship between
logarithms and,
T530–T531

F

Factored form
of polynomial, *T419*
of quadratic function,
T418
Factorial, T276–T277
Factor Theorem, *T445–T446*
proof of, *T458–T459*
Fermat's Little Theorem,
T721
variation of, to test for
primes, *T730–T731*
Fibonacci sequence,
T822–T824
Finite sets, *T712*
Fisher, R.A., T396
Fisher's exact test,
T404–T405
Fixed-shift letter-substitution
cryptosystem, *T716–T717*
Four-dimensional analog of a
cube, forming,
T679–T680
Four-dimensional model,
T677–T679
analog of a sphere in,
T677–T679
distance between points
in, *T677–T679*
midpoint of a segment
in, *T677–T679*
Fractals, *T781–T787*
Fractal tree, T191–T194
Frequency distributions
histogram of, T338–T339
for the number of
successes compared to
proportion of
successes, T341–T342
Frequency table, T337–T338
in estimating
probability, T338–T339
Function formulas, recursive
formulas and, *T781–T787*
Function graphs, translation
of, *T467*
Function(s)
absolute maximum and
minimum, *T426*
composition, T184–T185,
T194–T196, *T488*
decreasing, T195–T196
definition of, in terms of
ordered pairs and sets,
T712
derivative of, T43–T47
difference quotient for
estimating the
derivative, T37–T38
end behavior, *T424–T425,
T428–T430*
exponential, T24–T25,
T39–T43, T202–T203
finding equation of
inverse of a, T187–T188
increasing, T195–T196
inverse cosine,
T197–T199
inverse sine, T197–T199
inverses, T182–T199
linear, T22–T24,
T37–T38
linearizing, T230–T258
definition of,
T233–T234

local maxima and
minima, *T426*
logarithmic, T200,
T206–T207
multiplicity of zeroes,
T427–T428
natural log, *T517–T522*
one-to-one, T183–T184
piecewise-defined,
T197–T199
power, T39–T43
quadratic, T23–T25
square root, T234–T235
trigonometric, cosecant,
cotangent, secant,
T539–T542
Fundamental theorem of
algebra, *T450–T451,
T453–T454, T583–T584*
$f'(x)$, T34–T35
estimating by using
difference quotient for,
T35–T48, T55
estimating from graph
of $f(x)$, T43–T47
using to find
characteristics of the
graph of $f(x)$, T31–T33,
T51–T53
$f(x)$
patterns in and rate of
change of, T27–T29
properties of $f'(x)$ and
the graph of, T51–T52
rule in approximating
slope of graph, T51–T52

G

Galois, Evariste, *T448*
General Multiplication Rule
to find probability of
any two events, T292
Geometric mean, *T812–T820*
Geometric series, T317–T319,
T326–T328
Geometric transformations
complex numbers and,
T601–T604
inverses of, T195–T196
relationship between
multiplication of
complex numbers and,
in plane, *T586–T587*
Golden Ratio, *T822–T824*
Graphs
binomial distributions,
T360–T374
complete, T301–T302,
T310
cycle, T301–T302
derivative from function
graphs, T43–T47
edge coloring, T301–T302
estimating rate of
change, T13–T14
function inverse,
T186–T190
rate of change, using to
estimate net change,
T67–T72
velocity graph used to
sketch distance,
T31–T33

H

Half-angle identities,
T560–T561
Heading, T103–T104
Hill cipher, *T717*
general version of,
T729–T730
security of, *T717–T718*
Histograms
estimating mean and
standard deviation,
T338–T339
of frequency
distribution, T338–T339
Horizontal asymptote, *T467*
Horizontal line test,
T192–T194
Horizontal planes, equations
of, and planes parallel to
them, *T653*
Horner, William George
Horner's Method,
T443–T444
Hybrid cryptography, protocol
for, *T725*
Hyperbolas, *T632*
asymptotes of, *T638–T640*
branch of, *T638–T640*
drawing with conic
graph paper, *T643–T644*
equations of asymptotes
of, *T638–T640,
T649–T650*
foci of, *T638–T640,
T643–T644*
locus-of-points
definition of,
T637–T638
parametric equations
for, *T638–T640,
T649–T650*
standard forms of
equation of, *T638–T640*
symmetry lines of,
T638–T640
vertices of, *T638–T640*
Hyperbolic paraboloid, *T681*
Hyperboloid
of one sheet, *T680–T681*
of two sheets, *T681*
Hypercube, *T679–T680*
Hypergeometric formula,
T357–T358

I

Identities, half-angle,
T560–T561
Imaginary number *i*,
T449–T450, T583–T584
Imaginary numbers, find roots
of, *T591*
Imaginary part of *a* + *bi*,
T457–T458
Independent events,
multiplication rule for,
T290–T292
Induction, Principle of
Mathematical, T310
Infinite series, *T532–T533*
Infinite sets, *T712*
having same number of
elements, *T712*

Nth roots of unity, *T592–T594*
  regular polygons and,
    T602–T604
Null hypothesis, T380–T381
Null set, *T700–T702*

O

Oblique asymptote,
  T468–T471
Observational study, T392
Odd function, *T556–T558*
Ohm's Law, *T456–T457*
One-to-one correspondence,
  T712
One-to-one function,
  T183–T184
One-way function, *T724*
Opposite-angle identities,
  T548–T550
Optimization, T4–T95,
  *T431–T433, T471–T472,
  T480–T482*
OR (logical operator),
  T694–T695
Orbits, simulating,
  T158–T162
  circular, T158–T161
  elliptical, T160–T162
Order in counting,
  T274–T275
Ordered triple of numbers,
  T628, T645

P

Parabolas, *T632, T635–T636*
  directrix of, *T635–T636*
  focus of, *T635–T636*
  locus-of-points derived
    from, *T635–T636*
  parametric equations
    for, T148–T153,
    T635–T636
  vertex form of equation
    for, *T635–T636*
Parabolic cylindrical surface,
  T668–T669
Paraboloid, circular, *T631,
  T666–T668*
Parallel planes, equations of,
  T659–T660
Parameter, T143–T144
Parametric equations,
  T141–T144
  versus circles,
    T156–T157
  for circular motion,
    T153–T162
  combining, T166–T168
  for a curve, *T437–T438*
  for elliptical motion,
    T160–T161, T170–T171,
    T633–T635
  inverse functions and,
    T195–T199
  for lines with constant
    velocity, T147
  for parabolic motion,
    T148–T153
  for several forces, T152
Parametric function of
  calculator, T141–T142

Parametric models
  for linear motion,
    T141–T148
  for nonlinear motion,
    T148–T162
Parshall, Karen, *T444–T445*
Pascal, Blaise, T294
Pascal's triangle, T293–T299,
  T303–T305
  binomial expansions
    and, T294
  combinations and, T295
Percent change, use in
  spreadsheets, *T799–T805*
Perimeter
  limits, *T785–T787*
  recursive formulas,
    T781–T783
  similar figures and,
    T781–T783
Permutations, T273–T282
  counting formulas for,
    T276–T278
  features on a calculator,
    T279–T280
  $P(n, k)$, T279–T280
Phi (ϕ), T131–T133
Piecewise-defined function,
  T197–T199
π defined as an infinite series,
  T532–T533
Placebo effect, T392–T394
Plane symmetries
  testing for, *T661*
Poincaré, Henri, T319–T322
Points in three-space,
  T628–T629, T645
  distance between, *T653*
  plotting and
    interpreting, *T646–T647*
Polar coordinates, T127, *T548*
  relationship between
    rectangular coordinates
    for a point and, *T548*
Polynomial division,
  T446–T447
  area model for,
    T455–T456
  connection between
    processes of synthetic
    substitution and, *T461*
Polynomial functions,
  T418–T431
  characteristics of cubic,
    T427–T428
  characteristics of degree n,
    absolute maximum/
    minimum, *T428–T430*
  local maxima/minima,
    T428–T430
  shape, *T428–T430*
  connection between
    graph of, and graphs
    associated with linear
    factors of, *T433–T435*
  derivatives of, *T435–T436*
  end behavior of,
    T424–T425
  estimating zeroes of,
    using bisection
    algorithm, *T461–T463*
  Factor Theorem,
    T445–T446
  finding, using method of
    undetermined

coefficients, *T423–T425*
  Rational Zeroes
    Theorem, *T446–T447*
  shapes of, *T422,
    T430–T431*
  sign diagram for
    sketching graphs of,
    T432–T433
  zeroes of, in writing
    function equation,
    T418–T422
  zeroes of multiplicity,
    T427–T428
Polynomials
  degree of, *T419*
  factored form of, *T421,
    T441–T442*
  factoring, *T444–T448*
  factors of cubic,
    T433–T435
  linear factor of, *T419*
  nested multiplication
    form of, *T441–T442*
  number of complex
    roots for, *T450–T451*
  standard form of,
    T441–T442
  term, *T419*
Position vectors, T127
Power function
  derivative of, T39–T43
  inverses of, T188–T190
  translated, T256–T258
Power models, linearizing,
  T249, T256–T258
Power of a Power Property,
  T511
Power Property of
  Logarithms, T210
  proof by induction,
    T317–T319
Power set of a set, *T711*
Powers of i, *T459–T460*
Prime numbers, of ≤ n,
  T225–T227
  testing large, to see if
    they are prime,
    T730–T731
Principle of Mathematical
  Induction, T309–T312
  proof of DeMoivre's
    Theorem using, *T591*
Private key, *T723*
Probability
  Addition Rule for,
    T290–T292
  and binomial
    distributions,
    T360–T365
  conditional, T300–T301
  distributions, T337–T343
  of an event A, T290
  Multiplication Rule for,
    T290–T293
  normal distributions
    and, T377–T380
  $P(B|A)$, T292
  Venn diagrams and,
    T710–T711
Product of Powers Property,
  T511
Product Property of
  Logarithms, T208–T210
Product-sum trig identities,
  T580–T582
Proper subset, *T700–T702*
Proportionality, constant of,
  T254–T256

Proportions, and spreadsheets,
  T778–T780, T799–T821
  of successes, T339–T342,
    T347–T350
Protocol, *T725*
Public key, *T723*
Public-key cryptography
  protocol for, *T725*
  protocol for digital
    signature using, *T725*
  using, to authenticate
    data, *T725*
Public-key cryptosystem,
  T723–T727
  comparison of
    symmetric-key
    and, *T725–T726*
  in ensuring authenticity,
    T726
  in providing
    confidentiality, *T726*
Pythagoras and irrational
  numbers, *T448–T449*
Pythagorean trigonometric
  identities, *T544–T547*
Pythagorean Theorem, using
  the, to develop 3-D
  distance formula, *T654*

Q

Quadratic equation
  determining whether
    real or complex
    number roots of,
    T459–T460
  solving with
    spreadsheets,
    T778–T780
  standard form, combining
    real and imaginary
    numbers as solution to,
    T449–T450
Quadratic functions
  derivative of, T37–T38
  estimating instantaneous
    rates of change of,
    T23–T25
Quartic polynomial function,
  writing equation in
  three-space of, *T421*
Quadratic roots of unity,
  T591
Quotient trigonometric
  identities, *T545*
Quotient of Powers Property,
  T511
Quotient Property of
  Logarithms, T208–T210

R

Radians, T155
Randomization test, T396
Rare event, T338–T339
Rate of change
  absolute value function
    and, T54–T55
  average, T9–T14,
    T21–T30
  estimating at a point,
    T5–T14
  estimating from a table,
    T6–T7, T13–T14

for familiar functions, T22–T43
instantaneous, T4–T19
of linear functions, T22–T24, T55
and slopes of graphs of functions, T30–T33
Ratio, T212–T213
Rational functions, *T467–T468*
asymptotes of, *T472–T476*
functions that are *not*, *T476–T477*
behavior of, near asymptotes, *T472–T476*
domain and range of, *T471–T476*
end behavior of, *T472–T476*
finding local and absolute maxima/ minima of, *T472–T476*
identifying asymptotes of, *T472–T477*
interpreting graphs of, *T468–T469, T476–T477*
inverses of, *T488*
linearizing data and, *T485–T487*
relationships between graphs and equations of, *T476–T477*
role of parameters in, *T485–T487*
similar triangles and, *T482–T485*
zeroes of, *T472–T476*
Rational numbers versus irrational, *T448–T449, T710–T711*
Rational Zeroes Theorem, *T446–T447*
Real numbers
additive inverse of, *T721–T722*
complex roots of, *T591*
effect of multiplying nonzero complex number by, *T457–T458*
multiplicative inverse of, *T721–T722*
ordering property of, *T452–T453*
set of, *T710–T711*
Real part of $a + bi$, *T457–T458*
Reciprocal trig functions, *T539–T542*
Reciprocal trig identities, *T545*
Rectangles, using to estimate definite integral, T72–T75
Rectangular coordinates
of a point, *T628–T629, T645*
relationship between polar coordinates and, *T548*
Recursion, T308–T313
Recursive formulas and spreadsheets, *T755–T775, T781–T787*
Relation between two sets *A* and *B*, T712
Relatively prime, two integers are, *T729–T730*
Relief line, *T629*
comparing vertical cross sections of a surface and, *T632*

Relief map, *T629*
interpreting, *T630*
making, *T630*
relationship between contour map and, *T630*
Remainder Theorem, *T459–T460*
Repeated factors, connection between multiple zeroes and, *T447*
Repetition in counting, T274–T275
Residuals, T238–T239, T247
Resultant of vectors, T107–T108
Right triangles, special, *T551–T552*
Roots of unity, geometry of, *T591*
ROT13 cipher, security of, *T717–T718*
ROT13 cryptosystem, *T716*
Rotation matrix, *T559–T560*
Rotations
and complex number arithmetic, *T583–T595*
inverse functions, T195–T196
Rotations of point about origin, connection between complex number arithmetic and, *T588–T589*
RSA cryptosystem, *T723*
decrypting using, *T723–T724*
encrypting using, *T723–T724*
processes of decryption used in, *T726*
processes of encryption used in, *T726*
security of, *T724*
why it works, *T724*
RSA Public-Key Cryptosystem, *T723*
Ruffini, Paolo, *T443–T444, T448*

S

Sample space of the experiment, *T705–T706*
Sample survey, T391
Sampling
with replacement, T357–T358
without replacement, T357–T358
Scalar multiple of vectors, T105–T106, T131–T133
Scalar multiplication
distributive property of, T109–T111, T131–T133
Secant (sec) function, *T539–T542*
domain, range, and period of, *T539–T542*
graphs of, *T539–T542*
Security, *T715–T719*
of Caesar cipher, *T717–T718*

of Hill cipher, *T717–T718*
of ROT13 cipher, *T717–T718*
Semi-log graph paper, T215–T216
graphs of functions displayed on, T215–T216
Set, T280–T281, *T693–T694*
complement of, *T699–T700*
disjoint, *T700–T702*
elements of, *T693–T694*
empty, T280–T281, *T700–T702*
null, *T700–T702*
operations on, *T695–T700*
power set of, *T711*
proper, *T700–T702*
relation between, *T712*
subset, T280–T281, *T699–T700*
universal, *T699–T700*
Set builder notation, *T694–T695*
Set difference, *T697–T698*
Sets of numbers, relationships between, *T458–T459*
Set theory, *T693–T694*
Significance test, T380–T384
Sine (sin) function
circular functions, *T537–T538*
derivative of, *T560–T561*
polynomial approximation of, *T444*
Sine(s)
double angle identity for, *T554, T558–T559*
finding exact values of, *T551–T552*
right triangle ratios, T111–T112
sum and difference identities for, *T559–T560*
Single-bar errors, detecting and correcting, *T736*
Single-digit errors, detecting, *T740–T742*
Size transformations and inverses, T195–T196
and complex numbers, *T586–T589*
Space-shapes, sketching, *T621–T622*
Speed
average, T12–T13
instantaneous, T12–T13
Spheres
cross sections of, *T622–T623*
equations of, *T654, T676–T677, T680–T681*
surface of revolution, *T666*
volume of, T191–T192
Spiral similarity, by using complex numbers, *T601–T602*
Spreadsheets
absolute values (ABS), *T778–T780*
cell references in formulas, *T756*
designing, *T769*
fill down command, *T756, T771–T772*

fixed cell references, *T756*
histograms, *T792–T794*
IF-THEN-ELSE, *T774–T777*
INT, *T806–T807*
logarithms (LOG), *T778–T780*
logical test functions, *T774–T777*
PI( ), *T773–T775*
scientific notation, *T772–T773*
SORT function, *T806–T807*
SQRT function, *T772–T773, T812–T820*
SUM function, *T763–T766, T771–T772*
variable cell references, *T756*
Square root functions, linearizing, T234–T235
Standard deviation
for probability distributions, T364–T365
with spreadsheets, *T775–T778*
Standard position, angle in, *T537–T538*
Standard score, T377–T378
Statistically significant, T380–T381
Straightening functions, T231–T238
Subset, T280–T281, *T699–T700*
Substitution ciphers, *T716–T717, T727–T728*
keywords in, *T727–T728*
Substitution of variable, *T461, T565–T567*
Successes
converting number of to proportion of, T339–T342, T363
probability of, T289–T294, T360–T365
proportion of, formulas for mean and standard deviation, T367–T368
Sum identities, *T548*
for cosine and sine functions, *T550, T559–T560*
product to, *T555–T556*
for tangent function, *T555–T556*
using, *T551–T552*
Sum-product trig identities, *T580–T582*
Sums of functions and derivatives of sums of functions, T57–T59
Surface of revolution, *T666–T671*
approximating volume, *T676–T679*
axis of rotation, *T666*
cone as, *T666–T668*
finding equations of, *T666–T671*
sketching, *T666–T671*
Surfaces
cylindrical, *T668–T669*
determining symmetry, using equation of, *T661–T665*

Vertical asymptote, *T467*
Vertical cross sections of a
  surface, comparing
  relief lines and, *T632*
Vertical line test, T192–T194
Vertical planes, equations of,
  and planes parallel to
  them, *T653*

W

Waiting-time situations
  compared to binomial
  situations, T341–T342
Whole numbers as a set,
  T710–T711

X

$(x \in A)$ (symbol), *T693–T694*
x-, y-, and z-axes, *T628–T629*
x-, y-, and z-intercepts, *T661,
  T665, T673–T676*
xy-plane, *T628–T629*
xz-plane, *T628–T629*

Y

Yang Hui, *T443–T444*
y-values, effect of
  transforming on shape
  of data plot, T233–T234
yz-plane, *T628–T629*

Z

Zero multiplicity,
  T427–T428
  connection between graph
  of function and,
  T427–T430
Z_n, *T721–T722*
  addition and
  multiplication tables for
  arithmetic in,
  T729–T730
  multiplicative inverses in,
  T732
  solving equations in,
  T729–T730
z-score, T377

z-test
  calculator with, T387,
  T406–T407
  for difference of two
  proportions, T396–T397
  for a proportion,
  T380–T381

Index of Contexts